NOBEL PRIZE LIBRARY

BECKETT

BJÖRNSON

BUCK

BUNIN

Nobel Prize Library

PUBLISHED UNDER THE SPONSORSHIP OF THE

NOBEL FOUNDATION & THE SWEDISH ACADEMY

Samuel Beckett

Björnstjerne Björnson

Pearl Buck

Ivan Bunin

ALEXIS GREGORY, *New York*, AND
CRM PUBLISHING, *Del Mar, California*

CONTENTS

Samuel Beckett

1969

———————————————

"For a body of work that, in new forms

of fiction and the theater, has transmuted

the destitution of modern man into his

exaltation"

———————————————

Illustrated by AVIGDOR ARIKHA

PRESENTATION ADDRESS

By *KARL RAGNAR GIEROW*

PERMANENT SECRETARY

OF THE SWEDISH ACADEMY

IF KEEN IMAGINATION and logic are stirred together to the point of absurdity, the result is either a paradox or an Irishman. If it is an Irishman, the paradox is automatically included. There have indeed been times when the Nobel Prize has been shared. Paradoxically, that is what has happened this year, when one single Prize has been conferred on one man, two languages, and a third nation, itself divided.

Samuel Beckett was born in Dublin in 1906; it was in Paris that the world came to know this famous author almost a half-century later. Within three years he published five works that carried him at once to the peak of the literary world: *Molloy,* a novel, in 1951; its sequel, *Malone Dies,* in the same year; a play, *Waiting for Godot,* in 1952, and *The Unnameable,* the novel that completed the cycle of Molloy and Malone, in the following year, which was also the time of publication of *Watt,* another novel. With these works modern literature was endowed at a stroke with one of its richest chapters.

The dates refer only to the sudden appearance of the books. None of the five had just been written, nor were they composed in the order in which they appeared. They owed their origins both to the circumstances of the times and to Beckett's own earlier development. Perhaps it is only in the light of his more recent works that one can discern the true dimensions of *Murphy,* a novel written in 1938, and of his studies of Joyce (1929) and Proust (1931), focusing with clarity on the point from which he embarked. For Beckett, the forerunner of new modes of expression in the novel and the drama, is a man of traditions, because he is also a member of the family of Joyce, Proust and Kafka; and in their beginnings his dramatic works had deep common roots with the French literature of the 1890's and Alfred Jarry's *Ubu-Roi*.

From more than one point of view, the novel *Watt* might be regarded as a change of phase in this extraordinary production. Composed between 1942 and 1944 in the south of France, to which Beckett, who had long lived in Paris, had managed to flee after the Nazi occupation, this book represented a farewell to the English language that was to endure for many years; it was in French that he gained his reputation, and he did not return to his native language until some fifteen years later. But the climate too had changed when he resumed writing after the completion of *Watt*. The other works that have made him famous were written between 1945 and 1949. Their base was the Second World War; it was after that conflict that his work matured and acquired its message.

What was involved, however, was not the war in its literal sense, nor the events of the front or the Resistance, in which Beckett himself had participated, but, rather, what came afterward when peace returned, shredding the curtain that veiled the last depth of hell and revealing, in a horrific vision, the extent of inhuman degradation to which humanity could attain, whether in obedience to orders or to its own instincts, and how it could survive such a depravity. Thus the decadence of man is a theme that often recurs in Beckett's works, and in this degree his view of life, displayed even more emphatically against its background of broad farce at once grotesque and tragic, can be labeled negativism, a negativism incapable of interruption until it has run its full course. It must go on to the end, for it is only there that the miracle of revelation of tragic thought and poetry can take place.

What does the negative offer us, once it has been developed? A positive, a brighter image in which black itself is transformed into brilliance, in which the areas in the deepest shadow are precisely those that reflect the source of light. Its name is compassion. Its predecessors are beyond counting, and not only in the accumulation of horrors in Greek tragedies from which Aristotle derived his theory of catharsis, of purification through pity and terror. Man has gained more strength from the bitter depths of Schopenhauer than from the riches of nature of Schelling; he has found more divine grace in the anguished doubt of Pascal than in the blind faith of Leibniz in reason in the best of all possible worlds, and again—to confine oneself to that Irish heritage that has added its contribution to the alimentation of Beckett's work—he has gained far less profit from the pallid pastoral idyll of Oliver Goldsmith than from the black-furied depiction of the human species by Dean Swift.

The crucial point in Beckett's conception of the world is found here, in the difference between a facile pessimism confined within the insensibilities of skepticism and the pessimism that is so painfully earned and that endeavors to meet man in his most unarmored misery. The first arises out of the fact that nothing has value, and this is as well its limitation. The second strives to build from a diametrically opposite concept. For what is without worth can never be debased. Proof of the degradation of man—and we have been its witnesses as perhaps no generation before us has been—does not exist if one denies all value to man. But the more the evidence makes us suffer, the deeper the recognition of man's true worth. This is the source of inner purification, the life-giving strength *in spite of everything* that springs from Beckett's black pessimism. It embraces a love for mankind the more compassionate because it has known the extremes of revulsion, a despair that must reach the farthest limit of suffering in order to learn that that frontier vanishes when compassion disappears. Out of this condition bordering on annihilation the work of Samuel Beckett rises like a *Miserere* of the whole of mankind, and in its desolate elegiac tones there echo the release of the tortured and the solace of shipwrecked souls.

This is perhaps most clearly evident in the two masterpieces, *Waiting for Godot* and *Happy Days*. Each might be looked upon as the exegesis of the Biblical text appropriate to it. That of the first is "Art thou he who should come, or are we to await another?" What the two vagabonds of the play must confront is the meaningless cruelty of existence in its most brutal form. This may be a human one; no law is more cruel than those of creation itself, and the singular place that man occupies in it arises out of the fact that only he enforces those laws with deliberate malignity. But if we imagine a providence—and therefore a creator of this limitless suffering that man is capable of inflicting and enduring—then in what guise will that force appear that we, like the two tramps in the play, shall meet sometimes, somewhere? Beckett's answer to this question is the title of the play. We know no more of the identity of this Godot at the end of the play than at the close of the last act of our own lives. When

[5]

the curtain falls, we suspect nothing of that force whose ravages have been displayed before our eyes. But we are aware of one thing, something that can never be taken from us by what we have suffered in all its horror: our anticipation. This is man's metaphysical choice in the face of the perpetual, uncertain wait depicted in the simplicity of that great work, *Waiting for Godot.*

The Biblical allusion contained in the other play deals rather with men's earthly choices, their relations with one another, and here is heard the voice that crieth in the wilderness. In his explication of the text Beckett has much to say of the capacity for irresponsible illusion in a man set down without hope in the midst of the desert. But the theme is something else. The exterior event consists in the man's isolation as more and more sand covers him until in the end he is completely buried in his loneliness. But one thing remains and still rises above the suffocating silence: his head, his voice that cries in the wilderness, man's inextinguishable need to seek other men as long as he lives, to speak to his fellows and to find a common deliverance.

The Swedish Academy regrets that Samuel Beckett is not with us today. He has selected as his representative, however, the man who first recognized the importance of the work that we honor today, his Paris publisher, M. Jérôme Lindon. I beg you, sir, to accept from His Majesty the King the Nobel Prize for Literature awarded by the Academy to Samuel Beckett.

HAPPY DAYS

A PLAY IN TWO ACTS

By SAMUEL BECKETT

Act I

Expanse of scorched grass rising center to low mound. Gentle slopes down to front and either side of stage. Back an abrupter fall to stage level. Maximum of simplicity and symmetry.

Blazing light.

Very pompier trompe-l'oeil backcloth to represent unbroken plain and sky receding to meet in far distance.

Imbedded up to above her waist in exact center of mound, WINNIE. *About fifty, well preserved, blond for preference, plump, arms and shoulders bare, low bodice, big bosom, pearl necklet. She is discovered sleeping, her arms on the ground before her, her head on her arms. Beside her on ground to her left a capacious black bag, shopping variety, and to her right a collapsible collapsed parasol, beak of handle emerging from sheath.*

To her right and rear, lying asleep on ground, hidden by mound, WILLIE.

[7]

Long pause. A bell rings piercingly, say ten seconds, stops. She does not move. Pause. Bell more piercingly, say five seconds. She wakes. Bell stops. She raises her head, gazes front. Long pause. She straightens up, lays her hands flat on ground, throws back her head and gazes at zenith. Long pause.

WINNIE   (*gazing at zenith*). Another heavenly day. (*Pause. Head back level, eyes front, pause. She clasps hands to breast, closes eyes. Lips move in inaudible prayer, say ten seconds. Lips still. Hands remain clasped. Low.*) For Jesus Christ sake Amen. (*Eyes open, hands unclasp, return to mound. Pause. She clasps hands to breast again, closes eyes, lips move again in inaudible addendum, say five seconds. Low.*) World without end Amen. (*Eyes open, hands unclasp, return to mound. Pause.*) Begin, Winnie. (*Pause.*) Begin your day, Winnie. (*Pause. She turns to bag, rummages in it without moving it from its place, brings out toothbrush, rummages again, brings out flat tube of toothpaste, turns back front, unscrews cap of tube, lays cap on ground, squeezes with difficulty small blob of paste on brush, holds tube in one hand and brushes teeth with other. She turns modestly aside and back to her right to spit out behind mound. In this position her eyes rest on* WILLIE. *She spits out. She cranes a little further back and down. Loud.*) Hoo-oo! (*Pause. Louder.*) Hoo-oo! (*Pause. Tender smile as she turns back front, lays down brush.*) Poor Willie — (*examines tube, smile off*) — running out — (*looks for cap*) — ah well — (*finds cap*) — can't be helped — (*screws on cap*) — just one of those old

[8]

things — (*lays down tube*) — another of those
old things — (*turns towards bag*) — just can't
be cured — (*rummages in bag*) — cannot be
cured — (*brings out small mirror, turns back
front*) — ah yes — (*inspects teeth in mirror*) —
poor dear Willie — (*testing upper front teeth
with thumb, indistinctly*) — good Lord!
— (*pulling back upper lip to inspect gums, do.*)
— good God! — (*pulling back corner of mouth,
mouth open, do.*) — ah well — (*other corner,
do.*) — no worse — (*abandons inspection,
normal speech*) — no better, no worse — (*lays
down mirror*) — no change — (*wipes fingers on
grass*) — no pain — (*looks for toothbrush*)—
hardly any — (*takes up toothbrush*) — great
thing that — (*examines handle of brush*) —
nothing like it — (*examines handle, reads*) —
pure . . . what? — (*pause*) — what? — (*lays
down brush*) — ah yes — (*turns towards bag*)
— poor Willie — (*rummages in bag*) — no zest
— (*rummages*) — for anything — (*brings out
spectacles in case*) — no interest — (*turns back
front*) — in life — (*takes spectacles from case*)
— poor dear Willie — (*lays down case*) — sleep
forever — (*opens spectacles*) — marvelous gift
— (*puts on spectacles*) — nothing to touch it —
(*looks for toothbrush*) — in my opinion —
(*takes up toothbrush*) — always said so —
(*examines handle of brush*) — wish I had it
— (*examines handle, reads*) — genuine . . .
pure . . . what? — (*lays down brush*) — blind
next — (*takes off spectacles*) — ah well — (*lays
down spectacles*) — seen enough — (*feels in
bodice for handkerchief*) — I suppose — (*takes
out folded handkerchief*) — by now — (*shakes
out handkerchief*) — what are those wonderful
lines — (*wipes one eye*) — woe woe is me —

[9]

(*wipes the other*) — to see what I see — (*looks
for spectacles*) — ah yes — (*takes up spectacles*)
— wouldn't miss it — (*starts polishing
spectacles, breathing on lenses*)— or would I?
— (*polishes*) — holy light — (*polishes*) — bob
up out of dark — (*polishes*) — blaze of hellish
light. (*Stops polishing, raises face to sky, pause,
head back level, resumes polishing, stops
polishing, cranes back to her right and down.*)
Hoo-oo! (*Pause. Tender smile as she turns
back front and resumes polishing. Smile off.*)
Marvelous gift — (*stops polishing, lays down
spectacles*) — wish I had it — (*folds handkerchief*) — ah well — (*puts handkerchief back
in bodice*) — can't complain — (*looks for
spectacles*) — no no — (*takes up spectacles*) —
mustn't complain — (*holds up spectacles, looks
through lens*) — so much to be thankful for —
(*looks through other lens*) — no pain — (*puts
on spectacles*) — hardly any — (*looks for
toothbrush*) — wonderful thing that — (*takes
up toothbrush*) — nothing like it — (*examines
handle of brush*) — slight headache sometimes
— (*examines handle, reads*) — guaranteed . . .
genuine . . . pure . . . what? — (*looks closer*) —
genuine pure . . . — (*takes handkerchief from
bodice*) — ah yes — (*shakes out handkerchief*)
— occasional mild migraine — (*starts wiping
handle of brush*) — it comes — (*wipes*) — then
goes — (*wiping mechanically*) — ah yes —
(*wiping*) — many mercies — (*wiping*) — great
mercies — (*stops wiping, fixed lost gaze,
brokenly*) — prayers perhaps not for naught —
(*pause, do.*) — first thing — (*pause, do.*) —
last thing — (*head down, resumes wiping, stops
wiping, head up, calmed, wipes eyes, folds
handkerchief, puts it back in bodice, examines*

handle of brush, reads) — fully guaranteed . . .
genuine pure . . . — (*looks closer*) — genuine
pure . . . (*Takes off spectacles, lays them and
brush down, gazes before her.*) Old things.
(*Pause.*) Old eyes. (*Long pause.*) On, Winnie.
(*She casts about her, sees parasol, considers it
at length, takes it up and develops from sheath
a handle of surprising length. Holding butt of
parasol in right hand she cranes back and down
to her right to hang over* WILLIE.) Hoo-oo!
(*Pause.*) Willie! (*Pause.*) Wonderful gift.
(*She strikes down at him with beak of
parasol.*) Wish I had it. (*She strikes again.
The parasol slips from her grasp and falls
behind mound. It is immediately restored to
her by* WILLIE's *invisible hand.*) Thank you,
dear. (*She transfers parasol to left hand, turns
back front and examines right palm.*) Damp.
(*Returns parasol to right hand, examines left
palm.*) Ah well, no worse. (*Head up,
cheerfully.*) No better, no worse, no change.
(*Pause. Do.*) No pain. (*Cranes back to look
down at* WILLIE, *holding parasol by butt as
before.*) Don't go off on me again now dear
will you please, I may need you. (*Pause.*)
No hurry, no hurry, just don't curl up on me
again. (*Turns back front, lays down parasol,
examines palms together, wipes them on grass.*)
Perhaps a shade off color just the same.
(*Turns to bag, rummages in it, brings out
revolver, holds it up, kisses it rapidly, puts it
back, rummages, brings out almost empty
bottle of red medicine, turns back front, looks
for spectacles, puts them on, reads label.*) Loss
of spirits . . . lack of keenness . . . want of
appetite . . . infants . . . children . . . adults . . .
six level . . . tablespoonfuls daily — (*head up,*

smile) — the old style! — (*smile off, head down, reads*) — daily . . . before and after . . . meals . . . instantaneous . . . (*looks closer*) . . . improvement. (*Takes off spectacles, lays them down, holds up bottle at arm's length to see level, unscrews cap, swigs it off head well back, tosses cap and bottle away in* WILLIE'*s direction. Sound of breaking glass.*) Ah that's better! (*Turns to bag, rummages in it, brings out lipstick, turns back front, examines lipstick.*) Running out. (*Looks for spectacles.*) Ah well. (*Puts on spectacles, looks for mirror.*) Mustn't complain. (*Takes up mirror, starts doing lips.*) What is that wonderful line? (*Lips.*) Oh fleeting joys — (*lips*) — oh something lasting woe. (*Lips. She is interrupted by disturbance from* WILLIE. *He is sitting up. She lowers lipstick and mirror and cranes back and down to look at him. Pause. Top back of* WILLIE'*s bald head, trickling blood, rises to view above slope, comes to rest.* WINNIE *pushes up her spectacles. Pause. His hand appears with handkerchief, spreads it on skull, disappears. Pause. The hand appears with boater, club ribbon, settles it on head, rakish angel, disappears. Pause.* WINNIE *cranes a little further back and down.*) Slip on your drawers, dear, before you get singed. (*Pause.*) No? (*Pause.*) Oh I see, you still have some of that stuff left. (*Pause.*) Work it well in, dear. (*Pause.*) Now the other. (*Pause. She turns back front, gazes before her. Happy expression.*) Oh this is going to be another happy day! (*Pause. Happy expression off. She pulls down spectacles and resumes lips.* WILLIE *opens newspaper, hands invisible. Tops of yellow sheets appear on either side of his head.* WINNIE *finishes lips, inspects them in mirror held a little further away.*) Ensign crimson. (WILLIE *turns page.* WINNIE *lays down lipstick and mirror, turns towards bag.*) Pale flag.

WILLIE *turns page.* WINNIE *rummages in bag, brings out small ornate brimless hat with crumpled feather, turns back front, straightens hat, smooths feather, raises it towards head, arrests gesture as* WILLIE *reads.*

WILLIE His Grace and Most Reverend Father in God Dr. Carolus Hunter dead in tub.

Pause.

WINNIE (*gazing front, hat in hand, tone of fervent reminiscence*). Charlie Hunter! (*Pause.*) I close my eyes — (*she takes off spectacles and does so, hat in one hand, spectacles in other,* WILLIE *turns page*) — and am sitting on his knees again, in the back garden at Borough Green, under the horse-beech. (*Pause. She opens eyes, puts on spectacles, fiddles with hat.*) Oh the happy memories!

Pause. She raises hat towards head, arrests gesture as WILLIE *reads.*

WILLIE Opening for smart youth.

Pause. She raises hat towards head, arrests gesture, take off spectacles, gazes front, hat in one hand, spectacles in other.

WINNIE My first ball! (*Long pause.*) My second ball! (*Long pause. Closes eyes.*) My first kiss!

[13]

(*Pause.* WILLIE *turns page.* WINNIE *opens eyes.*) A Mr. Johnson, or Johnston, or perhaps I should say John*stone*. Very bushy moustache, very tawny. (*Reverently.*) Almost ginger! (*Pause.*) Within a toolshed, though whose I cannot conceive. We had no toolshed and he most certainly had no toolshed. (*Closes eyes.*) I see the piles of pots. (*Pause.*) The tangles of bast. (*Pause.*) The shadows deepening among the rafters.

Pause. She opens eyes, puts on spectacles, raises hat towards head, arrests gesture as WILLIE *reads.*

WILLIE   Wanted bright boy.

Pause. WINNIE *puts on hat hurriedly, looks for mirror.* WILLIE *turns page.* WINNIE *takes up mirror, inspects hat, lays down mirror, turns towards bag. Paper disappears.* WINNIE *rummages in bag, brings out magnifying-glass, turns back front, looks for toothbrush. Paper reappears, folded, and begins to fan* WILLIE's *face, hand invisible.* WINNIE *takes up tooth-brush and examines handle through glass.*

WINNIE   Fully guaranteed . . . (WILLIE *stops fanning*) . . . genuine pure . . . (*Pause.* WILLIE *resumes fanning.* WINNIE *looks closer, reads.*) Fully guaranteed . . . (WILLIE *stops fanning*) . . . genuine pure . . . (*Pause.* WILLIE *resumes fanning.* WINNIE *lays down glass and brush, takes handkerchief from bodice, takes off and polishes spectacles, puts on spectacles, looks for glass, takes up and polishes glass, lays down glass, looks for brush, takes up brush and wipes*

[14]

handle, lays down brush, puts handkerchief
back in bodice, looks for glass, takes up glass,
looks for brush, takes up brush and examines
handle through glass.) Fully guaranteed . . .
(WILLIE *stops fanning*) . . . genuine pure . . .
(*pause*, WILLIE *resumes fanning*) . . . hog's
(WILLIE *stops fanning, pause*) . . . setae.
(*Pause.* WINNIE *lays down glass and brush,*
paper disappears, WINNIE *takes off*
spectacles, lays them down, gazes front.) Hog's
setae. (*Pause.*) That is what I find so wonderful, that not a day goes by — (*smile*) — to speak
in the old style — (*smile off*) — hardly a day,
without some addition to one's knowledge
however trifling, the addition I mean, provided
one takes the pains. (WILLIE'*s hand reappears*
with a postcard which he examines close to
eyes.) And if for some strange reason no
further pains are possible, why then just close
the eyes — (*she does so*) — and wait for the
day to come — (*open eyes*) — the happy day
to come when flesh melts at so many degrees
and the night of the moon has so many hundred
hours. (*Pause.*) That is what I find so com-
forting when I lose heart and envy the brute
beast. (*Turning towards* WILLIE.) I hope
you are taking in — (*She sees postcard, bends*
lower.) What is that you have there, Willie,
may I see? (*She reaches down with hand and*
WILLIE *hands her card. The hairy forearm*
appears above slope, raised in gesture of giving,
the hand open to take back, and remains in this
position till card is returned. WINNIE *turns*
back front and examines card.) Heavens what
are they up to! (*She looks for spectacles, puts*
them on and examines card.) No but this is just
genuine pure filth! (*Examines card.*) Make any

nice-minded person want to vomit! (*Impatience of* WILLIE'*s fingers. She looks for
glass, takes it up and examines card through
glass. Long pause.*) What does that creature in
the background think he's doing? (*Looks
closer.*) Oh no really! (*Impatience of fingers.
Last long look. She lays down glass, takes edge
of card between right forefinger and thumb,
averts head, takes nose between left forefinger
and thumb.*) Pah! (*Drops card.*) Take it away!
(WILLIE'*s arm disappears. His hand reappears
immediately, holding card.* WINNIE *takes off
spectacles, lays them down, gazes before her.
During what follows* WILLIE *continues to
relish card, varying angles and distance from
his eyes.*) Hog's setae. (*Puzzled expression.*)
What exactly is a hog? (*Pause. Do.*) A sow of
course I know, but a hog . . . (*Puzzled
expression off.*) Oh well what does it matter,
that is what I always say, it will come back,
that is what I find so wonderful, all comes back.
(*Pause.*) All? (*Pause.*) No, not all. (*Smile.*)
No no. (*Smile off.*) Not quite. (*Pause.*) A part.
(*Pause.*) Floats up, one fine day, out of the
blue. (*Pause.*) That is what I find so wonderful.
(*Pause. She turns towards bag. Hand and card
disappear. She makes to rummage in bag, arrests
gesture.*) No. (*She turns back front. Smile.*)
No no. (*Smile off.*) Gently Winnie. (*She
gazes front.* WILLIE'*s hand reappears, takes
off hat, disappears with hat.*) What then?
(*Hand reappears, takes handkerchief from
skull, disappears with handkerchief. Sharply,
as to one not paying attention.*) Winnie!
(WILLIE *bows head out of sight.*) What *is*
the alternative? (*Pause.*) What *is* the al —

(WILLIE *blows nose loud and long, head and
hands invisible. She turns to look at him. Pause.
Head reappears. Pause. Hand reappears with
handkerchief, spreads it on skull, disappears.
Pause. Hand reappears with boater, settles it on
head, rakish angle, disappears. Pause.*) Would
I had let you sleep on. (*She turns back front.
Intermittent plucking at grass, head up and
down, to animate following.*) Ah yes, if only I
could bear to be alone, I mean prattle away
with not a soul to hear. (*Pause.*) Not that I
flatter myself you hear much, no Willie, God
forbid. (*Pause.*) Days perhaps when you hear
nothing. (*Pause.*) But days too when you
answer. (*Pause.*) So that I may say at all times,
even when you do not answer and perhaps hear
nothing, Something of this is being heard, I am
not merely talking to myself, that is in the
wilderness, a thing I could never bear to do —
for any length of time. (*Pause.*) That is what
enables me to go on, go on talking that is.
(*Pause.*) Whereas if you were to die — (*smile*)
— to speak in the old style — (*smile off*) — or go
away and leave me, then what would I do, what
could I do, all day long, I mean between the
bell for waking and the bell for sleep? (*Pause.*)
Simply gaze before me with compressed lips.
(*Long pause while she does so. No more
plucking.*) Not another word as long as I drew
breath, nothing to break the silence of this
place. (*Pause.*) Save possibly, now and then,
every now and then, a sigh into my looking-
glass. (*Pause.*) Or a brief . . . gale of laughter,
should I happen to see the old joke again.
(*Pause. Smile appears, broadens and seems
about to culminate in laugh when suddenly*

[17]

replaced by expression of anxiety.) My hair!
(*Pause.*) Did I brush and comb my hair?
(*Pause.*) I may have done. (*Pause.*) Normally
I do. (*Pause.*) There is so little one *can* do.
(*Pause.*) One does it all. (*Pause.*) All one can.
(*Pause.*) 'Tis only human. (*Pause.*) Human
nature. (*She begins to inspect mound, looks
up.*) Human weakness. (*She resumes inspection
of mound, looks up.*) Natural weakness. (*She
resumes inspection of mound.*) I see no comb.
(*Inspects.*) Nor any hairbrush. (*Looks up.
Puzzled expression. She turns to bag, rummages
in it.*) The comb is here. (*Back front. Puzzled
expression. Back to bag. Rummages.*) The
brush is here. (*Back front. Puzzled expression.*)
Perhaps I put them back, after use. (*Pause.
Do.*) But normally I do not put things back,
after use, no, I leave them lying about and put
them back all together, at the end of the day.
(*Smile.*) To speak in the old style. (*Pause.*)
The sweet old style. (*Smile off.*) And yet
. . . I seem . . . to remember . . . (*Suddenly
careless.*) Oh well, what does it matter, that
is what I always say, I shall simply brush and
comb them later on, purely and simply, I have
the whole — (*Pause. Puzzled.*) Them? (*Pause.*)
Or it? (*Pause.*) Brush and comb it? (*Pause.*)
Sounds improper somehow. (*Pause. Turning a
little towards* WILLIE.) What would you say,
Willie? (*Pause. Turning a little further.*) What
would you say, Willie, speaking of your hair,
them or it? (*Pause.*) The hair on your head, I
mean. (*Pause. Turning a little further.*) The
hair on your head, Willie, what would you say
speaking of the hair on your head, them or it?

Long pause.

[18]

WILLIE   It.

WINNIE   (*turning back front, joyful*). Oh you are going
           to talk to me today, this is going to be a happy
           day! (*Pause. Joy off.*) Another happy day.
           (*Pause.*) Ah well, where was I, my hair, yes,
           later on, I shall be thankful for it later on.
           (*Pause.*) I have my   (*raises hands to hat*)   yes,
           on, my hat on — (*lowers hands*) — I cannot take
           it off now. (*Pause.*) To think there are times
           one cannot take off one's hat, not if one's life
           were at stake. Times one cannot put it on, times
           one cannot take it off. (*Pause.*) How often I
           have said, Put on your hat now, Winnie, there
           is nothing else for it, take off your hat now,
           Winnie, like a good girl, it will do you good,
           and did not. (*Pause.*) Could not. (*Pause. She
           raises hand, frees a strand of hair from under
           hat, draws it towards eye, squints at it, lets it
           go, hand down.*) Golden you called it, that day,
           when the last guest was gone — (*hand up in
           gesture of raising a glass*) — to your golden . . .
           may it never . . . (*voice breaks*) . . . may it
           never . . . (*Hand down. Head down. Pause.
           Low.*) That day. (*Pause. Do.*) What day?
           (*Pause. Head up. Normal voice.*) What now?
           (*Pause.*) Words fail, there are times when even
           they fail. (*Turning a little towards* WILLIE.)
           Is that not so, Willie? (*Pause. Turning a little
           further.*) Is not that so, Willie, that even words
           fail, at times? (*Pause. Back front.*) What is one
           to do then, until they come again? Brush and
           comb the hair, if it has not been done, or if
           there is some doubt, trim the nails if they are
           in need of trimming, these things tide one over.
           (*Pause.*) That is what I mean. (*Pause.*) That is
           all I mean. (*Pause.*) That is what I find so

wonderful, that not a day goes by — (*smile*) —
to speak in the old style — (*smile off*) —
without some blessing — (WILLIE *collapses
behind slope, his head disappears,* WINNIE
turns towards event) — in disguise. (*She cranes
back and down.*) Go back into your hole now,
Willie, you've exposed yourself enough.
(*Pause.*) Do as I say, Willie, don't lie sprawling there in this hellish sun, go back into your
hole. (*Pause.*) Go on now, Willie. (WILLIE
invisible starts crawling left towards hole.)
That's the man. (*She follows his progress with
her eyes.*) Not head first, stupid, how are you
going to turn? (*Pause.*) That's it . . . right
round . . . now . . . back in. (*Pause.*) Oh I know
it is not easy, dear, crawling backwards, but it
is rewarding in the end. (*Pause.*) You have left
your vaseline behind. (*She watches as he crawls
back for vaseline.*) The lid! (*She watches as
he crawls back towards hole. Irritated.*) Not
head first, I tell you! (*Pause.*) More to the right.
(*Pause.*) The *right,* I said. (*Pause. Irritated.*)
Keep your tail down, can't you! (*Pause.*) Now.
(*Pause.*) There! (*All these directions loud.
Now in her normal voice, still turned towards
him.*) Can you hear me? (*Pause.*) I beseech
you, Willie, just yes or no, can you hear me,
just yes or nothing.

Pause.

WILLIE   Yes.

WINNIE   (*turning front, same voice*). And now?

WILLIE   (*irritated*). Yes.

WINNIE   (*less loud*). And now?

WILLIE   (*more irritated*). Yes.

WINNIE   (*still less loud*). And now? (*A little louder.*) And now?

WILLIE   (*violently*). Yes!

WINNIE   (*same voice*). Fear no more the heat o' the sun. (*Pause.*) Did you hear that?

WILLIE   (*irritated*). Yes.

WINNIE   (*same voice*). What? (*Pause.*) What?

WILLIE   (*more irritated*). Fear no more.

        Pause.

WINNIE   (*same voice*). No more what? (*Pause.*) Fear no more what?

WILLIE   (*violently*). Fear no more!

WINNIE   (*normal voice, gabbled*). Bless you Willie I do appreciate your goodness I know what an effort it costs you, now you may relax I shall not trouble you again unless I am obliged to, by that I mean unless I come to the end of my own resources which is most unlikely, just to know that in theory you can hear me even though in fact you don't is all I need, just to feel you there within earshot and conceivably on the qui vive is all I ask, not to say anything I would not wish you to hear or liable to cause you pain, not to be just babbling away on trust as it is were not knowing and something gnawing at me. (*Pause for breath.*) Doubt. (*Places index and second finger on heart area,*

moves them about, brings them to rest.) Here.
(*Moves them slightly.*) Abouts. (*Hand away.*)
Oh no doubt the time will come when before
I can utter a word I must make sure you heard
the one that went before and then no doubt
another come another time when I must learn
to talk to myself a thing I could never bear to
do such wilderness. (*Pause.*) Or gaze before me
with compressed lips. (*She does so.*) All day
long. (*Gaze and lips again.*) No. (*Smile.*) No
no. (*Smile off.*) There is of course the bag.
(*Turns towards it.*) There will always be the
bag. (*Back front.*) Yes, I suppose so. (*Pause.*)
Even when you are gone, Willie. (*She turns a
little towards him.*) You *are* going, Willie, aren't
you? (*Pause. Louder.*) You *will* be going
soon, Willie, won't you? (*Pause. Louder.*)
Willie! (*Pause. She cranes back and down to
look at him.*) So you have taken off your
straw, that is wise. (*Pause.*) You do look snug,
I must say, with your chin on your hands and
the old blue eyes like saucers in the shadows.
(*Pause.*) Can you see me from there I wonder,
I still wonder. (*Pause.*) No? (*Back front.*) Oh
I know it does not follow when two are
gathered together — (*faltering*) — in this way
— (*normal*) — that because one sees the other
the other sees the one, life has taught me that
. . . too. (*Pause.*) Yes, life I suppose, there is no
other word. (*She turns a little towards him.*)
Could you see me, Willie, do you think, from
where you are, if you were to raise your eyes
in my direction? (*Turns a little further.*) Lift
up your eyes to me, Willie, and tell me can you
see me, do that for me, I'll lean back as far as I
can. (*Does so. Pause.*) No? (*Pause.*) Well
never mind. (*Turns back painfully front.*) The

earth is very tight today, can it be I have put
on flesh, I trust not. (*Pause. Absently, eyes
lowered.*) The great heat possibly. (*Starts to
pat and stroke ground.*) All things expanding,
some more than others. (*Pause. Patting and
stroking.*) Some less. (*Pause. Do.*) Oh I can
well imagine what is passing through your mind,
it is not enough to have to listen to the woman,
now I must look at her as well. (*Pause. Do.*)
Well it is very understandable. (*Pause. Do.*)
Most understandable. (*Pause. Do.*) One does
not appear to be asking a great deal, indeed at
times it would seem hardly possibly — (*voice
breaks, falls to a murmur*) — to ask less — of a
fellow-creature — to put it mildly — whereas
actually — when you think about it — look into
your heart — see the other — what he needs —
peace — to be left in peace — then perhaps the
moon — all this time — asking for the moon.
(*Pause. Stroking hand suddenly still. Lively.*)
Oh I say, what have we here? (*Bending head to
ground, incredulous.*) Looks like life of some
kind! (*Looks for spectacles, puts them on,
bends closer. Pause.*) An emmet! (*Recoils.
Shrill.*) Willie, an emmet, a live emmet!
(*Seizes magnifying-glass, bends to ground
again, inspects through glass.*) Where's it gone?
(*Inspects.*) Ah! (*Follows its progress through
grass.*) Has like a little white ball in its arms.
(*Follows progress. Hand still. Pause.*) It's gone
in. (*Continues a moment to gaze at spot
through glass, then slowly straightens up, lays
down glass, takes off spectacles and gazes
before her, spectacles in hand. Finally.*) Like a
little white ball.

Long pause. Gesture to lay down spectacles.

[23]

WILLIE   Eggs.

WINNIE   (*arresting gesture*). What?

Pause.

WILLIE   Eggs. (*Pause. Gesture to lay down glasses.*)
Formication.

WINNIE   (*arresting gesture*). What?

Pause.

WILLIE   Formication.

*Pause. She lays down spectacles, gazes before
her. Finally.*

WINNIE   (*murmur*). God. (*Pause.* WILLIE *laughs
quietly. After a moment she joins in. They
laugh quietly together.* WILLIE *stops. She
laughs on a moment alone.* WILLIE *joins in.
They laugh together. She stops.* WILLIE
*laughs on a moment alone. He stops. Pause.
Normal voice.*) Ah well what a joy in any case
to hear you laugh again, Willie, I was
convinced I never would, you never would.
(*Pause.*) I suppose some people might think us
a trifle irreverent, but I doubt it. (*Pause.*) How
can one better magnify the Almighty than by
sniggering with him at his little jokes,
particularly the poorer ones? (*Pause.*) I think
you would back me up there, Willie. (*Pause.*)
Or were we perhaps diverted by two quite
different things? (*Pause.*) Oh well, what does
it matter, that is what I always say, so long
as one . . . you know . . . what is that wonderful

line . . . laughing wild . . . something something
laughing wild amid severest woe. (*Pause.*) And
now? (*Long pause.*) Was I lovable once,
Willie? (*Pause.*) Was I ever lovable? (*Pause.*)
Do not misunderstand my question, I am not
asking you if you loved me, we know all about
that, I am asking you if you found me lovable —
at one stage. (*Pause.*) No? (*Pause.*) You can't?
(*Pause.*) Well I admit it is a teaser. And you
have done more than your bit already, for the
time being, just lie back now and relax, I shall
not trouble you again unless I am compelled to,
just to know you are there within hearing and
conceivably on the semi-alert is . . . er
paradise enough. (*Pause.*) The day is now well
advanced. (*Smile.*) To speak in the old style.
(*Smile off.*) And yet it is perhaps a little soon
for my song. (*Pause.*) To sing too soon is a
great mistake, I find. (*Turning towards bag.*)
There is of course the bag. (*Looking at bag.*)
The bag. (*Back front.*) Could I enumerate
its contents? (*Pause.*) No. (*Pause.*) Could
I, if some kind person were to come along and
ask, What all have you got in that big black bag,
Winnie? give an exhaustive answer? (*Pause.*)
No. (*Pause.*) The depths in particular, who
knows what treasures. (*Pause.*) What comforts.
(*Turns to look at bag.*) Yes, there is the bag.
(*Back front.*) But something tells me, Do not
overdo the bag, Winnie, make use of it of
course, let it help you . . . along, when stuck,
by all means, but cast your mind forward,
something tells me, cast your mind forward,
Winnie, to the time when words must fail —
(*she closes eyes, pause, opens eyes*) — and do
not overdo the bag. (*Pause. She turns to look
at bag.*) Perhaps just one quick dip. (*She turns*

*back front, closes eyes, throws out left arm,
plunges hand in bag and brings out revolver.
Disgusted.*) You again! (*She opens eyes, brings
revolver front and contemplates it. She weighs
it in her palm.*) You'd think the weight of this
thing would bring it down among the . . . last
rounds. But no. It doesn't. Ever uppermost,
like Browning. (*Pause.*) Brownie . . . (*Turning
a little towards* WILLIE.) Remember
Brownie, Willie? (*Pause.*) Remember how
you used to keep on at me to take it away from
you? Take it away, Winnie, take it away,
before I put myself out of my misery. (*Back
front. Derisive.*) *Your* misery! (*To revolver.*)
Oh I suppose it's a comfort to know you're
there, but I'm tired of you. (*Pause.*) I'll leave
you out, that's what I'll do. (*She lays revolver
on ground to her right.*) There, that's your
home from this day out. (*Smile.*) The old style!
(*Smile off.*) And now? (*Long pause.*) Is
gravity what it was, Willie, I fancy not.
(*Pause.*) Yes, the feeling more and more that
if I were not held — (*gesture*) — in this way,
I would simply float up into the blue. (*Pause.*)
And that perhaps some day the earth will yield
and let me go, the pull is so great, yes, crack all
round me and let me out. (*Pause.*) Don't you
ever have that feeling, Willie, of being sucked
up? (*Pause.*) Don't you have to cling on
sometimes, Willie? (*Pause. She turns a little
towards him.*) Willie.

Pause.

WILLIE   *Sucked* up?

WINNIE   Yes love, up into the blue, like gossamer.
(*Pause.*) No? (*Pause.*) You don't? (*Pause.*)

Ah well, natural laws, natural laws, I suppose
it's like everything else, it all depends on the
creature you happen to be. All I can say is for
my part is that for me they are not what they
were when I was young and . . . foolish and
. . . (*faltering, head down*) . . . beautiful . . .
possibly . . . lovely . . . in a way . . . to look at.
(*Pause. Head up.*) Forgive me, Willie, sorrow
keeps breaking in. (*Normal voice.*) Ah well
what a joy in any case to know you are there,
as usual, and perhaps awake, and perhaps taking
all this in, some of all this, what a happy day
for me . . . it will have been. (*Pause.*) So far.
(*Pause.*) What a blessing nothing grows,
imagine if all this stuff were to start growing.
(*Pause.*) Imagine. (*Pause.*) Ah yes, great
mercies. (*Long pause.*) I can say no more.
(*Pause.*) For the moment. (*Pause. Turns to
look at bag. Back front. Smile.*) No no. (*Smile
off. Looks at parasol.*) I suppose I might — (*takes
up parasol*) — yes, I suppose I might . . . hoist
this thing now. (*Begins to unfurl it. Following
punctuated by mechanical difficulties overcome.*) One keeps putting off — putting up —
for fear of putting up — too soon — and the day
goes by — quite by — without one's having put
up — at all. (*Parasol now fully open. Turned
to her right she twirls it idly this way and that.*)
Ah yes, so little to say, so little to do, and the
fear so great, certain days, of finding oneself
. . . left, with hours still to run, before the bell
for sleep, and nothing more to say, nothing
more to do, that the days go by, certain days
go by, quite by, the bell goes, and little or
nothing said, little or nothing done. (*Raising
parasol.*) That is the danger. (*Turning front.*)
To be guarded against. (*She gazes front,*

[27]

holding up parasol with right hand. Maximum pause.) I used to perspire freely. (*Pause.*) Now hardly at all. (*Pause.*) The heat is much greater. (*Pause.*) The perspiration much less. (*Pause.*) That is what I find so wonderful. (*Pause.*) The way man adapts himself. (*Pause.*) To changing conditions. (*She transfers parasol to left hand. Long pause.*) Holding up wearies the arm. (*Pause.*) Not if one is going along. (*Pause.*) Only if one is at rest. (*Pause.*) That is a curious observation. (*Pause.*) I hope you heard that, Willie, I should be grieved to think you had not heard that. (*She takes parasol in both hands. Long pause.*) I am weary, holding it up, and I cannot put it down. (*Pause.*) I am worse off with it up than with it down, and I cannot put it down. (*Pause.*) Reason says, Put it down, Winnie, it is not helping you, put the thing down and get on with something else. (*Pause.*) I cannot. (*Pause.*) I cannot move. (*Pause.*) No, something must happen, in the world, take place, some change, I cannot, if I am to move again. (*Pause.*) Willie. (*Mildly.*) Help. (*Pause.*) No? (*Pause.*) Bid me put this thing down, Willie, I would obey you instantly, as I have always done, honored and obeyed. (*Pause.*) Please, Willie. (*Mildly.*) For pity's sake. (*Pause.*) No? (*Pause.*) You can't? (*Pause.*) Well I don't blame you, no, it would ill become me, who cannot move, to blame my Willie because he cannot speak. (*Pause.*) Fortunately I am in tongue again. (*Pause.*) That is what I find so wonderful, my two lamps, when one goes out the other burns brighter. (*Pause.*) Oh yes, great mercies. (*Maximum pause. The parasol goes on fire. Smoke, flames if feasible. She sniffs, looks up,*

throws parasol to her right behind mound,
cranes back to watch it burning. Pause.) Ah
earth you old extinguisher. (*Back front.*)
I presume this has occurred before, though I
cannot recall it. (*Pause.*) Can you, Willie?
(*Turns a little towards him.*) Can you recall
this having occurred before? (*Pause. Cranes*
back to look at him.) Do you know what has
occurred, Willie? (*Pause.*) Have you gone off
on me again? (*Pause.*) I do not ask if you are
alive to all that is going on, I merely ask if you
have not gone off on me again. (*Pause.*) Your
eyes appear to be closed, but that has no
particular significance we know. (*Pause.*)
Raise a finger, dear, will you please, if you are
not quite senseless. (*Pause.*) Do that for me,
Willie please, just the little finger, if you are
still conscious. (*Pause. Joyful.*) Oh all five, you
are a darling today, now I may continue with
an easy mind. (*Back front.*) Yes, what ever
occurred that did not occur before and yet . . .
I wonder, yes, I confess I wonder. (*Pause.*)
With the sun blazing so much fiercer down,
and hourly fiercer, is it not natural things
should go on fire never known to do so, in this
way I mean, spontaneous like. (*Pause.*) Shall I
myself not melt perhaps in the end, or burn, oh
I do not mean necessarily burst into flames, no,
just little by little be charred to a black cinder,
all this — (*ample gesture of arms*) — visible
flesh. (*Pause.*) On the other hand, did I ever
know a temperate time? (*Pause.*) No. (*Pause.*)
I speak of temperate times and torrid times,
they are empty words. (*Pause.*) I speak of
when I was not yet caught — in this way —
and had my legs and had the use of my legs,
and could seek out a shady place, like you,

[29]

when I was tired of the sun, or a sunny place
when I was tired of the shade, like you, and
they are all empty words. (*Pause.*) It is no
hotter today than yesterday, it will be no hotter
tomorrow than today, how could it, and so on
back into the far past, forward into the far
future. (*Pause.*) And should one day the earth
cover my breasts, then I shall never have seen
my breasts, no one ever seen my breasts.
(*Pause.*) I hope you caught something of that,
Willie, I should be sorry to think you had
caught nothing of all that, it is not every day I
rise to such heights. (*Pause.*) Yes, something
seems to have occurred, something has seemed
to occur, and nothing has occurred, nothing at
all, you are quite right, Willie. (*Pause.*) The
sunshade will be there again tomorrow, beside
me on this mound, to help me through the day.
(*Pause. She takes up mirror.*) I take up this
little glass, I shiver it on a stone — (*does so*) —
I throw it away — (*does so far behind her*) — it
will be in the bag again tomorrow, without a
scratch, to help me through the day. (*Pause.*)
No, one can do nothing. (*Pause.*) That is what
I find so wonderful, the way things . . . (*voice
breaks, head down*) . . . things . . . so
wonderful. (*Long pause, head down. Finally
turns, still bowed, to bag, brings out
unidentifiable odds and ends, stuffs them back,
fumbles deeper, brings out finally musical-box,
winds it up, turns it on, listens for a moment
holding it in both hands, huddled over it, turns
back front, straightens up and listens to tune,
holding box to breast with both hands. It plays
the Waltz Duet "I love you so" from* The
Merry Widow. *Gradually happy expression.
She sways to the rhythm. Music stops. Pause.*

*Brief burst of hoarse song without words —
musical-box tune — from* WILLIE. *Increase
of happy expression. She lays down box.*) Oh
this will have been a happy day! (*She claps
hands.*) Again, Willie, again! (*Claps.*) Encore,
Willie, please! (*Pause. Happy expression off.*)
No? You won't do that for me? (*Pause.*) Well
it is very understandable, very understandable.
One cannot sing just to please someone,
however much one loves them, no, song
must come from the heart, that is what I
always say, pour out from the inmost, like a
thrush. (*Pause.*) How often I have said, in evil
hours, Sing now, Winnie, sing your song, there
is nothing else for it, and did not. (*Pause.*)
Could not. (*Pause.*) No, like the thrush, or
the bird of dawning, with no thought of
benefit, to oneself or anyone else. (*Pause.*) And
now? (*Long pause. Low.*) Strange feeling.
(*Pause. Do.*) Strange feeling that someone is
looking at me. I am clear, then dim, then gone,
then dim again, then clear again, and so on,
back and forth, in and out of someone's eye.
(*Pause. Do.*) Strange? (*Pause. Do.*) No, here
all is strange. (*Pause. Normal voice.*)
Something says, Stop talking now, Winnie, for
a minute, don't squander all your words for the
day, stop talking and do something for a
change, will you? (*She raises hands and holds
them open before her eyes. Apostrophic.*) Do
something! (*She closes hands.*) What claws!
(*She turns to bag, rummages in it, brings out
finally a nailfile, turns back front and begins to
file nails. Files for a time in silence, then the
following punctuated by filing.*) There floats
up — into my thoughts — a Mr. Shower — a Mr.
and perhaps a Mrs. Shower — no — they are

holding hands — his fiancée then more likely —
or just some — loved one. (*Looks closer at
nails.*) Very brittle today. (*Resumes filing.*)
Shower — Shower — does the name mean
anything — to you, Willie — evoke any reality,
I mean — for you, Willie — don't answer if you
don't — feel up to it — you have done more —
than your bit — already — Shower — Shower.
(*Inspects filed nails.*) Bit more like it. (*Raises
head, gazes front.*) Keep yourself nice, Winnie,
that's what I always say, come what may, keep
yourself nice. (*Pause. Resumes filing.*) Yes —
Shower — Shower — (*stops filing, raises head,
gazes front, pause*) — or Cooker, perhaps I
should say Cooker. (*Turning a little towards
WILLIE.*) Cooker, Willie, does Cooker strike
a chord? (*Pause. Turns a little further.
Louder.*) Cooker, Willie, does Cooker ring a
bell, the name Cooker? (*Pause. She cranes back
to look at him. Pause.*) Oh really! (*Pause.*)
Have you no handkerchief, darling? (*Pause.*)
Have you no delicacy? (*Pause.*) Oh, Willie,
you're not eating it! Spit it out, dear, spit it
out! (*Pause. Back front.*) Ah well, I suppose
it's only natural. (*Break in voice.*) Human.
(*Pause. Do.*) What *is* one to do? (*Head down.
Do.*) All day long. (*Pause. Do.*) Day after day.
(*Pause. Head up. Smile. Calm.*) The old style!
(*Smile off. Resumes nails.*) No, done him.
(*Passes on to next.*) Should have put on my
glasses. (*Pause.*) Too late now. (*Finishes
left hand, inspects it.*) Bit more human.
(*Starts right hand. Following punctuated
as before.*) Well anyway — this man
Shower — or Cooker — no matter — and
the woman — hand in hand — in the other hands
bags — kind of big brown grips — standing there

gaping at me — and at last this man Shower —
or Cooker — ends in er anyway — stake my life
on that — What's she doing? he says — What's
the idea? he says — stuck up to her diddies in
the bleeding ground — coarse fellow — What
does it mean? he says — What's it meant to
mean? — and so on — lot more stuff like that
— usual drivel — Do you hear me? he says —
I do, she says, God help me — What do you
mean, he says, God help you? (*Stops filing,
raises head, gazes front.*) And you, she says,
what's the idea of you, she says, what are you
meant to mean? It is because you're still on
your two flat feet, with your old ditty full of
tinned muck and changes of underwear,
dragging me up and down this fornicating
wilderness, coarse creature, fit mate — (*with
sudden violence*) — let go of my hand and drop
for God's sake, she says, drop! (*Pause. Resumes
filing.*) Why doesn't he dig her out? he says —
referring to you, my dear — What good is she
to him like that? — What good is he to her like
that? — and so on — usual tosh — Good! she
says, have a heart for God's sake — Dig her out,
he says, dig her out, no sense in her like that —
Dig her out with what? she says — I'd dig her
out with my bare hands, he says — must have
been man and — wife. (*Files in silence.*) Next
thing they're away — hand in hand — and the
bags — dim — then gone — last human kind —
to stray this way. (*Finishes right hand, inspects
it, lays down file, gazes front.*) Strange thing,
time like this, drift up into the mind. (*Pause.*)
Strange? (*Pause.*) No, here all is strange.
(*Pause.*) Thankful for it in any case. (*Voice
breaks.*) Most thankful. (*Head down. Pause.
Head up. Calm.*) Bow and raise the head, bow

and raise, always that. (*Pause.*) And now?
(*Long pause. Starts putting things back in bag,
toothbrush last. This operation, interrupted by
pauses as indicated, punctuates following.*) It
is perhaps a little soon — to make ready — for
the night — (*stops tidying, head up, smile*) —
the old style! — (*smile off, resumes tidying*) —
and yet I do — make ready for the night —
feeling it at hand — the bell for sleep — saying
to myself — Winnie — it will not be long now,
Winnie — until the bell for sleep. (*Stops
tidying, head up.*) Sometimes I am wrong.
(*Smile.*) But not often. (*Smile off.*) Sometimes
all is over, for the day, all done, all said, all
ready for the night, and the day not over, far
from over, the night not ready, far, far from
ready. (*Smile.*) But not often. (*Smile off.*) Yes,
the bell for sleep, when I feel it at hand, and so
make ready for the night — (*gesture*) — in this
way, sometimes I am wrong — (*smile*) — but
not often. (*Smile off. Resumes tidying.*) I used
to think — I say I used to think — that all these
things — put back into the bag — if too soon —
put back too soon — could be taken out again —
if necessary — if needed — and so on —
indefinitely — back into the bag — back out
of the bag — until the bell — went. (*Stops
tidying, head up, smile.*) But no. (*Smile
broader.*) No no. (*Smile off. Resumes
tidying.*) I suppose this — might seem
strange — this — what shall I say — this
what I have said — yes — (*she takes up
revolver*) — strange — (*she turns to put
revolver in bag*) — were it not — (*about to put
revolver in bag she arrests gesture and turns
back front*) — were it not — (*she lays down
revolver to her right, stops tidying, her head up*) —

[34]

that all seems strange. (*Pause.*) Most strange.
(*Pause.*) Never any change. (*Pause.*) And more
and more strange. (*Pause. She bends to mound
again, takes up last object, i.e. toothbrush, and
turns to put it in bag when her attention is
drawn to disturbance from* WILLIE. *She
cranes back and to her right to see. Pause.*)
Weary of your hole, dear? (*Pause.*) Well I
can understand that. (*Pause.*) Don't forget
your straw. (*Pause.*) Not the crawler you were,
poor darling. (*Pause.*) No, not the crawler
I gave my heart to. (*Pause.*) The hands and
knees, love, try the hands and knees. (*Pause.*)
The knees! The knees! (*Pause.*) What a curse,
mobility! (*She follows with eyes his progress
towards her behind mound, i.e. towards place
he occupied at beginning of act.*) Another foot,
Willie, and you're home. (*Pause as she observes
last foot.*) Ah! (*Turns back front laboriously,
rubs neck.*) Crick in my neck admiring you.
(*Rubs neck.*) But it's worth it, well worth it.
(*Turning slightly towards him.*) Do you know
what I dream sometimes? (*Pause.*) What I
dream sometimes, Willie. (*Pause.*) That you'll
come round and live this side where I could see
you. (*Pause. Back front.*) I'd be a different
woman. (*Pause.*) Unrecognizable. (*Turning
slightly towards him.*) Or just now and then,
come round this side just every now and then
and let me feast on you. (*Back front.*) But you
can't, I know. (*Head down.*) I know. (*Pause.
Head up.*) Well anyway — (*looks at toothbrush in her hand*) — can't be long now —
(*looks at brush*) — until the bell. (*Top back of*
WILLIE's *head appears above slope.* WINNIE
looks closer at brush.) Fully guaranteed . . .
(*head up*) . . . what's this it was? (WILLIE's

[35]

hand appears with handkerchief, spreads it on skull, disappears.) Genuine pure . . . fully guaranteed . . . (WILLIE's *hand appears with boater, settles it on head, rakish angle, disappears*) . . . genuine pure . . . ah! hog's setae. (*Pause.*) What is a hog exactly? (*Pause. Turns slightly towards* WILLIE.) What exactly is a hog, Willie, do you know, I can't remember. (*Pause. Turning a little further, pleading.*) What *is* a hog, Willie, please!

Pause.

WILLIE   Castrated male swine. (*Happy expression appears on* WINNIE's *face.*) Reared for slaughter.

Happy expression increases. WILLIE *opens newspaper, hand invisible. Tops of yellow sheets appear on either side of his head.* WINNIE *gazes before her with happy expression.*

WINNIE   Oh this *is* a happy day! This will have been another happy day! (*Pause.*) After all. (*Pause.*) So far.

Pause. Happy expression off. WILLIE *turns page. Pause. He turns another page. Pause.*

WILLIE   Opening for smart youth.

Pause. WINNIE *takes off hat, turns to put it in bag, arrests gesture, turns back front. Smile.*

WINNIE   No. (*Smile broader.*) No no. (*Smile off. Puts on hat again, gazes front, pause.*) And now?

(*Pause.*) Sing. (*Pause.*) Sing your song,
Winnie. (*Pause.*) No? (*Pause.*) Then pray.
(*Pause.*) Pray your prayer, Winnie.

Pause. WILLIE *turns page. Pause.*

WILLIE   Wanted bright boy.

Pause. WINNIE *gazes before her.* WILLIE
turns page. Pause. Newspaper disappears.
Long pause.

WINNIE   Pray your old prayer. Winnie.

Long pause.

CURTAIN

Act II

Scene *as before.*

WINNIE *imbedded up to neck, hat on head,*
eyes closed. Her head, which she can no longer
turn, nor bow, nor raise, faces front motionless
throughout act. Movements of eyes as
indicated.

Bag and parasol as before. Revolver
conspicuous to her right on mound.

Long pause.

Bell rings loudly. She opens eyes at once. Bell
stops. She gazes front. Long pause.

WINNIE   Hail, holy light. (*Long pause. She closes her
eyes. Bell rings loudly. She opens eyes at once.
Bell stops. She gazes front. Long smile. Smile
off. Long pause.*) Someone is looking at me
still. (*Pause.*) Caring for me still. (*Pause.*)
That is what I find so wonderful. (*Pause.*)
Eyes on my eyes. (*Pause.*) What is that un-
forgettable line? (*Pause. Eyes right.*) Willie.
(*Pause. Louder.*) Willie. (*Pause. Eyes front.*)
May one still speak of time? (*Pause.*) Say it is
a long time now, Willie, since I saw you.
(*Pause.*) Since I heard you. (*Pause.*) May one?
(*Pause.*) One does. (*Smile.*) The old style!
(*Smile off.*) There is so little one can speak of.
(*Pause.*) One speaks of it all. (*Pause.*) All one
can. (*Pause.*) I used to think . . . (*pause*) . . . I
say I used to think that I would learn to talk
alone. (*Pause.*) By that I mean to myself, the
wilderness. (*Smile.*) But no. (*Smile broader.*)
No no. (*Smile off.*) Ergo you are there.
(*Pause.*) Oh no doubt you are dead, like the
others, no doubt you have died, or gone away
and left me, like the others, it doesn't matter,
you are there. (*Pause. Eyes left.*) The
bag too is there, the same as ever, I can
see it. (*Pause. Eyes right. Louder.*) The
bag is there, Willie, as good as ever, the
one you gave me that day . . . to go to market.
(*Pause. Eyes front.*) That day. (*Pause.*) What
day? (*Pause.*) I used to pray. (*Pause.*) I say
I used to pray. (*Pause.*) Yes, I must confess I
did. (*Smile.*) Not now. (*Smile broader.*) No
no. (*Smile off. Pause.*) Then . . . now . . . what
difficulties here, for the mind. (*Pause.*) To
have been always what I am — and so changed
from what I was. (*Pause.*) I am the one, I say
the one, then the other. (*Pause.*) Now the one,

then the other. (*Pause.*) There is so little one
can say, one says it all. (*Pause.*) All
one can. (*Pause.*) And no truth in it anywhere.
(*Pause.*) My arms. (*Pause.*) My breasts.
(*Pause.*) What arms? (*Pause.*) What breasts?
(*Pause.*) Willie. (*Pause.*) What Willie?
(*Sudden vehement affirmation.*) My Willie!
(*Eyes right calling.*) Willie! (*Pause. Louder.*)
Willie! (*Pause. Eyes front.*) Ah well, not to
know, not to know for sure, great mercy, all I
ask. (*Pause.*) Ah yes . . . then . . . new . . .
beechen green . . . this . . . Charlie . . . kisses . . .
this . . . all that. . . deep trouble for the mind.
(*Pause.*) But it does not trouble mine. (*Smile.*)
Not now. (*Smile broader.*) No no. (*Smile off.
Long pause. She closes eyes. Bell rings loudly.
She opens eyes. Pause.*) Eyes float up that seem
to close in peace . . . to see . . . in peace. (*Pause.*)
Not mine. (*Smile.*) Not now. (*Smile broader.*)
No no. (*Smile off. Long pause.*) Willie.
(*Pause.*) Do you think the earth has lost its
atmosphere, Willie? (*Pause.*) Do you, Willie?
(*Pause.*) You have no opinion? (*Pause.*) Well
that is like you, you never had any opinion
about anything. (*Pause.*) It's understandable.
(*Pause.*) Most. (*Pause.*) The earthball. (*Pause.*)
I sometimes wonder. (*Pause.*) Perhaps not
quite all. (*Pause.*) There always remains
something. (*Pause.*) Of everything. (*Pause.*)
Some remains. (*Pause.*) If the mind were to go.
(*Pause.*) It won't of course. (*Pause.*) Not
quite. (*Pause.*) Not mine. (*Smile.*) Not now.
(*Smile broader.*) No no. (*Smile off. Long
pause.*) It might be the eternal cold. (*Pause.*)
Everlasting perishing cold. (*Pause.*) Just
chance, I take it, happy chance. (*Pause.*) Oh
yes, great mercies, great mercies. (*Pause.*) And

now? (*Long pause.*) The face. (*Pause.*) The
nose. (*She squints down.*) I can see it . . .
(*squinting down*) . . . the tip . . . the nostrils . . .
breath of life . . . that curve you so admired . . .
(*pouts*) . . . a hint of lip . . . (*pouts again*) . . .
if I pout them out . . . (*sticks out tongue*) . . .
the tongue of course . . . you so admired . . . if
I stick it out . . . (*sticks it out again*) . . . the
tip . . . (*eyes up*) . . . suspicion of brow . . .
eyebrow . . . imagination possibly . . . (*eyes
left*) . . . cheek . . . no . . . (*eyes right*) . . . no
. . . (*distends cheeks*) . . . even if I puff them out . . .
(*distends cheeks*) . . . even if I puff them out . . .
(*eyes left, distends cheeks again*) . . . no . . . no
damask. (*Eyes front.*) That is all. (*Pause.*) The
bag of course . . . (*eyes left*) . . . a little blurred
perhaps . . . but the bag. (*Eyes front. Offhand.*)
The earth of course and sky. (*Eyes right.*)
The sunshade you gave me . . . that day . . .
(*pause*) . . . that day . . . the lake . . . the reeds.
(*Eyes front. Pause.*) What day? (*Pause.*)
What reeds? (*Long pause. Eyes close. Bell
rings loudly. Eyes open. Pause. Eyes right.*)
Brownie of course. (*Pause.*) You remember
Brownie, Willie, I can see him. (*Pause.*)
Brownie is there, Willie, beside me. (*Pause.
Loud.*) Brownie is there, Willie. (*Pause. Eyes
front.*) That is all. (*Pause.*) What would I do
without them? (*Pause.*) What would I do
without them, when words fail? (*Pause.*) Gaze
before me, with compressed lips. (*Long pause
while she does so.*) I cannot. (*Pause.*) Ah yes,
great mercies, great mercies. (*Long pause.
Low.*) Sometimes I hear sounds. (*Listening
expression. Normal voice.*) But not often.
(*Pause.*) They are a boon, sounds are a boon,
they help me . . . through the day. (*Smile.*) The

old style! (*Smile off.*) Yes, those are happy
days, when there are sounds. (*Pause.*) When I
hear sounds. (*Pause.*) I used to think . . .
(*pause*) . . . I say I used to think they were in
my head. (*Smile.*) But no. (*Smile broader.*)
No no. (*Smile off.*) That was just logic.
(*Pause.*) Reason. (*Pause.*) I have not lost my
reason. (*Pause.*) Not yet. (*Pause.*)
Not all. (*Pause.*) Some remains. (*Pause.*)
Sounds. (*Pause.*) Like little . . . sunderings,
little falls . . . apart. (*Pause. Low.*) It's things,
Willie. (*Pause. Normal voice.*) In the bag,
outside the bag. (*Pause.*) Ah yes, things
have their life, that is what I always say,
things have a life. (*Pause.*) Take my
looking-glass, it doesn't need me. (*Pause.*)
The bell. (*Pause.*) It hurts like a knife.
(*Pause.*) A gouge. (*Pause.*) One cannot ignore
it. (*Pause.*) How often . . . (*pause*) . . . I say
how often I have said, Ignore it, Winnie, ignore
the bell, pay no heed, just sleep and wake, sleep
and wake, as you please, open and close the
eyes, as you please, or in the way you find most
helpful. (*Pause.*) Open and close the eyes,
Winnie, open and close, always that. (*Pause.*)
But no. (*Smile.*) Not now. (*Smile broader.*)
No no. (*Smile off. Pause.*) What now?
(*Pause.*) What now, Willie? (*Long pause.*)
There is my story of course, when all else fails.
(*Pause.*) A life. (*Smile.*) A long life. (*Smile
off.*) Beginning in the womb, where life used to
begin, Mildred has memories, she will have
memories, of the womb, before she dies, the
mother's womb. (*Pause.*) She is now four or
five already and has recently been given a big
waxen dolly. (*Pause.*) Fully clothed, complete
outfit. (*Pause.*) Shoes, socks, undies, complete

set, frilly frock, gloves. (*Pause.*) White mesh.
(*Pause.*) A little white straw hat with a chin
elastic. (*Pause.*) Pearly necklet. (*Pause.*) A
little picture-book with legends in real print
to go under her arm when she takes her walk.
(*Pause.*) China blue eyes that open and shut.
(*Pause. Narrative.*) The sun was not well up
when Milly rose, descended the steep . . .
(*pause*) . . . slipped on her nightgown,
descended all alone the steep wooden stairs,
backwards on all fours, though she had been
forbidden to do so, entered the . . . (*pause*) . . .
tiptoed down the silent passage, entered the
nursery and began to undress Dolly. (*Pause.*)
Crept under the table and began to undress
Dolly. (*Pause.*) Scolding her . . . the while.
(*Pause.*) Suddenly a mouse — (*Long pause.*)
Gently, Winnie. (*Long pause. Calling.*)
Willie! (*Pause. Louder.*) Willie! (*Pause. Mild
reproach.*) I sometimes find your attitude a
little strange, Willie, all this time, it is not like
you to be wantonly cruel. (*Pause.*) Strange?
(*Pause.*) No. (*Smile.*) Not here. (*Smile
broader.*) Not now. (*Smile off.*) And yet . . .
(*Suddenly anxious.*) I do hope nothing is amiss.
(*Eyes right, loud.*) Is all well, dear? (*Pause.
Eyes front. To herself.*) God grant he did not
go in head foremost! (*Eyes right, loud.*)
You're not stuck, Willie? (*Pause. Do.*) You're
not jammed, Willie? (*Eyes front, distressed.*)
Perhaps he is crying out for help all this time
and I do not hear him! (*Pause.*) I do of course
hear cries. (*Pause.*) But they are in my head
surely. (*Pause.*) It is possible that . . . (*Pause.
With finality.*) No no, my head was always
full of cries. (*Pause.*) Faint confused cries.
(*Pause.*) They come. (*Pause.*) Then go.

(*Pause.*) As on a wind. (*Pause.*) That is what
I find so wonderful. (*Pause.*) They cease.
(*Pause.*) Ah yes, great mercies, great
mercies. (*Pause.*) The day is now well
advanced. (*Smile. Smile off.*) And yet it
is perhaps a little soon for my song. (*Pause.*)
To sing too soon is fatal, I always
find. (*Pause.*) On the other hand it is
possible to leave it too late. (*Pause.*) The bell
goes for sleep and one has not sung. (*Pause.*)
The whole day has flown — (*smile, smile off*)
— flown by, quite by, and no song of
any class, kind or description. (*Pause.*)
There is a problem here. (*Pause.*) One
cannot sing . . . just like that, no. (*Pause.*)
It bubbles up, for some unknown reason, the
time is ill chosen, one chokes it back. (*Pause.*)
One says, Now is the time, it is now or never,
and one cannot. (*Pause.*) Simply cannot sing.
(*Pause.*) Not a note. (*Pause.*) Another thing,
Willie, while we are on this subject. (*Pause.*)
The sadness after song. (*Pause.*) Have you
run across that, Willie? (*Pause.*) In the course
of your experience. (*Pause.*) No? (*Pause.*)
Sadness after intimate sexual intercourse one is
familiar with of course. (*Pause.*) You would
concur with Aristotle there, Willie, I fancy.
(*Pause.*) Yes, that one knows and is prepared
to face. (*Pause.*) But after song . . . (*Pause.*) It
does not last of course. (*Pause.*) That is what I
find so wonderful. (*Pause.*) It wears away.
(*Pause.*) What are those exquisite lines?
(*Pause.*) Go forget me why should something
o'er that something shadow fling . . . go forget
me . . . why should sorrow . . . brightly
smile . . . go forget me . . . never hear me . . .
sweetly smile . . . brightly sing . . . (*Pause.*

[43]

With a sigh.) One loses one's classics. (*Pause.*)
Oh not all. (*Pause.*) A part. (*Pause.*) A part
remains. (*Pause.*) That is what I find so
wonderful, a part remains, of one's classics, to
help one through the day. (*Pause.*) Oh yes,
many mercies, many mercies. (*Pause.*)
And now? (*Pause.*) And now, Willie?
(*Long pause.*) I call to the eye of the
mind . . . Mr. Shower — or Cooker. (*She
closes her eyes. Bell rings loudly, She opens her
eyes. Pause.*) Hand in hand, in the other hands
bags. (*Pause.*) Getting on . . . in life. (*Pause.*)
No longer young, not yet old. (*Pause.*)
Standing there gaping at me. (*Pause.*) Can't
have been a bad bosom, he says, in its day.
(*Pause.*) Seen worse shoulders, he says, in my
time. (*Pause.*) Dose she feel her legs? he says.
(*Pause.*) Is there any life in her legs? he says.
(*Pause.*) Has she anything on underneath? he
says. (*Pause.*) Ask her, he says, I'm shy.
(*Pause.*) Ask her what? she says. (*Pause.*) Is
there any life in her legs. (*Pause.*) Has she
anything underneath. (*Pause.*) Ask her
yourself, she says. (*Pause. With sudden
violence.*) Let go of me for Christ sake and
drop! (*Pause. Do.*) Drop dead! (*Smile.*) But
no. (*Smile broader.*) No no. (*Smile off.*) I
watch them recede. (*Pause.*) Hand in hand —
and the bags. (*Pause.*) Dim. (*Pause.*) Then
gone. (*Pause.*) Last human kind — to stray this
way. (*Pause.*) Up to date. (*Pause.*) And now?
(*Pause. Low.*) Help. (*Pause. Do.*) Help,
Willie. (*Pause. Do.*) No? (*Long pause.
Narrative.*) Suddenly a mouse . . . (*Pause.*)
Suddenly a mouse ran up her little thigh and
Mildred, dropping Dolly in her fright, began
to scream — (WINNIE *gives a sudden*

piercing scream) — and screamed and
screamed — (WINNIE *screams twice*) —
screamed and screamed and screamed
and screamed till all came running, in
their night attire, papa, mamma, Bibby
and . . . old Annie, to see what was the
matter . . . (*pause*) . . . what on earth could
possibly be the matter. (*Pause.*) Too
late. (*Pause.*) Too late. (*Long pause. Just
audible.*) Willie. (*Pause. Normal voice.*) Ah
well, not long now, Winnie, can't be long now,
until the bell for sleep. (*Pause.*) Then you may
close your eyes, then you *must* close your eyes
— and keep them closed. (*Pause.*) Why say
that again? (*Pause.*) I used to think . . .
(*pause*) . . . I say I used to think there was no
difference between one fraction of a second
and the next. (*Pause.*) I used to say . . .
(*pause*) . . . I say I used to say, Winnie, you are
changeless, there is never any difference
between one fraction of a second and the next.
(*Pause.*) Why bring that up again? (*Pause.*)
There is so little one can bring up, one brings
up all. (*Pause.*) All one can. (*Pause.*) My neck
is hurting me. (*Pause. With sudden violence.*)
My neck is hurting me! (*Pause.*) Ah that's
better. (*With mild irritation.*) Everything
within reason. (*Long pause.*) I can do no more.
(*Pause.*) Say no more. (*Pause.*) But I must say
more. (*Pause.*) Problem here. (*Pause.*) No,
something must move, in the world, I can't any
more. (*Pause.*) A zephyr. (*Pause.*) A breath.
(*Pause.*) What are those immortal lines?
(*Pause.*) It might be the eternal dark. (*Pause.*)
Black night without end. (*Pause.*) Just chance,
I take it, happy chance. (*Pause.*) Oh yes,
abounding mercies. (*Long pause.*) And now?

(*Pause.*) And now, Willie? (*Long pause.*)
That day. (*Pause.*) The pink fizz. (*Pause.*)
The flute glasses. (*Pause.*) The last guest gone.
(*Pause.*) The last bumper with the bodies
nearly touching. (*Pause.*) The look. (*Long
pause.*) What day? (*Long pause.*) What look?
(*Long pause.*) I hear cries. (*Pause.*) Sing.
(*Pause.*) Sing your old song, Winnie.

*Long pause. Suddenly alert expression. Eyes
switch right.* WILLIE's *head appears to her
right round corner of mound. He is on all
fours, dressed to kill — top hat, morning coat,
striped trousers, etc., white gloves in hand.
Very long bushy white Battle of Britain
moustache. He halts, gazes front, smooths
moustache. He emerges completely from
behind mound, turns to his left, halts, looks up
at* WINNIE. *He advances on all fours towards
center, halts, turns head front, gazes front,
strokes moustache, straightens tie, adjusts hat,
advances a little further, halts, takes off hat and
looks up at* WINNIE. *He is now not far from
center and within her field of vision. Unable to
sustain effort of looking up he sinks head to
ground.*

WINNIE   (*mondaine*). Well this is an unexpected
pleasure! (*Pause.*) Reminds me of the day you
came whining for my hand. (*Pause.*) I
worship you, Winnie, be mine. (*He looks up.*)
Life a mockery without Win. (*She goes off
into a giggle.*) What a get up, you do look a
sight! (*Giggles.*) Where are the flowers?
(*Pause.*) That smile today. (WILLIE *sinks
head.*) What's that on your neck, an anthrax?
(*Pause.*) Want to watch that, Willie, before it

gets a hold on you. (*Pause.*) Where were you
all this time? (*Pause.*) What were you doing
all this time? (*Pause.*) Changing? (*Pause.*) Did
you not hear me screaming for you? (*Pause.*)
Did you get stuck in your hole? (*Pause. He
looks up.*) That's right, Willie, look at me.
(*Pause.*) Feast your old eyes, Willie. (*Pause.*)
Does anything remain? (*Pause.*) Any remains?
(*Pause.*) No? (*Pause.*) I haven't been able to
look after it, you know. (*He sinks his head.*)
You are still recognizable, in a way. (*Pause.*)
Are you thinking of coming to live this side
now . . . for a bit maybe? (*Pause.*) No?
(*Pause.*) Just a brief call? (*Pause.*) Have you
gone deaf, Willie? (*Pause.*) Dumb? (*Pause.*)
Oh I know you were never one to talk, I
worship you Winnie be mine and then nothing
from that day forth only titbits from Reynolds'
News. (*Eyes front. Pause.*) Ah well, what
matter, that's what I always say, it will have
been a happy day, after all, another happy day.
(*Pause.*) Not long now, Winnie. (*Pause.*) I
hear cries. (*Pause.*) Do you ever hear cries,
Willie? (*Pause.*) No? (*Eyes back on*
WILLIE.) Willie. (*Pause.*) Look at me again,
Willie. (*Pause.*) Once more, Willie. (*He looks
up. Happily.*) Ah! (*Pause. Shocked.*) What
ails you, Willie, I never saw such an expression!
(*Pause.*) Put on your hat, dear, it's the sun,
don't stand on ceremony, I won't mind. (*He
drops hat and gloves and starts to crawl up
mound towards her. Gleeful.*) Oh I say, this
is terrific! (*He halts, clinging to mound with
one hand, reaching up with the other.*) Come
on, dear, put a bit of jizz into it, I'll cheer you
on. (*Pause.*) Is it me you're after, Willie . . .
or is it something else? (*Pause.*) Do you want

to touch my face . . . again? (*Pause.*) Is it a kiss you're after, Willie . . . or is it something else? (*Pause.*) There was a time when I could have given you a hand. (*Pause.*) And then a time before that again when I did give you a hand. (*Pause.*) You were always in dire need of a hand, Willie. (*He slithers back to foot of mound and lies with face to ground.*) Brrum! (*Pause. He rises to hands and knees, raises his face towards her.*) Have another go, Willie, I'll cheer you on. (*Pause.*) Don't look at me like that! (*Pause. Vehement.*) Don't look at me like that! (*Pause. Low.*) Have you gone off your head, Willie? (*Pause. Do.*) Out of your poor old wits, Willie?

Pause.

WILLIE   (*just audible*). Win.

Pause. WINNIE's *eyes front. Happy expression appears, grows.*

WINNIE   Win. (*Pause.*) Oh this *is* a happy day, this will have been another happy day! (*Pause.*) After all. (*Pause.*) So far.

Pause. She hums tentatively beginning of song, then sings softly, musical-box tune.

> Though I say not
> What I may not
> Let you hear,
> Yet the swaying
> Dance is saying,
> Love me dear!
> Every touch of fingers

[48]

Tells me what I know,
Says for you,
It's true, it's true,
You love me so!

Pause. Happy expression off. She closes her
eyes. Bell rings loudly. She opens her eyes. She
smiles, gazing front. She turns her eyes, smiling,
to WILLIE, *still on his hands and knees*
looking up at her. Smile off. They look at each
other. Long pause.

CURTAIN

POEMS IN ENGLISH

By SAMUEL BECKETT

[Selections]

---

from ECHO'S BONES

Enueg I

Exeo in a spasm
tired of my darling's red sputum
from the Portobello Private Nursing Home
its secret things
and toil to the crest of the surge of the steep perilous bridge
and lapse down blankly under the scream of the hoarding
round the bright stiff banner of the hoarding
into a black west
throttled with clouds.

Above the mansions the algum-trees
the mountains
my skull sullenly
clot of anger
skewered aloft strangled in the cang of the wind
bites like a dog against its chastisement.

I trundle along rapidly now on my ruined feet
flush with the livid canal;
at Parnell Bridge a dying barge
carrying a cargo of nails and timber

rocks itself softly in the foaming cloister of the lock;
on the far bank a gang of down and outs would seem to be mending
        a beam.

Then for miles only wind
and the weals creeping alongside on the water
and the world opening up to the south
across a travesty of champaign to the mountains
and the stillborn evening turning a filthy green
manuring the night fungus
and the mind annulled
wrecked in wind.

I splashed past a little wearish old man,
Democritus,
scuttling along between a crutch and a stick,
his stump caught up horribly, like a claw, under his breech,
smoking.
Then because a field on the left went up in a sudden blaze
of shouting and urgent whistling and scarlet and blue ganzies
I stopped and climbed the bank to see the game.
A child fidgeting at the gate called up:
"Would we be let in Mister?"
"Certainly" I said "you would."
But, afraid, he set off down the road.
"Well" I called after him "why wouldn't you go on in?"
"Oh" he said, knowingly,
"I was in that field before and I got put out."
So on,
derelict,
as from a bush of gorse on fire in the mountain after dark,
or, in Sumatra, the jungle hymen,
the still flagrant rafflesia.

Next:
a lamentable family of gray verminous hens,
perishing out in the sunk field,

trembling, half asleep, against the closed door of a shed,
with no means of roosting.
The great mushy toadstool,
green-black,
oozing up after me,
soaking up the tattered sky like an ink of pestilence,
in my skull the wind going fetid,
the water . . .

Next:
on the hill down from the Fox and Geese into Chapelizod
a small malevolent goat, exiled on the road,
remotely pucking the gate of his field;
the Isolde Stores a great perturbation of sweaty heroes,
in their Sunday best,
come hastening down for a pint of nepenthe or moly or half and half
from watching the hurlers above in Kilmainham.

Blotches of doomed yellow in the pit of the Liffey;
the fingers of the ladders hooked over the parapet,
soliciting;
a slush of vigilant gulls in the gray spew of the sewer.

Ah the banner
the banner of meat bleeding
on the silk of the seas and the arctic flowers
that do not exist.

Enueg II

world world world world
and the face grave
cloud against the evening

de morituris nihil nisi

and the face crumbling shyly
too late to darken the sky
blushing away into the evening
shuddering away like a gaffe

veronica mundi
veronica munda
give us a wipe for the love of Jesus

sweating like Judas
tired of dying
tired of policemen
feet in marmalade
perspiring profusely
heart in marmalade
smoke more fruit
the old heart the old heart
breaking outside congress

doch I assure thee
lying on O'Connell Bridge
goggling at the tulips of the evening
the green tulips
shining round the corner like an anthrax
shining on Guinness's barges

the overtone the face
too late to brighten the sky
doch doch I assure thee

from QUATRE POÈMES

1. Dieppe

again the last ebb
the dead shingle
the turning then the steps
towards the lighted town

4.

I would like my love to die
and the rain to be falling on the graveyard
and on me walking the streets
mourning she who sought to love me

*(translated from the French
by the author)*

TEXTS FOR NOTHING: 10

By SAMUEL BECKETT

Translated by the author from the French

Give up, but it's all given up, it's nothing new, I'm nothing new. Ah
so there was something once, I had something once. It may be thought
there was, so long as it's known there was not, never anything, but
giving up. But let us suppose there was not, that is to say let us suppose
there was, something once, in a head, in a heart, in a hand, before all
opened, emptied, shut again and froze. This is most reassuring, after
such a fright, and emboldens me to go on, once again. But there is not
silence. No, there is utterance, somewhere someone is uttering. Inanities,
agreed, but is that enough, is that enough, to make sense? I see what
it is, the head has fallen behind, all the rest has gone on, the head and
its anus the mouth, or else it has gone on alone, all alone on its old
prowls, slobbering its shit and lapping it back off the lips like in the
days when it fancied itself. But the heart's not in it any more, nor is the
appetite what it was. So home to roost it comes among my other assets,
home yet again, and no trickery involved, that old past ever new, ever
ended, ever ending, with all its hidden treasures of promise for tomorrow,
and of consolation for today. And I'm in good hands again, they hold
my head from behind, intriguing detail, as at the hairdresser's, the
forefingers close my eyes, the middle fingers my nostrils, the thumbs
stop up my ears, but imperfectly, to enable me to hear, but imperfectly,
while the four remaining busy themselves with my jaws and tongue, to
enable me to suffocate, but imperfectly, and to utter, for my good, what
I must utter, for my future good, well-known ditty, and in particular to
observe without delay, speaking of the passing moment, that worse have
been known to pass, that it will pass in time, a mere moment of respite
which but for this first aid might have proved fatal, and that one day
I shall know again that I once was, and roughly who, and how to go on,
and speak unaided, nicely, about number one and his pale imitations.
And it is possible, just, for I must not be too affirmative at this stage,

it would not be in my interest, that other fingers, quite a different gang, other tentacles, that's more like it, other charitable suckers, waste no more time trying to get it right, will take down my declarations, so that at the close of the interminable delirium, should it ever resume, I may not be reproached with having faltered. This is awful, awful, at least there's that to be thankful for. And perhaps beside me, and all around, other souls are being licked into shape, souls swooned away, or sick with over-use, or because no use could be found for them, but still fit for use, or fit only to be cast away, pale imitations of mine. Or has it knelled here at last for our committal to flesh, as the dead are committed to the ground, in the hour of their death at last, and at the place where they die, to keep the expenses down, or for our reassignment, souls of the stillborn, or dead before the body, or still young in the middle of the ruins, or never come to life through incapacity or for some other reason, or the immortal type, there must be a few of them too, whose bodies were always wrong, but patience there's a true one in pickle, among the unborn hordes, the true sepulchral body, for the living have no room for a second. No, no souls, or bodies, or birth, or life, or death, you've got to go on without any of that junk, that's all dead with words, with excess of words, they can say nothing else, they say there is nothing else, that here it's that and nothing else, but they won't say it eternally, they'll find some other nonsense, no matter what, and I'll be able to go on, no, I'll be able to stop, or start, another guzzle of lies but piping hot, it will last my time, it will be my time and place, my voice and silence, a voice of silence, the voice of my silence. It's with such prospects they exhort you to have patience, whereas you are patient, and calm, somehow somewhere calm, what calm here, ah that's an idea, say how calm it is here, and how fine I feel, and how silent I am, I'll start right away, I'll say what calm and silence, which nothing has ever broken, nothing will ever break, which saying I don't break, or saying I'll be saying, yes, I'll say all that tomorrow, yes, tomorrow evening, some other evening, not this evening, this evening it's too late, too late to get things right, I'll go to sleep, so that I may say, hear myself say, a little later, I've slept, he's slept, but he won't have slept, or else he's sleeping now, he'll have done nothing, nothing but go on, doing what, doing what he does, that is to say, I don't know, giving up, that's it, I'll have gone on giving up, having had nothing, not being there.

THE LIFE AND WORKS OF SAMUEL BECKETT

By JOHN MONTAGUE

SAMUEL BARCLAY BECKETT was born in Dublin on April 13, 1906. Before discussing the work of this most elusive of contemporary writers it seems best to begin with a few facts "to bring the balloon of the mind . . . into its narrow shed," to quote his great Irish predecessor as Nobel Prizewinner, the poet Yeats.

But immediately the balloon begins to tremble. For the Dublin city records list the month of his birth as May, not April. An innocent enough slip, one might think, but the infant's name seems to be spelled "Barelay" and not "Barclay." When one adds to this strange prophetic mistake the fact that April 13 was not merely a Friday, but a Good Friday, we seem to be in the presence of a destiny. One of Beckett's heroes, Murphy, consults the stars before he seeks a job, but here Christianity, numerology, *and* spelling agree to form the sign of suffering. That the stars hesitate as the sacrificial ram's horns uncurl to form those of the bull only means that the destiny will be delayed, for who would *willingly* accept such a burden?

Beckett's father, William, earned his living as a quantity surveyor. Again we are made aware of the science of numbers and we remember the outraged cry of Mr. Rooney in *All That Fall* (1957): "Not count! One of the few satisfactions in life!" Repeatedly in Beckett's work, whether it is Molloy counting his sucking stones, or the omniscient author enumerating the physical details of the prostitute Celia in *Murphy* (1938), we are made aware of the importance of exact measurement.

According to Beckett himself, he was fascinated by his father's workroom; decades later, those same detailed plans seem to find an echo in the elaborate stage directions which upset so many egotistic directors. Otherwise, there is very little to connect the lean intellectual silhouette of the young Beckett with his solid, bowler-hatted father who would naturally have more in common with his elder son, William, who became an engineer and joined the family business. But heredity is an area in which one should not come to conclusions too quickly: what about the high incidence of bowler hats in the later writings of Samuel Beckett?

> . . . The hat, as hard as iron, superbly domed above its narrow guttered rim, is marred by a wide crack or rent extending in front from the crown down and intended probably to facilitate the introduction of the skull . . . And though the edges of the split brim close on the brow like the jaws of

[59]

a trap, nevertheless the hat is attached, by a string, for safety, to the topmost button of the coat, because, never mind. And were there nothing more to be said about the structure of this hat, the important thing would still remain unsaid, meaning of course its color, of which all that can be said is this, that a strong sun full upon it brings out shimmers of buff and pearl gray and that otherwise it verges on black, without however ever really approaching it.

One thing his father certainly did transmit to him was a love for the landscape of south Dublin. Not far from their home, in Foxrock, a residential suburb, lies Leopardstown racecourse, where William Beckett used to bring his boys: there is a photograph which shows William sitting in the stands, cigar in one hand, umbrella in the other, a jovial citizen. "A nice man, a gay man," as his son still says fondly.

It is this racecourse, and the little railway station beside it, which figure in *All That Fall* (1957) and *Watt* (1953). And beyond and around them are the soft Dublin mountains: "No, they are no more than hills, they raise themselves gently, faintly blue, out of the confused plain. It was there somewhere he was born, in a fine house, of loving parents. Their slopes are covered with ling and furze, its hot yellow bells, better known as gorse."

It is these hills, and the seacoast around Dublin, which Belacqua, the hero of Beckett's first stories, loved to wander. Decades later, the aged Krapp remembers the lost pleasures of youth: "Be again on Croghan on a Sunday morning, in the haze, with the bitch, stop and listen to the bells . . ." And in *Embers* (1959), Henry recalls his dead father's love for that light, that side of the bay: "you always loved light, not long past

noon and all the shore in shadow and the sea out as far as the island." Although Beckett has chosen to live the greater part of his adult life outside Ireland, that country has provided him with a primal landscape to which he has paid homage as few writers have done. No wonder that when he speaks of Anglo-Irish writers, he speaks with special affection of Synge for his descriptions of the Irish countryside and of the glens of Dublin and Wicklow.

One sometimes wonders if there is not some connection between this landscape and the mother figure in Beckett's work. He is one of the few writers who claim to have a knowledge of what it was like to have been in the womb. Sitting on the grass above Dublin Bay, Belacqua Shah, his first hero, longs to be back in the caul, "on his back, in the dark, for ever."

This same desire afflicts many of Beckett's later heroes. Molloy lives in his mother's room and relates a frightening pilgrimage toward her image. The main character of *An Abandoned Work* remembers his mother at the window, in her nightgown crying and gesticulating, as he sets out on his journey. Cursed or longed for or both, the figure of the mother has great power in Beckett's work, and Beckett seems to have been very attached to his own mother, May Beckett, whom he returned to visit in Ireland each year.

Certainly she was the member of the family to whom he bore most resemblance. He says, "My mother was profoundly religious." Although as an adult Beckett rejected religion—his work is haunted by the hymns she taught him. The portrait of the religious fanatic, Miss Fitt, in *All That Fall*, may be satirical, but Mrs. Rooney joins her in singing: "The night is dark and I am far from ho-ome."

[60]

And the religious images in many of the plays may be traced back to his early churchgoing, especially in *Waiting for Godot* (1956). "I remember the maps of the Holy Land," says Estragon, as though recalling long hours at Sunday school. And Vladimir pedantically notes that of the four evangelists, only one speaks of the Good Thief. If Didi is a lapsed poet, Gogo seems, like the hero of *Murphy* (1938), to be a lapsed theologian. Although he admits to only one moment of religious emotion (at his First Communion, which might have some connection with his being born on a Good Friday), Beckett's strict Protestant upbringing marked him deeply, in particular by giving him access to the most common way of expressing suffering in the Western tradition.

So in the Biblically named *All That Fall*, landscape and religion join as the old woman, Maddy Rooney, stands mourning over Dublin like an Old Testament prophet: "Do not flatter yourselves for one moment, because I hold aloof, that my sufferings have ceased. No. The entire scene, the hills, the plain, the racecourse with its miles and miles of white rails and three red stands, the pretty little wayside station, even you yourselves, yes, I mean it, and over all the clouding blue, I see it all, I stand here and see it with my eyes . . . (*the voice breaks*) . . . Oh if you had my eyes . . . you would understand . . ."

Beckett's education, like his religious upbringing, was conventional and lasting in its effect. He attended a kindergarten in Stillorgan, near his home, run by two German ladies. From there he moved to a preparatory school in the center of Dublin, run by a Frenchman. Thus, unlike the majority of Irish children, he became aware at an early age of the existence of other nationalities.

Another more definite sign appeared when his parents chose to send him to Portora Royal School, one of the principal Protestant public schools in Ireland. Beckett very quickly found his place, distinguishing himself equally in the classroom and at games, an excellent example of what the English call "an all-rounder." Which is not surprising, considering his Uncle Jim was heavyweight champion of Trinity, represented Leinster in rugby, held all the Irish swimming championships at various times, and represented Ireland in water polo for over twenty years.

Apart from a few generals and the usual public figures, the main claim to fame of Portora was that it had produced Oscar Wilde, the only other modern dramatist in English who also wrote in French. Beckett has never pronounced on Wilde's work, but already a tradition was beginning to operate, if only in the sense of curiosity; he remembers being intrigued by the fact that Wilde's name was blacked out from the scholars roll of honor.

Beckett, like Wilde, went on to Trinity College, the university in the center of Dublin which is the alma mater of most of the great Anglo-Irish writers. Beckett's principal interest, like that of James Joyce, was in the Romance languages. The fantastically learned hero of his first stories is called after a character in Dante, the sluggard Belacqua. He also studied Spanish, becoming a great admirer of Calderón, especially his play, *Life Is a Dream*. But his principal studies were in French, under the brilliant and eccentric Professor Rudmose-Brown, who was a personal friend of the French poets Larbaud, Fargue, Jammes, and Vielé-Griffin. It was Rudmose-Brown who placed their work in the curriculum at Trinity along with that of Proust and Gide, thereby making the program of

French studies there one of the most advanced in Europe.

It was natural enough, therefore, that the young Beckett should find his way to France; first on a bicycle (also the first appearance of a later favorite symbol), touring the châteaux of the Loire in 1926, and then, as the most brilliant student of his year, to the Ecole Normale as lecturer in English. Here again, as with Portora, one notices, if not the hand, at least the nudge of destiny, for why should Trinity be one of the few universities with an exchange agreement with the famous French college? It was natural enough, too, that the young polyglot Beckett should find himself drafted to help the blind Irish master Joyce as he struggled with the exfoliating manuscript of *Finnegans Wake*. With Alfred Penon, his opposite number, who had spent a year at Trinity, he began the translation of the most famous section, "Anna Livia Plurabelle."

Since the two great Irish writers are so often linked, it seems relevant to stress the almost racial difference between them. Joyce was from a lower-middle-class Catholic family in north Dublin; but for scholarships he could never have gone to a Jesuit school and the new Catholic University. Yet one of the more curious aspects of Beckett's career is the way he absorbs the other Irish tradition, almost by osmosis. He shows only a glancing interest in the scholastic tradition that was so important to Joyce. The group of young poets, however, with whom Beckett was most associated in Dublin were all from the same university as Joyce, and when he comes to choose names for his characters, he invariably takes an Irish country name, like Murphy, Molloy, or Malone. While acknowledging Beckett as the last of the Anglo-Irish writers, properly speaking, one must recognize that his feeling for

the landscape and the people finally crosses all barriers of class and religion to create a kind of ideal Ireland, akin to the paintings of his friend, Jack B. Yeats.

This process may have been hastened by Joyce's influence. But Joyce's immediate influence was the integrity of his example, particularly in his linguistic experiments. It is fascinating to reflect, in view of Beckett's career, that he became friendly with Joyce just as the latter was becoming the high priest of *Transition*'s "revolution of the word." In the essay that Beckett wrote on *Finnegans Wake*, we find him expressing the same concern, declaring that "no language is so sophisticated as English. It is abstracted to death." When Joyce describes something, he goes back to the prelingual gesture behind the word: "Here form *is* content, content *is* form . . . His writing is not *about* something; it is *that something itself*."

In that same essay we find also a few sentences that suggest an emerging vision of his own. He praises Joyce, for example, for not taking birth for granted: and he declares "there is a great deal of the unborn infant in the lifeless octogenarian and a great deal of both in man at the apogee of his life's curve." He describes the world as "a continuous purgatorial process . . . in the sense that the vicious circle of humanity is being achieved . . . neither prize nor penalty; simply a series of stimulants to enable the kitten to catch its tail."

This vision deepens in his remarkable study, *Proust* (1931). As well as demonstrating his independence of Joyce, this eighty-page essay is probably the most lucid and relentless analysis of Proust's central vision that exists. He ignores the social historian and the expert on sexual deviation in order to go straight for the jugular vein of his pessimism, "the poisonous ingenuity of Time in the science of affliction." And he describes it in terms that leave no doubt about his sympathy—when he speaks of the Proustian equation where "the unknown, choosing its weapons from a hoard of values, is also the unknowable," he could be speaking of his own later work. And when he evokes the heavy burden of time, declaring that "there is no escape from the hours and the days. Neither from tomorrow nor from yesterday," we could be listening to a Molloy or Malone lamentation. If life is Purgatory, as he suggests in the Joyce essay, then it is because of original sin, the "sin of having been born."

"We are alone. We cannot know and we cannot be known." All that is needed to complete this early sketch of Beckett's universe is the appearance of the tramp hero and we find him in Belacqua, with his "ruined feet" and his tendency to pass most of his time in sordid Dublin pubs. Like the Proust essay, *More Pricks Than Kicks* (1934) is grossly overwritten, but it contains two interesting stories, a very moving meditation on the death of a lobster (not surprisingly called "Dante and the Lobster") and the "horribly comic" monologue of a love-sick young woman. Even in the other stories in this collection there are details of the emerging Beckett universe; the fascination with ritual ("there was always something one had to do next"), the attraction of bicycles and asylums, his envious portrait of a blind paralytic who had made a system of his disability, being wheeled every day to a certain situation to beg. Another pointer toward the future: at one point when the hero is being particularly pedantic, the author intervenes over his head to remark, "Pardon the French expressions, but the creature dreams in French."

Thus the early Beckett is very nearly a blueprint for the later, international model. The masterpiece of this period is *Murphy*, written during his years in London. After the Ecole Normale, Beckett returned to teach at his old university. But he soon resigned, pleading the absurdity of trying to teach what he himself did not understand. When his father died in 1933, he inherited a small yearly income which, with occasional literary labors, enabled him to lead the life he preferred.

Here, perhaps, one should halt, not so much to make a comparison as to pay a compliment to the *Zeitgeist*. The philosophical novel is not a new genre, but it returned to European literature in the late 1930s with works like Sartre's *La Nausée* (*Nausea*), published the same year as *Murphy*. In both we find a naturally solitary hero; I don't think that Beckett's phrase for Murphy, "a seedy solipsist" would go far amiss in describing Antoine Roquentin. And when Maurice Nadeau describes *La Nausée* as "*Un monde hermétiquement clos*," he could, as we shall shortly see, be speaking of Murphy's mind, if not of that of his fellow characters, hurled in pointless Newtonian motion.

The difference is that *Murphy* is a comic, if not hilarious, book; what other writer could begin with his hero stark naked in a rocking chair? For Murphy these are conditions not of erotic, but of mental bliss; the place he finds most interesting in the world is his own mind. Of its three zones "light, half-light, dark," he preferred the last.

> The third, the dark, was a flux of forms, a perpetual coming together and falling asunder of forms. . . . Crumbling into the fragments of a new becoming, without love or hate or any intelligible principle of change. Here there was nothing but commotion and the purest forms of commotion. Here he was not free, but a mote in the dark of absolute freedom. He did not move,

he was a point in the ceaseless uncon-ditioned generation and passing away of time . . .

Thus as his body set him free more and more in his mind, he took to spending less and less time in the light, spitting at the breakers of the world; and less in the half-light, where the choice of bliss introduced an element of effort; and more and more and more in the dark, in the will-lessness, a mote in its absolute freedom.

These pleasures, however, are what the rest of the world, especially the women who say they love him, wish to deny Murphy. Forced by his mistress to look for work, Murphy solves the problem in typical Beckett fashion by getting a job in an asylum, where he finds the self-absorption of the inmates totally admir-able. Murphy is a much more convinced solipsist than Belacqua, but the old-fash-ioned, though brilliant, intrigue which revolves around him competes with his vision. In the later novels, the other char-acters will be functions of the central figure's imagination: it was only when Beckett realized his genius for mono-logue that he began to discover his proper fictional mode. And to do that he had to write in French, a language not slippery with metaphors and puns, a lan-guage in which it is "easier to write without style."

And so we come to the crucial deci-sion of Beckett's life, his choice to write in French. There has been much specula-tion as to why and how this happened, but it seems clear that World War II acted as a watershed between his two careers. Up to then, Beckett was known as a minor Anglo-Irish writer and, at the beginning of the war, he was actually in Ireland with his mother. But he returned, declaring, according to the myth, that "France at war was better than Ireland at peace."

Like the few other public statements attributed to Beckett, this one seems de-signed to be a humorous red herring, to conceal his real feelings. Although he had little reason to love a country which had banned his fiction and humiliated him when he appeared as witness in a literary law case in 1937 (he was accused in cross-examination of not only writing doubtful books himself but also praising others who did, such as Marcel Proust), Ireland was no longer really an issue. With his long residence in France, his French friends and wife, Beckett was now more committed to Montparnasse than Fox-rock.

He was certainly not indifferent to the Nazi threat. In particular, he objected to anti-Semitism and when he saw his friends compelled to wear the Star of David and hostages being taken, he could not, to use his own phrase, "stand with his arms folded."

Of the Resistance group for which Beckett served as a "mail drop," the majority were captured; Beckett and his wife fled only a few minutes before the Gestapo came. They found a refuge in Roussillon, where Beckett worked as a farm laborer during the day and tried to write at night in order to forget the war.

Watt has only been recently published in French but it is crucial as a watershed between his two careers. For one thing, it is one of the most Irish of his books, as though his isolation made his home land-scape shine more brightly. It is also one of the most comic; the little lyrics, the lists of impossible names, and, above all, the story of the night Larry was born during dinner. Also in *Watt* is a wonder-ful lyric outburst on time:

The crocuses and the larch turning green every year a week before the

others and the pastures red with un-
eaten sheep's placentas and the long
summer days and the newmown hay
and the wood-pigeon in the morning
and the cuckoo in the afternoon and
the corncrake in the evening and the
wasps in the jam and the smell of the
gorse and the look of the gorse and the
apples falling and children walking in
the dead leaves and the larch turning
brown a week before the others and
the chestnuts falling and the howling
winds and the sea breaking over the
pier and the first fires and the hooves
on the road and the consumptive post-
man whistling *The Roses are blooming
in Picardy* and the standard oil lamp
and of course the snow and to be sure
the sleet and bless your heart the slush
and every fourth year the February
debacle and the endless April showers
and the crocuses and then the whole
bloody business starting all over again.

But the central theme is the verbal
breakdown, the cerebral crucifixion of
Watt, who discovers that he cannot describe what has happened to him even to
Sam, his neighbor in the asylum. English
reviewers did not take to this extraordinary vision of solitude and when next
we hear this lonely voice it will be in
French and even the friendly Sam will
have withdrawn to let the monologist,
whether Molloy, Moran, or Malone, hold
sway.

In 1945, Beckett was back in Paris,
after a brief period as an interpreter at
the military hospital of St. Lô. His first
works of this period did not satisfy him.
In *The Unnamable* (1953), there is a
contemptuous reference to "the pseudo-
couple" Mercier-Camier and the novel
named after them was not published until
1970. One can see why: although it is an
ingenious and amusing work, it is tech-
nically too close to his previous work in
English, and with its excess in dialogue,
it lies half-way between fiction and
drama. For the first time in Beckett's
work, one meets the couple, each on the
point of leaving the other, but always
staying, their exasperated exchanges
amounting to a way of life. When we
meet them again, it will be on the stage.
In the *nouvelles* written at that time,
Beckett comes closer to discovering his
proper fictional world. The friendly narrator of *Mercier et Camier* has disappeared; each creature tells his own story,
as best he can. Not that they are sure of
much except that they are not where they
were. "I did not know where I was," says
the main character of *The Expelled*
(1962), who has been wandering for a
whole day, after being thrown out of his
home, himself, and his hat.

In *The End*, the narrator has also been
expelled from some sort of institution,
with his hat attached to his buttonhole by
a string like a Chaplin tramp. There is an
obvious parallel between this exile from
society and Beckett's personal situation,
but the implications are wider then that.
Turning his back on the prewar world,
and the art that represented it, Beckett
begins to seek a language that will express the human condition at its most
naked, man brought to his knees by a
century of horrors. The protective powers of wit and pedantry disappear as, for
five extraordinary years, Beckett struggles to express his new vision, as stripped
as the sculptures of his friend, Gia-
cometti. In *The Expelled* he wrote:

I don't know why I told this story. I
could just as well have told another.
Perhaps some other time I'll be able to
tell another. Living souls, you will see
how alike they are.

In April 1951, *Molloy* appeared, the
first of Beckett's French books to be pub-

lished. The critical response was immediate: leading French critics all agreed that it was a major literary event while recognizing the unlikelihood of its ever becoming popular. Its resemblance to *The Expelled* (which appeared in French first in the revue *Fontaine*) was remarked, almost as though it were the fulfillment of a vague promise at the end of that work. But from now on it is the same solitary lament that is heard in Beckett's fiction, whatever the circumstances, for all details are equal and opposite in the universe of degradation.

For example, Molloy has not been expelled: he is in his mother's room. But he has had a terrible time getting there, and that journey is as real as the room, because it is that journey he is writing down. A man comes to take away the sheets of paper, and returns those of the week before. They are marked with signs, as though he were a printer returning proofs—which we now are reading.

And another, for the journey of Molloy is paralleled by that of Moran, who sets out to look for him. A dignified burgher, he is gradually broken down in the same way as the subject of his quest; but even bicycles, Beckett's favorite symbol of a happy relationship between body and mind, disintegrate in Molloy country. And so would we, if we dared follow, but there are recompenses which not even Goya would have dreamed of

To be literally incapable of motion at last, that must be something! My mind swoons when I think of it. And mute into the bargain! And perhaps as deaf as a post! And who knows as blind as a bat! And as likely as not your memory a blank! And just enough brain intact to allow you to exult! And to dread death like a regeneration.

This is pure Swift: what Beckett seems to be saying is that humanity is in such a condition that the only way to endure it is by a paralysis worse than death. The narrator of *Malone Dies,* the next volume in the trilogy, has advanced a little further than Molloy in the way of nothingness. He too is sitting in his room writing down stories, he too has been brought there "in an ambulance, a vehicle of some kind certainly." But the room is less like a womb then a skull, his own perhaps, and he has made no pilgrimage to get there; Molloy's maternal fixation has vanished, leaving nothing between him and death except the stories he spins. "I tell, therefore I am" is Malone's version of the Cartesian dilemma that obsesses Beckett.

The stories are about others, not himself, invented beings who fade into one another. The first is Sapo, a boy whose only interests are mental arithmetic and watching hawks: "He would stand rapt, gazing at the long pernings, the quivering poise, the wings lifted for the plummet drop, the wild reascent, fascinated by such extremes of need, of pride, of patience, and solitude." But he soon tires of this "dolt" and sends him to a typical family of French peasants, whom he describes so well that soon he is murmuring: "How plausible all that is." Especially the father "highly thought of as a bleeder and disjointer of pigs": "Then he would set forth, hugging under his arm, in their case, the great knives so lovingly whetted before the fire the night before, and in his pocket, wrapped in paper, the apron destined to protect his Sunday suit as he worked."

The contrast between the inert figure in the bed and his creatures constitute the structure of the book. They merge in the mysterious figure of Macmann, who is discovered overlooking a river that looks suspiciously like the author's native Liffey. Macmann is another in Beckett's series of tramps, and he finds refuge, like Murphy, in an asylum: the love affair he has with his keeper, Moll, is the most horribly comic comment on physical love since Swift's poems. Finally their creator decides to kill her first, then perhaps him: the thinking machine is running down. A day expedition from the asylum ends with a boatload drifting to sea as the syntax expires.

"What now? Who now? When now?" If *Molloy* is related to *The Expelled, The Unnamable* might be a development of *The Sedative*, another of the early *nouvelles* in which the narrator begins by wondering when exactly he has died. In the interval between the last two books of the trilogy, the narrator has died, but death, instead of being a solution, only complicates the language problem still further, because how do you describe states outside time or find a language for silence? We are now definitely in the dark, which Murphy desired so much, subject to all the anguish of a consciousness speaking of what it can never properly know.

We do learn, however, that all the characters in Beckett's novels are linked, part of a series proceeding toward zero, which, by definition, can never be achieved. And although the narrator keeps rejecting the old fictions as disguises for the author, they cannot help combining to create fresh horrors. Mahood comes to an almost complete stop, stuck like a flower in a jar outside a restaurant (it seems that there was a restaurant sign near the Vaugirard abattoirs that gave Beckett the idea). But Mahood is a frenzy of consciousness compared to Worm, who, as his names indicates, "Feeling nothing, knowing nothing, . . . exists nevertheless but not for himself, for others, others conceive him and say, Worm is, since we conceive him . . ."

Nevertheless even this philosophical polyp has an eye which is "always open." Like Faulkner's, Beckett's characters present themselves as aspects of one vision, except that his Yoknapatawpha County is interior. Or rather, to return to the essay on Proust, they all derive from one central experience, Beckett's almost mythical sense of the absurdity of existence: "we cannot know and we cannot be known." At the end of *The Unnamable,* all the fictional conventions have broken down but the voice continues "I can't go on, I'll go on."

Despite remarkable passages, beautiful as a prose poem of Baudelaire's, the trilogy is too relentless a statement of the Beckettian dilemma to appeal to the general public. But happily, when Beckett discovered his genius for monologue, he also turned to writing plays and it was with the first performance of *Waiting for Godot* in 1953 that he began to be popularly known. Three years after *The Bald Soprano* of Ionesco, the Theater of the Absurd, as it came to be called, had another champion. That the first performance of an unknown playwright, in a small theater, should have echoed around the world shows that the world was waiting for Beckett!

The remarkable thing about his plays is that they are in no way a simplification of his vision: *Waiting for Godot* was written between *Malone Dies* and *The Unnamable,* and is possibly more bleak than either. On a deserted country road, two hoboes wait for someone they call Godot; a man and his servant enter, and after they have staggered away, a small boy comes to say that Godot is not coming today. "Nothing happens, nobody comes, nobody goes, it's awful!" Estragon's cry toward the end of the first act sums up the action of the play, where indeed, as the critic Vivian Mercier has said, nothing happens, *twice.*

But once you have accepted the anguish of the void—"Nothing to be done" is the opening statement of the play— you are free to pass the time as you like, and Vladimir and Estragon are in one of the oldest theatrical traditions of all, that of Punch and Judy:

> Estragon: That's the idea, let's abuse each other. *They turn, move apart, turn again and face each other.*
> Vladimir: Moron!
> Estragon: Vermin!
> Valdimir: Abortion!
> Estragon: Morpion!
> Valdimir: Sewer-rat!
> Estragon: Curate!
> Vladimir: Cretin!
> Estragon: (*with finality*) Critic!
> Vladimir: Oh!

While there is no point in entering into the debate about the significance of Godot, it is clear enough that he is meant to stand for any vague hope that keeps us alive, even God. What counts in the play are the relationships: that between Pozzo and Lucky which illustrates the interdependency of master and servant, the kind of marriage between Gogo and Didi. Their games, their exchanges, their rituals enable them and us to forget our anguish; the air may be "full of our cries . . . but habit is a great deadener."

Speaking of the play himself, Beckett stresses the game element; for him, it was a halt, a turning aside from the relentless illogic of the trilogy. In this connection, there is a fascinating anecdote which partly explains Beckett's obsession with tramps. Shortly before the war, he was attacked by one in the street, the knife just missing the heart. When Beckett saw him in the Santé prison, afterwards, the tramp could not explain why he had done it: "I don't know, sir!" was his only answer.

> Vladimir: (*vexed*) Then why do you always come crawling back?
> Estragon: I don't know.
> Vladimir: No, but I do. It's because

you don't know how to defend yourself. I wouldn't have let them beat you.
> Estragon: You couldn't have stopped them.
> Vladimir: Why not?
> Estragon: They were ten of them.
> Vladimir: No, I mean before they beat you. I would have stopped you from doing whatever it was you were doing.
> Estragon: I wasn't doing anything.
> Vladimir: Then why did they beat you?
> Estragon: I don't know.

Endgame (1957) is a restatement of the same situation, with an altered emphasis. The road has become a room which, like the room in *Malone Dies,* seems to resemble the inside of a skull. The master-slave relationship has been made the center of the action; the only other characters are Nag and Nell, the parents of Hamm, who live like Mahood in dustbins at the side of the stage.

Much has been made of the resemblance between *King Lear* and *Endgame,* and the comparison, though exaggerated, suggests the quality of the play, with Hamm like a deposed king tended by his clown. Black humor plays over this desolate post-atomic landscape. "Nothing is as funny as unhappiness," says Nell, closed in her bin, and one is reminded of the terrible third section of *Gulliver's Travels.* Like Swift, Beckett cannot lightly accept the indignities of age, the mind chained to a rotting body. The Struldbrugs are doddering forbears of the parents in *Endgame,* all romance reduced to a scratch on the back.

It is tempting to see Beckett's three best-known plays as sharing the same relationship as the novels of the trilogy. With *Happy Days* (published in 1961 in English and in 1963 in French), we are back to monologue, with a female voice raised against the encroaching desert. But nearly all Beckett's later work is written for his favorite instrument, the isolated human voice, whether it is the narrator crawling through the mud in *How It Is* (*Comment c'est,* 1961) or Krapp playing with his tape recorder.

The first theme is probably the importance of habit. In his essay on Proust, Beckett described it as that "compromise effected between the individual and his environment" which protects us from reality, and which, as T. S. Eliot once reminded us, "mankind cannot endure." All Beckett's characters illustrate this bitter truth, whether unconsciously— Winnie enumerating the contents of her handbag in *Happy Days*—or by parodying it into an insane ritual of repetition—the sucking stones which Molloy transfers from pocket to pocket.

One very human form of habit is companionship, whether of friends or couples. Here Beckett's genius exposes us to another unpalatable truth about our condition. In his essay *Proust,* that depository of the future themes of Beckett, "the attempt to communicate where no communication is possible" is described as "horribly comic," while "friendship implies an almost piteous acceptance of face values." These two statements might be a gloss on the series of couples that inhabit his plays, from Didi and Gogo in *Waiting for Godot,* to Mr. and Mrs. Rooney toiling their way back from the station in *All That Fall,* and Winnie translating the groans of Willie as signs of hope. They may not communicate in the strict sense of the word, but their little exchanges of exasperation and tenderness enable them to go on.

And what of love, "the supreme theme of art and song," to return to Yeats? One does not usually think of Beckett in this connection, but there must be very few dramatic representations of "that desert of loneliness and recrimination that men call love" (I quote again from the essay on Proust) as stark as the triangle in *Play.* Buried to their necks in jars, two women besiege one man with their claims and counterclaims; it is clear that no one is listening to anyone else, but concerned with justifying their own ego. It is, indeed, "horribly comic."

But there is also the memory of love, so potent in the Proustian world. One of the most mysterious and beautiful passages in *Krapp's Last Tape* (a monologue written for the B.B.C. and first published in 1959) has him playing and replaying the love scene in the boat.

> I asked her to look at me and after a few moments—(*pause*) after a few moments she did, but the eyes just slits, because of the glare. I bent over her to get them in the shadow and they opened (*Pause, low*) Let me in. (*Pause*) . . . I lay down across her with my face in her breasts and my hand on her. We lay there without moving. But under us all moved, and moved us, gently, up and down, and from side to side.

Is Beckett mocking this memory as the echo of *For Whom the Bell Tolls* would seem to suggest? "But I wouldn't want them back" growls Krapp thirty years later, yet speaks of it as a period when "there was a chance of happiness."

The old man in *Eh Joe* is haunted by the memory of a girl who committed suicide; like Krapp he drove her away and now depends on the occasional visits of a whore to ease his body. Across the landscape of Beckett periodically steals the ghostly sound of his favorite tune, Schubert's "Death and the Maiden" and one remembers that a cousin he loved died young.

> I would like my love to die
> and the rain to be falling on the grave-
> yard

and on me walking the streets
mourning the first and last love to me.

But if the girl dies, the woman lives. The tenderness of the portrait of Celia, the prostitute in *Murphy,* is rare in Beckett, whose hero, in any case, considers his need for her as an intrusion on his thoughts. Generally the sole female companion of a Beckett character is a hag, whose decrepitude underlines the absurdity of looking for the soul through a hole "between the legs."

Is Beckett then mocking the indomitability of Winnie (does the Churchill echo seem only ironic accident?), as she fills the void with clichés? I think he admires her, just as he admires Mrs. Rooney, that massive Queen Lear, with the woes of the world on her back. At least the women keep going and they can even find a kind of poetry in deprivation. Our final image of *Happy Days* is of Winnie buried to the neck, singing like a mystic in praise of the blessed light which is destroying her. When the Nobel Committee wished to honor her creator, it seemed appropriate that the news should have reached him living in a flooded town at the edge of a desert.

THE 1969 PRIZE

By KJELL STRÖMBERG

In 1969 everyone of importance in literary circles both in France and abroad assumed that at last the time had come for the award of the Nobel Prize for Literature to André Malraux. By common accord he was the most remarkable of living French writers, the unchallenged master of a generation that had already sent several representatives—including Sartre and Camus—to that select circle of laureates. The author of *The Human Condition* seemed all the more eligible this year since he no longer exercised any governmental function that might give rise to some political hesitations among the literary arbiters of a neutral nation. Moreover, it was now five years since a French author had been honored in the person of Jean-Paul Sartre.

The Swedish Academy, as it developed, preferred another writer who wrote in French: Samuel Beckett of the School of the Absurd. This French-Irish author was one of 103 candidates that year. They included, in addition to Malraux, the Anglo-American poet, W. H. Auden, who, incidentally, had just left Stockholm after a much-publicized visit as the guest of honor of the Swedish Academy at the annual colloquium sponsored by its three Nobel Prize committees. Speaking more frankly than is the general practice, a member of the Literature Com-

mittee had told an interviewer for an Italian paper that the year's list of candidates included some very famous figures who had made their careers in other fields of work: notably General de Gaulle, Charlie Chaplin, and Ingmar Bergman, the Swedish film-maker. In addition to the usual perennial candidates, there was one new one: Vladimir Nabokov, the Russian-American author of *Lolita*, was sponsored by the P.E.N. Club of Sweden. There was also the name of Aleksandr Solzhenitsyn, who had remained true to his native country.

Samuel Beckett was first suggested for the Nobel Prize in 1957 by a professor of literature at the Sorbonne who had no known connections with the literary avant-garde. The Swedish Academy set out at once to make a thorough study of the new candidate. By that time Beckett had already produced the essential substance of his work. Hailed as the strikingly perfect expression of the alienation of the spirit in a shipwrecked world, at least one of his plays, *Waiting for Godot*, had attracted critical attention virtually everywhere. The first analysis of his work was devoted particularly to his fiction. One study by Erik Wahlund, an extremely able drama critic, is worth some attention here. Published later in the *Svenska Dagbladet,* his report took the form of a comparison of four dramatic authors reasonably well known as innovators: Beckett, Eugène Ionesco, Jean Genêt, and Vitold Gombrowicz.

Though fully recognizing Beckett's outstanding qualities, Wahlund stressed unequivocally that the author of *Waiting for Godot* had only this "single first-rank work" and that nothing in his later output had even approached its depths of thought or the almost undetectable precision-work of its structure. A single work—even if it be a masterpiece that could survive beyond the time and circumstances of its conception—seemed to this wary critic too tenuous a ground for the elevation of an author to the highest literary award that the whole world could confer. Wahlund himself preferred Ionesco, for the originality of his viewpoints and the variety of his subjects, his incisive dialogue, and his rich flow of black humor: these qualities, according to Wahlund, seemed more likely to bring fertility to the theater of the future—and therefore to claim the attention of a Nobel jury.

The final decision, however, lay with the permanent secretary of the Swedish Academy, Karl Ragnar Gierow, a lyric poet and a critic of refinement. He found Beckett entirely worthy and indeed superior to the others. The Swedish Academy met in plenary session on Thursday, October 23, and awarded the Nobel Prize to Samuel Beckett "for a body of work that, in new forms in fiction and the theater, has transmuted the destitution of modern man into his exaltation."

Then came the ticklish and utterly unavoidable question: would Mr. Beckett accept the Nobel Prize? It was common knowledge that he had always clung to a rigid isolation, living almost like a hermit with his wife, seeing no one except his publisher, Jérôme Lindon, and a very few friends, as withdrawn as himself, with whom now and then he would have a whisky or two in some small bar near his apartment in the Boulevard Arago. There was no reply to the telegram sent off at once to notify him of the award and invite him to receive it in Stockholm. His publisher was sought out in great haste by the Swedish Embassy in Paris; he explained that, anticipating the event, desirous of preserving his anonymity and fearful of publicity and all its attendant burdens, the author had left Paris and taken refuge in Nabeul, a small village deep inside Tunisia, which was cut off from the world by a recent flood.

In spite of all these precautions, a few reporters had managed to run Beckett to earth. Fortunately Beckett was not overly tempted by the excessive publicity that would have ensued had he emulated Sartre, who refused the award five years before. So, after a few days' thought and the observation to the press that he regarded his election as a disaster, the laureate-in-spite-of-himself answered the Swedish Academy affirmatively as far as the Prize was concerned but courteously declined—for reasons of health—to transport his person to Stockholm.

Perhaps the investiture of so difficult a writer under such outlandish conditions might have aroused varying reactions in world opinion. This was hardly the case. In most countries literary people congratulated the reluctant laureate with much feeling, and the great newspapers covered him with unqualified praise. Only his native Ireland sulked, refusing to acknowledge parenthood of a son who had turned his back on his native Gaelic in favor of two alien tongues: English and French.

Beckett had sent word that he did not wish to receive his Prize in the official fashion usually followed when a winner could not be present—that is, through his country's ambassador—and instead he was represented by Lindon, his French publisher. So it was Lindon who, after Gierow had blanketed the absent laureate in brilliantly phrased tribute, received from the hands of King Gustav Adolf the diploma, the gold medal, and the valuable check as the audience rose in courteous applause.

At the traditional banquet in the City Hall that followed the award ceremonial, the Irish Ambassador, Tadgh Seosamh O'Hodhráin, insisted on representing his honored compatriot at the king's table, where Lindon too had been seated, next to Marcus Wallenberg, the monarch of Sweden's high finance.

Lindon flew back to Paris the next morning, carrying the diploma and the medal, but not the check—made out in the comfortable amount of $75,000. Not knowing what to do with it, the payee preferred to leave it in Sweden for the time being.

Translated by Charles Lam Markmann.

Björnstjerne Björnson

1903

"As a tribute to his noble, magnificent, and versatile work as a poet, which has always been distinguished by both the freshness of its inspiration and the rare purity of its spirit"

Illustrated by GASTON BARRET

PRESENTATION ADDRESS

By C. D. AF WIRSÉN

PERMANENT SECRETARY
OF THE SWEDISH ACADEMY

AGAIN THIS YEAR the names of several candidates for the Nobel Prize for Literature have been submitted to the Swedish Academy for its approval, some of them authors of European reputation. The Academy thinks that this year it should give priority to the poet Björnstjerne Björnson. Although we have the pleasure of seeing the illustrious laureate at this ceremony, custom requires that I speak of him in the third person as I give an account of the Academy's decision. But I reserve the right to address a few personal remarks to him at the end.

Björnstjerne Björnson is so generally known and his works are so familiar to educated Swedes that it is unnecessary to give a comprehensive appreciation of his universally and gladly acknowledged merits. Therefore I shall limit myself on this solemn occasion to the following remarks.

The poet to whom with true satisfaction the Swedish Academy has awarded the Nobel Prize for Literature was born at Kvikne, Norway, where his father was a minister and where as a child he could listen to the waters of the Orkla boiling at the bottom of a gorge. The last years of his childhood, however, were spent at Naesset in the beautiful valley of Romsdal where his father had been transferred. The vicarage of Naesset is situated between the two inlets of Langfjord, Eidsvaag and Eirisfjord.

In that picturesque countryside of Norway, between these two fjords, the young boy often looked at the splendor of the sun setting behind the mountain or in the sea. There he learned to do farmwork. His love of

the rustic nature of his country and his intimate knowledge of the life of
the people date from that time. At the age of eleven he was sent to
school at Molde. He did not do brilliantly, but the development of a
great poet is not always measured by such standards. During his studies
he came across one author who was to have a profound influence on
his life: he began to read Sturleson. At this period, too, he became
acquainted with the stories of Asbjörnson and the works of Oehlenschläger and Walter Scott. At the age of seventeen he went to Christiania
(Oslo) to prepare for his baccalaureate, which he passed in 1852.

Björnson has said that he knew of his poetic vocation after he took part
in the First Student Assembly in Uppsala in 1856. In unforgettable words
he has given us his impressions of the church of Riddarholm lit up by the
rays of the setting sun, and of Stockholm in the splendor of the summer. Then he wrote *Mellen slagene* (Between the Battles, 1857) in a
fortnight, to be followed by other works, among them the story *Synnöve
Solbakken* (*Sunny Hill,* 1857). Henceforth the reputation of Björnson
was solidly established and an uninterrupted series of new works spread
his name all over the world.

Björnson is a great epic and dramatic writer, but he is also a great lyric
poet. *Synnöve Solbakken, Arne* (1858), and *En glad gut* (*A Happy Boy,*
1860) put him in the first rank of painters of contemporary life. In these
somber accounts he reveals himself as a man of the country and of the
old saga; indeed it has been said, not without reason, that he describes
the life of the peasant in the light of saga. But it should be added that
the peasants whom he knew so well since his Romsdal days have—in
the judgments of competent persons—preserved the laconic and reserved
manner of talking which the poet has reproduced with such felicity.
Although this reproduction is idealized and profoundly poetic, it is nonetheless faithful and true to nature.

As a dramatist Björnson has treated historical subjects, e.g. *Kong
Sverre* (1861); *Sigurd Jorsalfar* (Sigurd the Crusader, 1872); the
masterly *Sigurd Slembe* (Sigurd the Bad, 1862), in which the love of
Audhild brings some light into a somber situation and where the figure
of Finnepigen stands in the splendor of an aurora borealis; the passionate
drama *Maria Stuart i Shotland* (1864); and other creations of genius.
But he has been equally successful in his choice of contemporary sub-

jects, as in *Redaktören* (*The Editor,* 1874), *En fallit* (*The Bankrupt,* 1874), etc.

Even as an old man he has created a disinterested portrait of love in *Paul Lange og Tora Parsberg* (1898); in *Laboremus* (1901) he has extolled the right of the moral life against the natural forces of unrestrained passion. Finally, in *På Storhove* (At Storhove, 1902) he has paid dramatic homage to the guardian forces of the home as represented by Margareta, the faithful and constant support of her family. It should in fact be observed that Björnson's characters are of a rare purity, that his genius is always positive and in no way negative. His works are never adulterated; on the contrary they are pure metal, and whatever modifications the years and experience have imposed upon his point of view and that of others, he has never ceased to combat the claim of the senses to dominate man.

It is sometimes said that the Nobel Prize for Literature, designed for the best literary work, should preferably be awarded to young writers. That may be true, but even so the Academy believes it has met all reasonable demands. The creative power of this man of seventy-one is so great that he published *På Storhove* in 1902, and the works published afterward bear witness to the youthful spirit that he has been able to preserve.

As a lyric poet Björnson is exemplary for his fresh simplicity and his profound sentiments. His poems are an inspirational source of inexhaustible wealth, and the melodious character of his verse has tempted many a composer to set it to music. No country has a more beautiful anthem than *"Ja, vi elker dette Landet"* (Yes, we love this country) by Björnson, and when one reads the sublime song of *"Arnljot Gelline,"* in which the rhythms are like the majestic movements of waves, one likes to think that in future times the waves of memory will murmur *"i store maaneskinsklare Naetter"* (on clear moon-lit nights) as they play the name of the great national poet on the coasts of Norway.

Mr. Björnstjerne Björnson—Your genius has served the purest and most elevated ideas; it has put the highest demands on human life, in certain cases—*En hanske* (*A Gauntlet,* 1883)—even thought too high by many. But in their noble severity they are infinitely preferable to the laxness that is all too prevalent in the literature of our day. Your inspired

[79]

and universally acknowledged poetic achievement, rooted in nature and in the life of the people as well as in strong personal convictions, combines morality and a healthy poetic freshness. Hence the Swedish Academy has seen fit to render homage to your illustrious genius by awarding you the Nobel Prize for this year, and it respectfully asks His Majesty the King to deign to give you this proof of its admiration.

ACCEPTANCE SPEECH

By BJÖRNSTJERNE BJÖRNSON

I BELIEVE that the Prize I have received today will be regarded by the public as a gift from one nation to another. After the long struggle in which I have taken part to gain for Norway an equal place within the Union, a struggle which was often bitterly resented in Sweden, may I say that the decision is a credit to her name.

I am glad of this opportunity to express very briefly my views on the role of literature.

Let me, in the interest of brevity, evoke a picture I have had in my mind since my early youth, whenever I think of human progress. I see it as an endless procession in which men and women move steadily along. The line they follow is not invariably straight but it does take them forward. They are urged on by an irresistible force, purely instinctive at first but eventually more and more conscious. Not that human progress is ever entirely a matter of conscious effort, and no man has ever been able to make it so. It is in this no man's land between conscious progress and subconscious forging ahead that imagination is at work. In some of us, the gift of prescience is so great that it enables us to see far ahead to the new paths along which human progress will travel.

Nothing has ever molded our conscience so strongly as our knowledge of what is good and what is evil. Therefore, our sense of good and evil is so much a part of our conscience that, to this day, no one can disregard it and feel at ease with himself. That is why I have always been so puzzled by the idea that we writers should lay down our sense of good and evil before we take up our pens. The effect of this reasoning would be to turn our minds into cameras indifferent to good and evil, to beauty and ugliness alike!

I do not want to dwell here on the extent to which modern man—always assuming he is a sane individual—can shake off a conscience that is the heritage of millions of years, and by which all the generations of mankind have been guided to the present day. I shall merely ask why those who subscribe to this theory choose certain images instead of others? Is their choice a purely mechanical one? Why are the pictures that present themselves to their imagination almost invariably shocking? Are they sure that it is not they, in fact, who have chosen them?

I do not think we need to wait for the answer. They can no more shake off the ideas that have come down to them through centuries of inherited morality than we can. The only difference between them and ourselves is that, whereas we serve these ideas, they try to rebel against them. I should quickly add here that not all is immoral that appears to be so. Many of today's guiding ideas were revolutionary ones in the past. What I do say is that the writers who reject tendentiousness and purpose in their work are the very ones who display it in every word they write. I could draw countless examples from the history of literature to show that the more a writer clamors for spiritful freedom, the more tendentious his work is liable to be. The great poets of Greece were equally at home with mortals and immortals. Shakespeare's plays were a great Teutonic Valhalla with brilliant sunshine at times and violent tempests at others. The world to him was a battlefield, but his sense of poetic justice, his sublime faith in life and its infinite resources guided the battles.

We may invoke from their graves, as often as we wish, the characters of Molière and Holberg, to see nothing but a procession of figures in frilly costumes and wigs who, with affected and grotesque gestures, fulfill their mission. They are as tendentious as they are verbose.

I spoke just now of our Teutonic Valhalla. Did not Goethe and Schiller bring something of the Elysian fields into it? The sky was loftier and warmer with them, life and art happier and more beautiful. We may perhaps say that those who have basked in this warmth, in this sunshine— young Tegnér, young Oehlenschläger, and young Wergeland, not forgetting Byron and Shelley—have all had something of the Greek gods in them.

This time and this trend are gone now but I should like to mention two great men who belongs to it. First, I think of my old friend in Norway who is now ill. He has lit many a beacon along our Norwegian coast to guide the mariner, to warn him of the danger that lies ahead. I think, too, of a grand old man in a neighboring country to the east, whose light shines forth and gives happiness to many. Their spirit, their many years of work, were lit by a purpose that was ever brighter, like a flame in the evening wind.

I have said nothing here of the effect of tendentiousness on art, which it can make or mar.

If tendentiousness and art appear in the same proportion, all is well. Of the two great writers I have mentioned, it may well be that the former's warnings are so severe as to be frightening. And the latter may lure us with the charms of an ideal that passes human understanding and therefore frightens, too. But what is necessary is that our courage to live is strengthened, not weakened. Fear should not turn us back from the paths which open before us. The procession must go on. We must be confident that life is fundamentally good, that even after frightening disasters and the most tragic events, the earth is bathed in a flood of strength whose sources are eternal. Our belief in it is its proof.

In more recent times, Victor Hugo has been my hero. At the bottom of his brilliant imagination lies the conviction that life is good and it is that which makes his work so colorful. There are those who talk of his shortcomings, of his theatrical mannerisms. Let them. For me, all his deficiencies are compensated for by his *joie de vivre*. Our instinct of self-preservation insists on this, for if life did not have more good than evil to offer us, it would have come to an end long ago. Any picture of life that does not allow for this fact is a distorted picture. It is wrong to imagine, as some do, that it is the dark aspects of life which are bad for us. That is not true.

Weaklings and egotists cannot abide harsh facts but the rest of us can. If those who choose to make us tremble or blush were also able to hold out a promise that, for all that may befall us, life has happiness to offer us, we might say to ourselves: all right, we are faced in this plot and in these words with a mystery that is part of life, and we should be roused to fear or amusement according to the author's will. The trouble is that writers seldom achieve more than a sensation, and often not even that! We feel doubly dissatisfied, because the author's attitude to life is so negative and because he is not capable of leading us. Incompetence is always galling.

[83]

The greater the burden a man takes upon his shoulders, the stronger he must be to carry it. No words are unmentionable, no action or horror beyond powers of description, if one is equal to them.

A meaningful life—this is what we look for in art, in its smallest dewdrops as in its unleashing of the tempest. We are at peace when we have found it and uneasy when we have not.

The old ideas of right and wrong, as firmly established in our consciousness, have played their part in every field of our life; they are part of our search for knowledge and our thirst for life itself. It is the purpose of all art to disseminate these ideas and, for that, millions of copies would not be one too many.

This is the ideal I have tried to defend, as a respectful servant and enthusiast. I am not one of those who believe that an artist, a writer, is exempt from responsibility. On the contrary, his responsibility is greater than that of other men because he who is at the head of the procession must lead the way for those who follow.

I am deeply grateful to the Swedish Academy for recognizing my efforts in this direction and I now wish to raise my glass to the success of its work in promoting all that is sound and noble in literature.

BEYOND HUMAN MIGHT

By BJÖRNSTJERNE BJÖRNSON

Translated from the Norwegian by Edwin Björkman

ACT I

A deep chasm that ends in a turn toward the right. It is just possible to catch a glimpse of the sea in the background. Both sides of the chasm are dotted with small huts placed without the least suggestion of order. Some of them are nothing but deck houses, while others are made up of the whole stern part of some sailing-vessel. Other shanties lean against the steep sides of the chasm in such a way that the lanes in their rear are on a level with their upper stories. At the bottom of the chasm, in the foreground, is a sort of square with a fountain and a water-trough, both very dilapidated. Houses surround the open place.

In the extreme foreground, at the right, there stands a ramshackle old building. All its window-panes are broken. The front door is almost torn off and hangs across the doorway. A bent metal pole projects from the front of the house. It carries a signboard with the word "Hell" painted on it. The sign is nearly torn from its fastenings.

A muffled rumbling fills the place and hardly ever ceases. It comes from an iron bridge that spans the chasm. Now and then the whistle of an engine is heard, followed by the deafening clangor of a passing train. When this ceases, one hears again the hollow and comparatively
suppressed rumble of carriage-wheels and the tramp of horses.

Before the curtain rises, a funeral hymn is sung in unison. As the curtain rises, a coffin—the size of which shows that it holds the body of a grown-up person—is being carried out from one of the shanties at the left. It is followed by another coffin, apparently holding the body of a child, and then by a third that is still smaller.

The square is crowded with workmen, women, and children. All the men have bared their heads. Many of the men and women are crying. Some of the children are howling loudly. The people fall in behind the coffins, with FALK, *the minister, at their head. He wears the canonical dress of a pastor in the Established Church of Norway. Beside him, leaning on his arm, totters a man of advanced age,* ANDERS HOEL, *known as* BLIND ANDERS. *Thus the procession makes very slow progress.*

Everyone present falls into line. The procession passes along the bottom of the chasm until it reaches the bend, where it disappears to the right. The hymn continues to be heard long after the last people have passed out, the sound of it mounting upward as it recedes into the distance.

While the singing is still heard, an elderly man sneaks timidly out of the

*ramshackle building at the right. He
wears a long coat that falls in heavy folds
around him, and he acts as if he didn't
know where to turn. He stares at the
maltreated building and finally he sits
down on its front stoop which stands
separated from the house far out in the
square.*

*At that moment another man becomes
visible far up on the path along which
the procession passed. His clothes are
ragged, threadbare, and greasy. On his
head, which is very large, he wears a very
small cap. The shoe on his right foot is
almost new, but on the left foot he has
merely an upper to which a sole is
fastened with strings. His face is very
red. His hands are almost purple in color.
His hair is dark and cut very short.*

This man, whose name is OTTO HERRE,
*comes down the road with head erect and
swinging movements. On seeing the man
sitting on the stoop, he stops for a moment. Then he resumes his advance, but
more slowly.*

At last the man on the stoop—named
ANDERS KOLL, *but generally known as*
MOUSIE—*becomes aware of* HERRE *and
turns away from him.*

MOUSIE (*Muttering to himself*). I
guess he must 'a' got out after all.

HERRE. Behold the humble Mousie!
Seated in front of his torn-up hole. Sunk
in deep thought.

MOUSIE (*As before*). He's got a load
on, sure enough.

HERRE. Broken, the windows—and
sadly drooping, the sign—like a drink
that is dripping away. The stoop seized
by a hurricane and hurled across the
ocean of your destiny. And you yourself
clinging to this last remnant of the vessel
that was your life. (*A queer, clucking
sound is heard from* MOUSIE) And the
door! That door which has seen so many
beggars enter and so many kings pass
out! Now it's hanging there like a drunkard whom the bouncer is chucking into
the street.—That's how matters look
where the wrathful hand of virtue has
descended.

MOUSIE. So news gets into the jail,
too?

HERRE. They have made scrambled
eggs out of your furniture. Your glasses
and bottles have had to turn somersaults
to the accompaniment of their own
music.

MOUSIE. A fellow what's on his uppers
had better look out—there's still a lot of
glass around.

HERRE. And your well-filled whiskey
barrels——

MOUSIE (*With a sigh*). Oh, mercy—
yes!

HERRE. They were rolled out—turned
into torrents—by clerical command.

MOUSIE. He stood exactly where you
are now, giving his orders.

HERRE. But are there no authorities,
then? Is there to be no law at all down
here in Hell? Haven't you made a complaint?

MOUSIE. No, this strike here has made
'em clear crazy. If I had complained,
they'd 'ave torn me to pieces. They were
going to do it anyhow—they'd already
started. But then that fellow Bratt took a
hand.

HERRE. And all this because Maren
lost her reason—nice, honest Maren!

MOUSIE (*Half rising*). I couldn't help
that, could I?

HERRE. Maren, who killed both her
brats!—And I who have seen them running around here, sockless and curly-
haired! What is life anyhow?

MOUSIE. And then she killed herself—
herself, too!

HERRE. And she killed herself, too!
First the children—then herself. Like
Medea—the great Medea!

For naught, for naught, my babes, I
    nurtured you,

And all for naught I labored, travail-
worn,
Bearing sharp anguish in your hour of
birth.[1]

MOUSIE (*As before*). I couldn't help
that, could I?

HERRE. O calamity-producing Mousie:
speak thou the truth at this open grave!
Thus biddeth the Word. How much
more, then, at three open graves! *She had
bought the whiskey from you!* For she
had to get drunk before she could face
her gruesome task.

MOUSE. How could I know she was
getting ready to——? I am as clean of it as
a baby's shirt.

HERRE. Weep not, Mousie! It behooves
not your rank and profession. I assure
you that if I had been out—what I mean
to say is: if I had been here—then it
would not have happened. But how was
it that people didn't get their reason back
when they saw the whiskey running away
—literally running away?

MOUSIE. Oh, it ran like water in a
brook, man! Just like that!

HERRE. But didn't they go down on
their bellies? Didn't they lap it up? Didn't
they use the hollows of their hands for
cups? Didn't they come running with
pitchers and pails?

MOUSIE. It ran all over the parson's
feet. "That's where it belongs," he said.

HERRE. Bratt is powerful. But there are
limits to everything. Marvelous happenings! Like earthquakes! Is—has Bratt
taken the place of the Lord down here?

MOUSIE. Oh, I guess the Lord never
had such power in Hell as that fellow
has.

HERRE. He didn't follow the coffin. Or
I would have said howdy to him. We
were together at the university.

MOUSIE. No, he's in his office now.

_____
[1] Euripides, *Medea*. Trans. by Arthur S.
Way.

HERRE. In his office? But he isn't a
minister any longer!

MOUSIE. The strike office, I mean. It's
him that has started this strike here, and
all the money goes to him.

(ELSA, *nicknamed* THE FLEECE, *comes
in; she is brown-skinned and full-
bosomed.*)

MOUSIE. There's the Fleece.

HERRE. Good morning, my cup of hot
coffee! All my senses are drinking in
your fragrance. What are you after, anyhow?

THE FLEECE. None of your business,
Mr. Soak! So you've got out at last?

HERRE. I met the funeral, but failed to
notice your chaotic locks in it. All Hell
was there, but not you, its guardian
spirit. You were attending to some early
business, were you not?

THE FLEECE. Oh, leave me alone!—
Why didn't you go along with Maren and
her children? She used to be kind to you.
And that's more than she was to me.

HERRE. Maren *was* good. Why didn't I
go along? I'll tell you—tell you frankly:
had I gone, I should have had to speak!
Then I should have wiped out the sun,
the moon, and all the stars for everyone
who entered that chapel. I should have
said: it wasn't she who is lying here—
that nice, hard-working Maren—it wasn't
she who killed her children. It wasn't she
who took her own life sinfully. No, it
was those people up there that killed her.
Those cannibals that live in the big city
have eaten her—her and her children.
The strike went to her head. The strike
took her reason. For her nervous soul
possessed that fullness of conscience
which is lacking in her murderers. Under
such conditions she didn't dare to continue living. She couldn't bear the responsibility of letting her two little girls
face hunger and degradation. It seemed
to her that life was a beast of prey, and
she wanted to save them while they were
still—— (*He breaks down.*)

THE FLEECE. Really, now and then it does one good to listen to you. The way you put things——

HERRE. You're a fine woman, Elsa. There is nothing the matter with your heart.

MOUSIE. The end of it will be that they'll eat us all up, I suppose.

A COARSE MALE VOICE (*Heard from the houses at the left*). If we don't eat 'em first!

HERRE. What sort of mountain spirit was that? A word of warning out of the future. A message from the huts to the palaces.

THE FLEECE (*Softly to* MOUSIE). What made me come here was to tell *you* to look out, Anders.

MOUSIE (*In the same tone*). Lord, what's up now? Can't they leave me alone on top of this?

THE FLEECE (*As before*). I fell in with a cop up there, and he asked me if it was true you went around with a big bottle of whiskey in your coat-pocket.

MOUSIE. No, no, it isn't true. (*He puts his hand mechanically to the tail pocket of his coat.*)

THE FLEECE (*As before*). And if you sold it on the sly around here?

MOUSIE (*Rising, horrified*). There, you see! They want to ruin me outright!

HERRE (*Comes up to him and tries to put his arm around him*). Is that true? Have you—have you——?

MOUSIE (*Trying to get away*). Leave me alone! Leave me alone, I tell you! You—he-he, I'm so ticklish! Oh, you—he-he!

HERRE. There is something back there. When you move, it describes a ponderous circle.—Elsa!

MOUSIE. It isn't true!

THE FLEECE. I'll hold him for you!

MOUSIE. Don't touch me! I'll holler!

THE FLEECE. Then the police will come and take both you and your bottle.

A FEMALE VOICE (*From the right*).

What are you doing to the Mousie that makes it squeak so?

MOUSIE. No, no, no!

(HERRE *pulls a big bottle from* MOUSIE's *coat-pocket.*)

MOUSIE. It's ordered! It's an order, I tell you! It isn't mine any longer!

HERRE (*Having drunk deeply*)

Ordered or not——

It goes right to the spot.

THE FLEECE. Oh, well—let me now——!

HERRE (*After another draught*)

It's the noblest juice

You did ever produce!

THE FLEECE. Let me now—let me now!

HERRE.

All right! Do your worst,

You soul athirst!

MOUSIE. This is the worst kind of larceny.

THE FLEECE. Never in the world did I taste anything better.

HERRE. Ah! Those people up there—they know—they know pretty well why they want to keep us from this dream of the gods.

MOUSIE. You've drunk all my profit for many days.

HERRE. Have a drink yourself, you poison-bearer!

THE FLEECE (*In a low voice*). Do you know what I have been thinking of again and again these last days? (*Drawing closer to* HERRE) Why shouldn't we set fire to the whole city up there some stormy night? Just set fire to it!

HERRE. Pooh! Then that rabble would seek safety in the open. No (*mysteriously*), there are a number of mining galleries left in the rock on which the city is built. Left from the time when the river came through here. Right here where we are standing now. For *we* are living in the old river-bed. This whole Hell here is nothing but the old river-bed. These old galleries, which start back of the houses over there and run into the rock in all directions, should be looked up. Then they should be loaded with powder and dynamite and all sorts of explosives—with electric wires laid through it. Ha, ha, ha! What a revelation of stinking, rotten guts we should have then!

THE FLEECE. Hooray! What a hell-fry! (*She snatches the bottle from* MOUSIE *and takes a long drink.*)

MOUSIE. But then we'd have to fly, too, I suppose.

THE FLEECE (*Handing the bottle to* HERRE). Would we have to go along?

HERRE (*Having had a drink and then permitted* MOUSIE *to take back the bottle, he gives* ELSA *a grandiose look*). Could we wish for a more beautiful lot?—At times, when I have given some thought to the final exit of one Otto Berg Herre, my thoughts have pictured it something like this: accompanied by thousands through the dawn-red gates of immortality. At *my* command, like slaves obeying some Oriental master, they would have to change dress in order to follow me in festive garments. After a life full of big promises —but also full of cares and regrets and frequent misunderstandings—to reach one's goal at last, in the moment of death—what a coronation that would be! To see one's name flashed upon the sky in sun-gilt script and read by all the world! To seat oneself upon a *sedia curulis* built out of the bent necks of millionaires! Ah, ah—with one's feet on their money-bags! And all around one the curses and applause of mankind like the swelling blast of an orchestra—like a roaring sea of homage—ah!

A FEMALE VOICE (*From the right as before*). Now they're coming back!

MOUSIE (*Scared*). Who's coming?

THE FLEECE (*Speaking simultaneously with* MOUSIE). Coming, you say?

HERRE (*Simultaneously with* MOUSIE *and* ELSA). What is it?

A FEMALE VOICE. The funeral, don't you know? But they're still up above.

THE FLEECE. Well—then there's plenty of time.

MOUSIE (*In a low voice*). But these here galleries—there's a lot of people have been talking of them—but you can't get through them, they say.

HERRE. There we are—there we are!

MOUSIE. There's water in some and worse in others.

THE FLEECE. Yes, I have heard that, too.

HERRE. That's just like this race of slaves! The least difficulty, a little water, a few grains of sand—and it's enough to break the wings of their vengeance, to scare away their cravings for freedom and light!

A FEMALE VOICE. The parson's along!

HERRE (*Frightened*). The parson? Pastor Bratt?

A FEMALE VOICE. No, the real parson.

MOUSIE. Falk——

HERRE. Oh, that one! He's nothing but a humbug. And so I might tell him to his face any time. I saw enough of him in the Students' Society.

THE FLEECE. Now I'll clear out.

HERRE (*Softly to her*). I'll be with you in a moment.

MOUSIE. Would you—would you say that to the parson?

HERRE. What?

MOUSIE. What you said—what you called him——

HERRE. A humbug? Why, to tell him *that*——?

MOUSIE. Will you—if you will, I'll give you a crown—sure as you live!

HERRE. In advance!—In advance!

MOUSIE. No-o-o——

HERRE. In advance!

MOUSIE. And if you don't say it, then——?

HERRE. I'll go right up to him and tell him at once—on my word of honor! If you give it in advance!

MOUSIE. I'll give you half of it—there!

(*The procession has begun to stream down the path. At that moment a train passes across the bridge.* FALK *is now dressed in ordinary clothes. He is in the rear and a little behind the rest. As he appears,* HERRE *meets him and tries to get by him.*)

FALK. Why, dear me—isn't this Otto Herre—our *magister bibendi?*

HERRE (*Saluting him*). Yes, your grace! That is, what is left of him.

FALK (*To himself*). Dear me, dear me! (*He begins to search all his pockets.*)

HERRE. And yet, take it all in all, perhaps the better part of him. But the times have not been very propitious, your grace.

FALK. No, I can see that. (*In a lowered voice*) Come to me if you get real hard up. Today I haven't—I have really given away what little I had. Here's half a crown—it's all I have.

HERRE. Thanks, your grace! Many thousand thanks. It's as I have always told the people here: it's your heart that makes you a man of genius. (*He starts to leave.*)

MOUSIE (*Who has been hiding behind a corner, intercepts* HERRE *on his way up*). But—but——?

HERRE. You didn't give me more than half. (*He disappears.*)

FALK (*To* HANS BRAA). Could you believe that that man is timid and shrinking when sober? If I were like him, I suppose I should be drinking, too.

BRAA. Yes, we know. We have often noticed it.

FALK. He's like the Rose of Jericho: dry as dust and a commonplace gray. But when you put it into the water, it begins to expand, and it smiles like the Lord's own day.—Well, folks, I told you up there, at the graves, that I had something on my heart which it would be more fitting to speak of down here. (*He ascends the stoop, and the people group themselves around him*) What I began with up there, and what I ended with as well, was this: we must not judge her! That must be left to Him who knows us all. Peace be to her outworn heart! Peace to her name when mentioned among us!—The worst feature of things like this strike here is that they bring so many to despair. Some say it happens only to the weakest. What I say is that it happens to the finest, to those who feel their responsibility most keenly, and who for that reason often are the best. Just as the best, as a rule, suffer more, take upon themselves greater sacrifices, and pay more of the cost. (*It is evident that the workmen agree with him in this*) I don't want to put the blame on anybody. But I suppose there is more than one of you who have discovered how dreadful it is when the children come crying: "I want something more to eat—oh, mamma, I want something more to eat." (*The crowd is stirred; he continues quietly*) I contribute my own mite every day.

A MAN (*In subdued tones*). Yes, you've been good to us.

SEVERAL (*In the same way*). Yes, you have.

FALK. Otherwise I shouldn't have the right to come here and say anything at all. My opinion, my advice, is, that a strike as big as this one—the biggest we have ever had—mustn't last long. An unexpected amount of help has come from the outside. But there are too many mouths to be fed. There are already those who know what hunger means. And many more will have to learn it. But nothing is more contagious than despair. Bear that in mind! And so a time will come—may come sooner than you expect now—when no one remains capable of controlling the forces that have been let loose. I have seen signs of violence and murder——

BLIND ANDERS. Yes, violence and murder!

FALK. What was that you said, old man?

BRAA. Oh, Anders, he's got only one thing to talk of.

FALK. Well, let him talk!

BLIND ANDERS. It was this thing that happened—my poor——

FALK. Don't I know it? Didn't we follow her together?

BLIND ANDERS. No, not her. I had another daughter, younger than her—who got a place up there in the city, in one of the fine houses. And there they laid violent hands on her.

FALK. Yes, yes. We remember. But that isn't the question now, Anders.

BLIND ANDERS. But you were talking of "violence and murder." *That* was violence. And she took it so hard that it ended in murder, too. God help us and protect us!

FALK. My dear Anders, we know all this. (*He remains silent for a while*) To get back to our present problem—despair is a dangerous comrade, and it is already present among you. You must act in such fashion that you are not held responsible for what was never in your own minds.

BRAA. It's those people up in the city who are responsible.

FALK. The past, Hans Braa, is more to blame than the present. And those who bear the blame in the present are generally found on both sides.

BRAA. No, it's all with them, up there!

FALK. Not all of it!

SEVERAL. Yes, yes, all of it!

FALK. Do you dare to declare yourself quite free from blame?

ALL. Yes, yes!

FALK. Now your temper is up because you have been suffering. And I shall say no more about it. But if you *want* peace, then it's of *no* use for you to look upon the others as a lot of thieves.

BRAA. But when they *are* thieves?

SEVERAL. You bet they are!

FALK. Like those that were crucified, perhaps. You know, even thieves may be converted.

PETER STUA. Reg'lar beasts of prey, that's what they are!

FALK. That's going it one better! But let me tell you something now: you should leave threats and defiances to the rich. Theirs has been the power, and so they have grown accustomed to be brutal and to settle everything by force. Don't be stupid enough to take after them. Poverty has certain advantages which no wealth can gain. Don't throw them away! Poverty has its own blessings——

BRAA. Have you tried 'em, pastor?

FALK. I know rich and poor alike, and in many things the poor are better off than the rich.

HANS OLSEN. Yes, in rags and vermin.

FALK. That's *your* experience? (*A few laugh*) I'll tell you in what respects I think the poor are better off. They often know how to be content with very little. They are always kind to each other—truly self-sacrificing, that's what they are. And they have more patience, more forbearance——

A COARSE MALE VOICE (*From a house high up on the left side of the chasm*). Why don't you go and tell that to the rich?

(*Everybody turns to look in the direction from which the voice came.*)

FALK. I have done so! I cringe no more to the rich than to the poor.

COARSE MALE VOICE. Aw, we don't want any more of that Sunday-school drivel down here!

A FEMALE VOICE (*Heard as before from the right, far up along the hillside*). Why don't you listen instead, you Muck-Peter over there? You're the dirtiest bum in all Hell, you are!

COARSE MALE VOICE. Aw, shut up, you——!

FALK. That kind of forces—if despair is added to them—you think you can control them? No more than I can control the sea out there!—And now I want to tell you—for they have been to see me—that there are those among you who would like to go back to work again——

PETER STUA. Just let 'em try!

SEVERAL (*In quick succession*). Is that true?

ALMOST EVERYBODY. Yes, let 'em try! (*Wild excitement seizes the crowd*) We'll 'tend to them! Tell us who they are! Names! Names! (*Finally the crowd yells in time*) Names! Names!

FALK (*With a gesture of authority that stills the uproar*). Now you have violence in mind! If you knew them, you would use violence against them! And when it comes to that, then murder is not far off! (*Deep silence*) Then more than one of you would be ruined for life. And so would your children and your poor wives——

BLIND ANDERS. That's true!

BRAA. The people up there would have to answer for it.

FALK. Yes, if you could make them see *that,* then——

PETER STUA. They'll *have* to see it!

ASPELUND. The day will come when they'll see it.

FALK. But for that day *you* cannot wait. You must deal with them as they are, both men and conditions. Water won't run down-hill faster than the grade demands. To me it looks as if the Lord wanted you to practice patience until His time comes. And frequently it comes when we least expect it.

COARSE MALE VOICE (*From the left as before*). Aw, why the devil don't you quit?

FALK. You won't get very far by calling for the devil, folks! I fear you'll have to turn to Him who patiently lets His sun rise over good and evil——

FEMALE VOICE (*From the right*). There comes Bratt!

SEVERAL. Who—Bratt?

BRAA. Yes, he promised to come today.

A MAN (*Who has run up the path*). Yes, it's him!

(*All turn around. A few more toward the background; others follow them gradually. At last only three old women remain near FALK.*)

FALK. Well—why don't you go with the rest?

AN OLD WOMAN (*Embarrassed*). No, you're too nice for that.

FALK. Three—it isn't much! But then they mean it, at least! (*He steps down from the stoop.*)

BRAA (*In the background*). Three cheers for Bratt!

(*The crowd breaks into wild cheering. BRATT, who becomes visible at the bend leading to the right, waves his hand to silence them, but without effect. The ovation continues uninterruptedly until he reaches the stoop. BRATT mounts it, and for a while silence reigns.*)

BRATT. 'Way up there, where I was standing, I could hear my predecessor in this parish say that the Lord patiently lets His sun shine upon good and evil alike. What I want to say first of all is that, down here, the sun never shines.

(*The crowd laughs and repeats the last words.*)

BRATT. I have really met those who don't know that we down here are living at the bottom of a deep river. There used to be falls in the river, not far from its mouth. Those falls ate their way further and further back. That's what made this cleft in which we live. And that's what led to the discovery of all the wealth in the rocks on both sides of the river. Then they turned the water aside and started mining. That's what made the big city up there. But all the reward the workmen got for what they dragged out into the sunlight was that they were thrust out of the sunlight themselves, down into this place. They earned so much for the others that the ground up there became

too expensive for poor people. And so they had to be satisfied with what they could get for nothing down here. But to this place the sun never comes.

(*The people talk among themselves.*)

BRAA. That's the way it is.

FALK (*Before he leaves*). Be careful now, Bratt!

BRATT (*Looks for a moment at* FALK; *then he resumes*). Little by little it became the rule that all who went to waste up there in the big city, or who wasted themselves, were cast down here——

BRAA. Human garbage!

BRATT. Into "Hell," as they soon began to call it. . . . Here it is dark and cold. Here few work hopefully, and no one joyfully. Here the children won't thrive— they yearn for the sea and the daylight. They crave the sun. But it lasts only a little while, and then they give up. They learn that among those who have been cast down here there is rarely one who can climb up again.

SEVERAL. That's right.

BRATT. Here we are now. But those who own all that vacant land we call Sunnywold have just told us that it is something we cannot have. And at the highest point of that land, where the old fort used to stand, there Holger has reared his new palace—and there, in "The Castle," representatives of the factory owners from all over the country are to meet this evening. There they are to discuss how they can hold us down so that we may never get up.

COARSE MALE VOICE (*From the left*). Yes, let 'em try!

BRATT. I ask you, for Heaven's sake: let them by all means gather up there. That castle was built while the distress was increasing all around the country— as if in spite. It is quite as it should be that they meet there and give us their answer from there. I am told that the whole castle will be illuminated tonight!

COARSE MALE VOICE. Yes, let 'em try!

ALL (*As before*). Yes, let 'em try, let 'em try!

BRATT. But, friends, don't you understand that nothing could be better for us? This very day, when we have followed Maren and her two children to their graves——

BLIND ANDERS. Yes, Maren——

BRATT. Then they start an illumination! (*Excitement and anger are shown by the crowd*) By all means, let them go on like that! It will bring us many friends we didn't have before. And more than one will tremble before the God who is thus mocked. Let them illuminate! Those people who have taken the sun away from you! (*The crowd mutters*) You know, don't you, that everything that carries infection is best · at home where the sun cannot reach it? The sun kills off the microbes—those of the soul as well as of the body. The sun gives strength and cunning. The sun is company. The sun breeds faith! All this is known by the rich people up there. They learn it at school —and yet they let you live down here! They have let you live here where disease and rottenness live side by side with you—here, where children lose their color and thoughts their clearness —here, where clothes and minds alike grow moldy. They have preachers and churches; they have hymns and prayers; they have a tiny bit of charity, too—but a God they have not. (*Excitement*) Can we wait until they get one? Generation after generation, in misery and sin?— What was it that happened here three days ago? For whom were the bells tolling today? And we ask if it is possible to wait? A few homes for workmen here and there—do they end the bitter need of thousands? What is there to herald the coming of better things? A new generation up there? Listen to what their young people answer for themselves: "We want a good time!" And their books? The books and the youth together make the future. And what do the books say? Exactly the same as the youth: "Let us have a good time! Ours are the light and the lust of life, its colors and its joys!" That's what the youth and their books say.— They are right! It is all theirs! There is no law to prevent their taking life's sunlight and joy away from the poor people. For those who have the sun have also made the law.—But then the next question is whether we might not scramble up high enough to take part in the writing of a new law. (*This is received with thundering cheers*) What is needed is that one generation makes an effort strong enough to raise all coming generations into the vigorous life of full sunlight.

MANY. Yes, yes.

BRATT. But so far every generation has put it off on the next one. Until at last *our* turn has come to bear sacrifices and sufferings like unto those of death itself. Only a little while ago we saw one of us break down under them. But are you aware that she has not died in vain? Her desperation has struck panic in more than one conscience. Never before have the contributions to the strike fund poured in as they did yesterday and today. Several have given large sums— from one man alone we got two thousand today.

(*This news is received with enthusiasm.*)

BLIND ANDERS (*With emotion*). You don't tell me!

BRATT. What do you say about remembering her—her fears and her sufferings? As a symbol of the misery we want to end? As a cry of help from all those generations that have perished? As a desperate prayer for deliverance?

ALL (*Deeply moved*). Yes, yes!

BRATT. And let us all try our utmost in self-sacrifice! I am now getting along with one half of what I generally live on. No one knows how long the ordeal will last. I have persuaded many others to do like me. And they agree with me, that it feels like a consecration. As I stand here now, my hands are aflame and I seem to be charged with electricity. My senses are more keen, my faculties more clear— fused, as they are, into a passion for sacrifice. . . . You must practice the art of doing without! Controlling yourself, you control those others who need to be guided—and of those there is enough!— Keep up your courage! Every day brings new support from all quarters. Never before have the workers stood so close to their goal. Never before have we been united to the same extent. Never have we had a firmer grip or a better foothold. O that it might be granted the generation which is ours—that it might be granted —to raise the workers of this country out of the darkness and the dampness for all time to come—out of the cellar holes, so that they may live on the sunlit side of life!

(*A wave of emotion passes through the crowd.*)

BRATT (*Who has covered his face with his hands, says quietly as he looks up at the crowd again*). You had better go up to the strike office. The money is ready for you. (*There is a lot of happy excitement*) And when you have got your money, you must select the committee that is to call on Mr. Holger today. You remember—he is to have his answer today.

(*Everybody looks happier. Many go up to* BRATT *to press his hand as he steps down from the stoop. Then they hurry away toward the city in groups, eagerly talking. Just as* BRATT *himself is about to leave, after all the rest are gone,* ELIAS *appears.*)

ELIAS (*Coming from one of the houses at the right*). Bratt!

BRATT. Elias! (*Hurries toward him and leads him down the stage*) At last! Where have you been? Just when we needed you most, you disappeared.

ELIAS. I, too, had my work to do.

BRATT. Do you think I doubt it?

ELIAS (*Smiling*). And, for that matter, you have seen me.

BRATT. Without knowing you?

ELIAS. Yes. But—what did you want me for?

BRATT. First of all, I was afraid that the money we have been receiving—that entirely too much of it came from you. And I wanted to warn you, Elias.

ELIAS. Thanks! Do you know who was the last man Maren Haug talked with?

BRATT. You?

ELIAS. Yes, me.

BRATT. What did she say? That she was in despair——?

ELIAS. She said: "Someone has to die." That's what she said. "They'll never pay any attention to us before," she said.

BRATT. Was that what she said—? A case of conscious martyrdom, then? Do you think so?

ELIAS. I do.

BRATT. But more than one martyr has been out of his reason.

ELIAS. So they have.

BRATT. And the whiskey? Everybody says that she had been drinking.

ELIAS. To get courage, yes! Which is only one more proof, it seems to me.

BRATT. Why didn't she ask us for more assistance? She would have got it.

ELIAS. I, too, offered to help her.

BRATT. And then?

ELIAS. "I will only take it from outsiders," she said.

BRATT. Really!—Yes, there was something remarkable about that woman.— But it is wonderful! Oh, there is much that is great among the poor people down here.—So she offered herself as a sacrifice?

ELIAS. I am sure of it.

BRATT. I can see that it has made a deep impression on you. (ELIAS *nods assent*) You don't look well. You ought

to go to your sister. Have you seen her recently?

ELIAS. Not in the last few days.—Do you recall that remarkable boy and girl who were with her—the children of Sommer?

BRATT. Of course! It would be impossible to forget them.

ELIAS. They are not with her any longer.

BRATT. What does that mean? They were given to your sister, were they not?

ELIAS. No, their uncle has taken them now.

BRATT. Holger? But the last thing Sommer said was that your sister should have them.

ELIAS. That didn't matter. Now the uncle has taken them. "Their parents are dead," he said, "and I am their parents. I am going to make them my heirs, and they are to be brought up in accordance with *my* will."

BRATT. In accordance with *his* will! So they are also to become sweaters of labor?

ELIAS. Of course. Those people take the future itself away from us. It's a thing that haunts me night and day— even more than what happened to Maren. *For it is worse.* Think only, that they take the very future away from us.

BRATT (*Looking him firmly in the eye*). That kind of feeling should be turned into action, Elias!

ELIAS (*Meeting his glance firmly*). Well, there is no doubt about that!

BRATT (*Putting his arm within that of* ELIAS). Do you remember how you and your sister came to me down here?

ELIAS. Now, that's strange!

BRATT. What is?

ELIAS. Your mentioning that. For it is just what I have been thinking of all day.

BRATT. You came so radiantly. You had just got your inheritance from that American aunt of yours. You were rich.

ELIAS. And we came to find out what we could do with it.

BRATT. I showed you what I was doing. Your sister wouldn't join us—it was untried ground, she said. And instead she bought land and built her hospital up there. But you——

ELIAS (*Placing his free hand on that of* BRATT). I chose to stay with you!

BRATT (*Pointing in the direction from which* ELIAS *first appeared*). And the day you bought that miserable little house you were as happy as a lark.

ELIAS. And I haven't regretted it once. To me this is the only kind of life worth living.

BRAT (*Gravely*). But how is it then, Elias, that something has come between you and me?

ELIAS. What are you talking about?

BRATT. I can hear it in the ring of your voice right now! I could see it in you before you had spoken a word—that there is somebody who has taken you away from me!

ELIAS (*Freeing himself*). Nobody could! Nothing but death!

BRATT. But something has happened——?

ELIAS. So it has.

BRATT (*Anxiously*). What is it?

ELIAS (*After a moment's thought*). You ask me so many questions. May I ask you just *one*?

BRATT. My dear boy, what is it?

ELIAS (*With a peculiar forcefulness*). Both of us believe that God is something we have to work out within ourselves.

BRATT. Yes.

ELIAS. That He is evident in the eternal order of the universe, and that to man this order means justice—the growth of justice.

BRATT. And of goodness.

ELIAS. But isn't He evident in war also? Could He stand outside of that?

BRATT. Is *that* your question?

ELIAS. Yes.

BRATT (*After having looked at him for a moment*). There are so many kinds of war.

ELIAS. This is the kind I am thinking of: to sacrifice oneself in order to destroy those that will evil.

BRATT. If that kind of war comes within the order that is justice——?

ELIAS. Yes.

(*A* MAN IN BROWN *has stolen up close to them without being noticed by either one of them. At this moment he puts his head in between them, with his face close to that of* BRATT.)

BRATT. Ugh! What is the use of that sort of thing? Why must he always come like that?

MAN IN BROWN (*Crouching on his haunches, with his hands resting on his knees, begins to laugh wildly*). Ha—ha—ha—ha!

(*He hops around like a bird until, at a sign from* ELIAS, *he suddenly disappears.*)

BRATT. Is it never possible to have a talk with you without that fellow getting in between us?

ELIAS. What do you want me to do? He has attached himself to me. It is his one happiness in this world. Do you want me to chase him away?

BRATT. No, of course, I don't. But can't you keep him from breaking in like that whenever anybody is talking to you? That's too much.

ELIAS. He thinks it's funny. Why not let him do it, then? Otherwise he suffers so terribly. This very day I have had to promise him that we are to live and die together.

BRATT. What does that mean?

ELIAS. Oh, at times he has wonderfully lucid moments. So I had to promise him.

BRATT. You are *too* good, Elias.

ELIAS. No, *I* am not too good, but mankind has too much to bear. He with the rest. He is one of those Holger drove out of his employ because they dared to vote our ticket. It was more than the man could face, and so he went to pieces, and was thrust down to us.

BRATT. I know it.

ELIAS. Well—and then he began to follow me wherever I went. He would be crouching outside my house like a dog, so I had to let him in.

BRATT. But when you give yourself to everybody like that—then you impair your efficiency where it is most——

ELIAS (Interrupting). Pardon me for interrupting you, but I am so restless today. I cannot stand still and listen. And I have so little time to spare. I really came here just to see you. I wanted so badly to have a look at you!

BRATT. But what we were talking of, Elias——

ELIAS. Don't let us talk of it any more!

BRATT. Are we not to talk of it?

ELIAS. Afterward you will understand so much better. I cannot stand seeing so much wrong-doing! I cannot stand hearing that the others are going to win!

BRATT. Are the others going to win, you say? Has it got so far with you, that you can believe such a thing for a moment?

ELIAS. That far—yes! (Putting his hands around BRATT's head) I do love you! For all that you have been to me. From the first day you picked me up here—until your present moment of alarm.

BRATT. Yes, Elias, you do——

ELIAS. Now you must be quiet. I love you who everlastingly dare to believe, and to live in accordance with your belief. You who take hold so that the whole country can feel it. You whose cry goes right into our souls: "Courage, courage!" To the youth that means: "Push ahead—farther still!"

BRATT (Frightened). But farther than this, Elias—that would be to——

ELIAS. You mustn't say anything. Nor must I!

(He throws his arms around BRATT, hugging him as hard as he can; then he lets him go only to take hold of his head with both hands; having kissed him twice, he lets him go again, and runs out in the direction from which he first appeared.)

BRATT. But, Elias—? You have no right to run away without telling me what it is.—Still further—? Now? Horrible! (He runs after ELIAS) It must be stopped! (He calls out with all his might) Elias! (As the curtain falls, he is still heard crying) Listen, Elias! Elias!

CURTAIN

ACT II

An artistically furnished library of lofty proportions. The entire rear wall is covered by drapery. At the left there is an arched window, reaching from the floor to the ceiling. The walls on both sides of the window are covered with bookshelves that also reach to the ceiling. At the right, facing the window, there is an arched doorway, which is likewise flanked by bookshelves. A table stands in the foreground toward the left. A number of architectural drawings are lying on the table.

HOLGER (Seated in a huge armchair that stands between the table and the foremost bookcase). Then there is nothing but the basement floor to be changed?

HALDEN (Standing). Yes, and not much of that. But then there is the extension.

HOLGER. The extension? There is not going to be any extension. Did I forget to tell you about that?

HALDEN. You did.

[97]

HOLGER. The extension was meant for my nephew and niece. At that time we took for granted that they were going to live with Miss Sang.

HALDEN. Oh, are they not to live with Miss Sang?

HOLGER. They are to live with me. (*Pause.*)

HALDEN. Then there is hardly anything left to do.

HOLGER. There is no reason, then, why Miss Sang shouldn't move in. What do you say?

HALDEN. As I understand it, she was going to move in today.

HOLGER (*Looking hard at* HALDEN). You haven't seen her?

HALDEN (*Without looking at* HOLGER). Not for a long while.

(*A knocking at the door is heard, and* HALDEN *hastens to open it.*)

HOLGER (*Rising at once and going toward the door*). There she is now, perhaps.

(HALDEN *opens the door.*)

BRAA (*Still outside*). Is Holger here?

HOLGER (*Seating himself again*). Here I am.

HALDEN. A delegation of workmen.

HOLGER. So I can hear——

HALDEN. Well—can they come in?

HOLGER. Oh, yes, let them!

HANS BRAA, ASPELUND, *old* ANDERS HOEL, HENRIK SEM, HANS OLSEN, *and* PETER STUA *enter.*)

HOLGER (*Seated as before*). Who is that blind old man?

BRAA. That's Anders Hoel—he's the father of her——

HOLGER. Is he employed in any of the factories here in town?

BRAA. No, but his children——

HOLGER. I won't negotiate with anybody but the workmen from the factories.

BRAA. He's the father of Maren—her that we buried today—her and her two children. And so it seemed kind of

proper, as we thought, that he should come along and speak for——

HOLGER. That's all right. Take him outside.

(*Nobody moves. Nobody answers.*)

BLIND ANDERS. Am I to be put out?

BRAA. So he says.

BLIND ANDERS (*Quietly*). Is there anybody can tell more than I about the hard times down there?

BRAA. But he won't have it, don't you see?

BLIND ANDERS. We-ell? But he ought to know Maren ain't the only one I've lost.

HOLGER. Take that man out so we can start—eh?

HALDEN. Come, Anders, I'll help you out.

BLIND ANDERS. Who're you? Seems to me I know your voice——

HALDEN. This way, Anders.

BLIND ANDERS. No, I won't! I've been elected, I tell you!

SEVERAL (*At once*). You must!

BRAA. We can't get anything done before, don't you see!

BLIND ANDERS. Oh, you can't? Well, well—then I want to say a couple of words first.

HALDEN. No, no, Anders!

SEVERAL. Naw!

BLIND ANDERS. So you think—? All I wanted to tell him was that if she was here now, that smallest girl of mine— that poor little thing, what——

HOLGER (*Rising*). Get out, all of you! Eh?

ASPELUND (*To* BLIND ANDERS). Can't you hear? That's no joke! And it's we that'll have to pay.

(HOLGER *seats himself again.*)

BLIND ANDERS. Well, then we'll be quits. For what you've done, I've had to pay for.

HALDEN. Oh, be sensible now, Anders! Come along with me!

BLIND ANDERS. Who're you anyhow?

BRAA. It's Halden, don't you know?

BLIND ANDERS. Oh, it's Halden! He's all right, they say. Well—well, I'll go along with Halden.

HALDEN. That's a good fellow! And I'll see that you get something to brace you up.

BLIND ANDERS. But we're in that man Holger's house, ain't we?

HALDEN. Yes.

BLIND ANDERS. Of course, I ain't had nothing to eat but scraps o' bread for two days, but sooner than eat a bite or drink a drop of that man Holger's—(with deep emotion) sooner I'd do like them girls o' mine.

HALDEN. It's my own, what you're going to have.

BLIND ANDERS. Oh, so! Oh, well—yes —well——

HALDEN. Now we'll go, then?

BLIND ANDERS. Now we'll go. (Takes a step or two toward the door and turns around again) But now you'll have to tell that man Holger— Yes, you know, he is still sitting over there!

SEVERAL. Get out now, Anders!

BLIND ANDERS (In a thunderous voice). They thought a whole lot more of their honor than you do over there!— You and the likes of you!—Now I'm going! Now I've said what I wanted to. (He goes out slowly, led by HALDEN.)

HOLGER. Well, what is it you want?

BRAA. Today's the day we was to meet you, ain't it?

HOLGER. Oh, that's it? I had forgotten.

BRAA. We were looking for you down in the city first, but then they told us you were out here. (Pause.)

HOLGER. Well, you know that I represent all the factory owners now—eh?

ASPELUND. And we all the workmen. As far as that goes, it's all right. (Pause.)

HOLGER. Have you any proposition to make?

BRAA. Yes.

ASPELUND. Sure we have!

HOLGER. What is it?

BRAA. That we pick a board of arbitration together.

(HOLGER makes no reply.)

BRAA. And we thought of putting in a bill about it, too. So it could be made a law, don't you see?

(HOLGER remains silent.)

BRAA. We workmen feel as if there might be a future in that.

HOLGER. But we don't.

ASPELUND. Naw—you don't want anybody to get in between——

HOLGER (Without paying any attention to him). Have you any other propositions?

BRAA. We have authority, if you've got any others.

HOLGER. Propositions? No!

BRAA. Is it just as it was before?

HOLGER. No, it isn't.

ASPELUND (Quietly and timidly). Is there anything more than there was before?

HOLGER. No propositions. We make no propositions. Eh?

BRAA (Tensely). What is it, then?

HOLGER. Conditions, that's what it is!

BRAA (After an exchange of glances between the workmen, says in a subdued and hesitant manner). Might we hear what kind of condition it is?

HOLGER. I fear you are not done with striking yet. And if so, it's of no use.

(The workmen are seen talking among themselves.)

BRAA. We've agreed we'd like to hear it just the same.

HOLGER. The condition, you mean? There are several.

ASPELUND (In a wholly different tone). So, there's a lot of 'em! Well, is there any reason why we shouldn't hear about them? Now's as good a time as any.

HOLGER. There is this reason against it: that only the factory owners of this city have agreed to them so far. But we want everybody to agree with us. Every factory owner in the country. We are going to meet tonight. We are going to have a trade union, we too!

BRAA. So we've heard. But as the conditions have to do with us first of all, I think we might be told about them.

ASPELUND. Well, that's what *I* think, too.

HENRIK SEM *and* HANS OLSEN. Yes.

HOLGER. As you like. The first condition is that no workman can be a member of Bratt's union, or of any other union that hasn't our approval.

(*The workmen exchange glances, but without a word or change of mien.*)

HOLGER. The next one is that you cannot subscribe to Sang's paper, or to any other paper not approved by us.

HANS OLSEN. And I suppose we've got to go to church, too?

BRAA (*Silencing him with a gesture*). And what do we get if we agree?

HOLGER. What you had before. Eh?—However, I have to inform you that those are not the only conditions.

ASPELUND. I think if I was you, I'd try the other way around. Making the people a little happier instead.

HOLGER. It isn't in our power to make you happy.

ASPELUND. Oh, yes! Oh, yes! Let's have a share of the profits, and let's get land up here to live on——

HOLGER. People who want what belongs to others can never be happy. Eh?

HANS OLSEN. But those who've got hold of what belongs to others can be happy enough.

HOLGER (*Striking the table with his hand*). Have I got hold of what belongs to others? What would you be but for me? Eh? Who has built up all this—you or me?

HANS OLSEN. I guess there was a few who helped to build up—from the first—and now there's thousands that are helping.

HOLGER. Helping? Yes, my ink-well has also been helping? And the power, and the machines, and the telegraph, and the ships, and the workmen. I put the workmen last, because every so often they try to smash all the rest to pieces. And neither the ink-well nor the power nor the machines nor the telegraph can be called that stupid.

ASPELUND. You're playing a high game —I must say!

HOLGER. The game should have been still higher long ago. Eh? Then, perhaps, talent and capital might even have found time to make decent living conditions for the workmen.

HANS OLSEN. Yes, in Hell!

BRAA. No, no—that kind o' talk doesn't lead to anything.

ASPELUND. Yes, it does! It leads to what's bad.—For Heaven's sake, come and see how we're living down there!

HOLGER. Well, why do you strike, then? You're wasting a lot more than we could have given to help you.

BRAA. Why wouldn't you do *anything* before we struck?

ASPELUND. Why can't you do anything now? And be done with it?

HOLGER. I would call that putting money into your strike fund. Eh? No, *this* time you'll have to bear all the consequences of your behavior. For now *I* am in command. (*Long silence.*)

BRAA (*To the rest*). I guess we may just as well get out of here at once. We can't do anything here.

ASPELUND. No, Blind Anders will be doing about as much sitting outside.

HOLGER. It's my opinion, too, that we haven't got anything new to tell each other.—You'd better come back when you are done with all that strike nonsense. Eh?

BRAA. So we're to be done up this time, are we? P'r'aps it mightn't work after all!

ASPELUND. We've got something like

honor, too—just as Anders said before.

HANS OLSEN. The way you talk! We—honor? Naw, they've got all the honor! Them as take it from the women folks—and then send 'em off to America!

HOLGER. Although this has nothing to do with the strike, or with me either—let me tell you that, once for all—yet I'll answer it. It's the second time you've come forward with it. And it's all the time in your paper.—Every class has its own sense of honor. But it's by our women we can best measure how much of that kind of sense we have. Such as *our* honor is, such are they.

ASPELUND. Yes, there's a lot in that.

HOLGER. But when *your* women are such that they can be caught by hand like fledgling birds—what sort of honor have you got then?

PETER STUA. (*Who until then has not said a word*). I'll be damned if I stand for any more of that!

(*He swings himself across the table. HOLGER, who has risen to meet him, bends him backward against the table, as BRAA and ASPELUND run up to them from opposite sides.*)

BRAA. Cut out that kind of thing!

(*HOLGER and PETER STUA let go their hold of each other.*)

ASPELUND. You'd better wait. There'll be time for that too.

HOLGER. Now you'll have to get out!

HALDEN (*Rushes into the room*). What's up here?

ASPELUND. Oh, they've got to fighting about honor.

HANS OLSEN (*In a rage*). All you big fellows have a lot of sons in America that you don't want to hear of. And none of them comes back here to teach you what honor is.

HOLGER (*Having arranged his clothing*). Open the door, Halden!—Eh?

BRAA. (*Close to HOLGER*). There is something I must talk of. It can't wait.

HOLGER. But the rest will have to get out at once.

HANS OLSEN. Well, we ain't hankering to stay either. (*He goes out.*)

PETER STUA. We'll come back again. But I guess it'll be in a different way.

BRAA. Aw—get out now!

(*PETER STUA goes out.*)

ASPELUND (*Quietly, as he is leaving*). Yes, indeed, you're playing a mighty high game. (*He goes out.*)

HOLGER (*Sharply to BRAA*). What is it?

BRAA. You can see for yourself that there are some here that can't be controlled much longer. And it might be a good thing to keep that in mind.

HOLGER. Well, why don't you keep it in mind? Eh?

BRAA. Things might happen here which *everybody* would ask the Lord to spare us.

HOLGER. No, I wouldn't! For that would be the very best thing that could happen.

BRAA. That many thousands——

HOLGER. The more, the better!

BRAA. Well, I'll be hanged!

HOLGER. Eh? Now you are standing on our feet. And then we could put you at a proper distance again for at least another generation. And in the meantime something might happen.

BRAA. Well, then there is nothing left for me to say here. (*He goes out.*)

HOLGER (*To HALDEN*). I can't help thinking, whenever I see that fellow, there must be gentle blood in him.—And that's true of Peter Stua, too.—All who dare—all who dare to revolt—have upper-class blood in them. Careless crossing that, Halden!

HALDEN. Careless?

HOLGER. I like those fellows. Especially the one who came at me. Splendid chap. I should like to know who was his father.

Upper-class blood. It almost seems as if I could spot his nose. Eh? The rest are nothing but slaves. Born slaves. Pure and simple.—Was there anything you wanted, Halden?

HALDEN. Miss Sang has been waiting quite a while outside.

HOLGER. And why didn't you tell me at once? Eh? (*He hastens to the door and opens it; not seeing anybody, he steps into the next room; a moment later he is heard to say outside*) You mustn't think it's my fault. Eh? If I had only known——

RACHEL (*Beginning to speak while still outside*). Mr. Halden wanted to announce me. But I didn't think I ought to prevent the workmen from finishing their talk with you.

(*Both she and* HOLGER *are in the room by the time she stops speaking.*)

HOLGER. Well, they treated me to some of that bitter beer your paper has been brewing. (*At his words* RACHEL *is seen to flinch; he doesn't notice it, but leads her to a sofa, where he sits down beside her*) I have had to hear that those fellows have made my wealth, and that accordingly I am playing the part of an archthief. Eh? Quite an amusing tale! Here I have built up a market for the labor of many thousand men. Add to those all who are depending on them, and they make a whole city. And so one fine day, before I am through with it, they turn on me and tell me it is theirs! Eh? And when I won't make concessions at once, they rebel. I forgive them, and everything seems to be all right again—when a crazy preacher drops down among them and begins to proclaim the law of God. But the law of God is that everything should be turned topsy-turvy. Now we can't even build and live as we please, for then we are taking the sun away from *them*. To make up for this, the city is

asked to build houses for those people in Sunnywold—in Sunnywold, the pride and joy of the whole city! Why not lodge them in our own houses? And as it's the "law of God"—why not in heaven as well? Eh? (*Rising*) I tell you, Miss Sang, if we handed out everything we have, bag and baggage—in a year it would be all over with the factories, the capital, the trade, and all of us would be in the poorhouse! Eh?—I beg your pardon, Miss Sang! Here I am treating you to the same sort of bitter brew, only drawn from a different barrel. (*He seats himself again*) There is no one I respect more than you, my dear Miss Sang. But I happen to be made in such a way that my temper is a part of my motive power. And as there had been such a lot of it stored up during that meeting——

RACHEL (*Smiling*). Oh, I have to hear all sorts of things these days.

HOLGER. I thought you had already moved in, Miss Sang. And I came here only to hand over the deed to you. It was registered yesterday. (*He takes a document from the table*) Now the park and the house are yours under the law. And I regard it as a pleasure and an honor to have the chance of placing this deed in your hands.

(*Both rise.*)

RACHEL. A magnificent gift, indeed! Now my hospital ought to be secure or I'll prove myself sadly incapable. I thank you with all my heart, Mr. Holger. (*She takes his hand.*)

HOLGER. The document is a work of art, as you'll see. That's Halden's doing, of course.

RACHEL (*Opening the deed*). Yes, so it is. I'll have it nicely framed, and then I'll hang it right opposite the entrance. A thousand, thousand thanks! (*They bow to each other*) Is the deed entirely in my name?

[102]

HOLGER. Of course!

RACHEL. But it's a gift to the hospital?

HOLGER. It's a gift to you. And you will dispose of it.

RACHEL. Well, I hope only that I may prove equal to it——

HOLGER. You have already proved that.—When are you going to move in?

RACHEL. I thought of doing so at once if you have no objection?

HOLGER. There are some books here I want to take away. Nothing else.

RACHEL. You can't imagine how happy my sick people are made by this. Today we have knocked a hole in the wall between the hospital and the park. And everybody who could crawl out of bed had to come and watch the work.

HOLGER. I suppose you have a lot to attend to, and so we'll leave you—Halden and I.

RACHEL. Oh, there is something I wanted so badly to ask of you, Mr. Holger. Although, of course, you never listen when I ask you for something.

HOLGER. There is nobody, absolutely nobody, to whom I would rather listen. (*He motions her to be seated*) What is it? (*He seats himself again.*)

RACHEL. The big meeting of all the delegates that is to be held tonight—don't hold it in the Castle! Don't make any display! Don't illuminate the Castle!

HOLGER. The Castle is one of the finest pieces of architecture in this country. And the site of the old fort, where it is located, makes a very fine setting for it. Eh?

RACHEL. That's true. Mr. Halden has every right to be proud of his work. There is no one who disputes that. But——

HOLGER. But—yes? The workmen have declared the building and its location a direct affront to themselves.

RACHEL. Many cruel deeds were committed in the old fort.

HOLGER. And now they are covered up with beauty. Is there anything criminal in that? Eh?

RACHEL. The time during which the Castle was built——

HOLGER. The time? When times are hard is the best time to make work for people. Is there anything criminal in that either?

RACHEL. It has been misunderstood. Remember what happened during your housewarming.

HOLGER. A little dynamite—what of it? Sheer futility. Those deep old moats prevent them from getting near the place.

RACHEL. But don't give another excuse for it.

HOLGER. Not only will the banquet and the illumination be repeated, but I am going to put three bands at the big——

RACHEL. Oh, no, no!

HOLGER (*Rising*). Eh? Do you mean to say that we are to give way because of their evil plotting? Not while I am in command. It is just in times like these that the Castle has a message for certain people. Did you see it illuminated?

RACHEL. No, I didn't go out at all.

HOLGER. That's where you missed it. (*He goes toward the background*) Fortunately I had an artist on hand to paint it. A very clever fellow. Here you'll see.

(*He pulls aside the drapery in the rear, thus revealing a beautiful painting that covers the entire wall. It shows a medieval castle with towers and turrets, crenelated walls, and a broad moat in front. The upper edges of the building are outlined with electric lights and the whole structure is strongly illuminated. Further down on the picture may be seen a city with its harbor, which is protected toward the open sea by a long breakwater. There are electric lights along the breakwater, too. The atmospheric effect is that of a clear fall evening with waning light.*)

RACHEL (*Who has risen*). Yes, that's wonderful! Indeed, it's wonderful!

HOLGER. That's how I believe things are going to look when this earth once more finds a place for big personalities, who dare and can proclaim their own selves. When we get away from ant-heap ideas and centipedal dreams—back to big men with genius and will.

RACHEL. It's fascinating!

HOLGER. To me the most important feature of the whole struggle is to make room for personality. Here you may witness the restoration of a structure belonging to a time when personality did have elbow-room. With towers that rise and rule. With massive walls whose strength and shape inculcate a religion of pomp, of power. Eh?—Do you want it to stay here, or shall I take it away?

RACHEL. I want it taken away.

HOLGER (*Hurt*). You want——?

RACHEL. Yes.

HOGER (*To* HALDEN). You hear that? Will you please see that it is taken away at once.

(HALDEN *nods assent.*)

HOLGER. I mean it literally. At once. Eh?

(HALDEN *remains quiet as before and goes out.*)

HOLGER. There is something about that fellow—— (*He checks himself.*)

RACHEL. You don't like Halden?

HOLGER. Have you noticed that?

RACHEL. I noticed it the first time I saw the two of you together.

HOLGER. Oh—then! That was not to be wondered at. Your hospital was being built right outside my park. I heard that a young lady was using her private fortune in that way, and I became curious. Eh? And so, one day, I walked right into the place. And whom should I find there with you? Halden. He was your architect. And he hadn't said a word to me about it.

RACHEL. He doesn't say very many.

HOLGER. What is it that has corked him up?

RACHEL. I don't know. He has had to make his own way.

HOLGER. That's what all of us have had to do.

RACHEL. But I imagine it comes a little harder in America.

HOLGER. How did he come to be your architect?

RACHEL. Because he wanted to. And was willing to do the work for nothing.

HOLGER. Has he done it for nothing?

RACHEL. Everything.

HOLGER (*Takes a turn across the floor*). Did he come to you himself?

RACHEL. No, somebody else brought me a message from him.

HOLGER (*Stopping in his walk*). Can you tell me who that was? Can you—or don't you want to?

RACHEL. Yes. It was my brother.

HOLGER. Does Halden know your brother?

RACHEL. Yes—or rather, I don't know. My brother brought me that message from him: that's all I do know.

HOLGER. I have often wondered what kind of acquaintances that man might have. I am not one of them. (*He picks up his hat.*)

RACHEL. Well, that's more than I know.

HOLGER (*After a brief pause*). I hope that you may feel at home out here—you and your convalescents.

RACHEL. Thank you ever so much! You must come over when we are in here—so that all of them may have a chance of thanking you!

HOLGER. I will——

RACHEL (*Coming closer to him*). Have I made trouble for Halden by saying that he knew my brother? For, really, I don't know that he does.

HOLGER. You are greatly concerned about Halden.

RACHEL. I don't want to harm anybody.

HOLGER. You need have no fear.

RACHEL. And that other matter I spoke of—? For the sake of all the people, Mr. Holger, who may be tempted into wrong-doing——?

HOLGER. I have already told you: there is no one to whom I listen with greater pleasure than you. But you know also that we have different religions, you and I. Eh?

RACHEL. People are scared. They say that old mining galleries are still in existence under the Castle.

HOLGER. That's true of the greater part of the city.

RACHEL. Suppose they should try——?

HOLGER (*Placing himself right in front of her*). THAT WOULD BE THE BEST THING THAT COULD HAPPEN!

RACHEL (*Drawing away from him*). You are awful!

HOLGER. The religion of the masters, Miss Sang.

RACHEL. And this is what you want to teach your nephew and niece?

HOLGER. Yes, it is. I want to teach them the only thing that can save all of us.

RACHEL (*Urgently*). The damage you do will be tremendous then—! And you have no right to do it, either!

HOLGER. No right, eh? I, who bestow all I have on those two young people?

RACHEL. If you were to bestow ten times as much on them, Mr. Holger, it wouldn't give you the right to rob them of their souls.

HOLGER. Well, if I ever—eh?

RACHEL. Can it be called less than that? Everything those wonderful young creatures know and cherish—all that you want to take away from them.

HOLGER. In order to give them what is still better.

RACHEL. But which they despise, Mr.

Holger. No one has the right to shape the future by force—not by force!

HOLGER. That'll have to be fought out.

RACHEL. Whether the children should be taken away from their parents?

HOLGER. The parents are dead in this case.

RACHEL. No living parents have a greater right to their children than have these who are dead. And you know it, Mr. Holger.

HOLGER. Do you mean that I should respect the silly notions of the parents for that reason—even their silly notions? Credo and Spera! Parents who are capable of naming their children Credo and Spera—eh?

RACHEL. "I believe"—"thou shalt hope"—are those such silly notions? Thus had the parents disposed of these children before they were born. And that's something we ought to respect, Mr. Holger.

HOLGER. Respect silly notions! What kind of hope and faith is it a question of? (*In an amused tone*) It is not in this world, Miss Sang, that those who are first shall be last, and the last first.

RACHEL. That's something you know nothing about, Mr. Holger. The future will be settled by the masses—by the vast masses.

HOLGER. Hm—! That'll have to be fought out.

RACHEL. There is a current at work here that we cannot stop.

HOLGER (*Merrily*). Well, I'll get these two out of the current anyhow.

RACHEL. And you dare to do that, Mr. Holger?

HOLGER. Dare—? Please don't interfere with me in this.

RACHEL. You have refused to let me keep them. I can do nothing about that. But you cannot refuse me the right to influence them.

HOLGER. Oh, I cannot? Eh? The children are not going to obey me, you mean? THEN THEY MUST GO AWAY FROM HERE!

RACHEL (*Horrified*). Away from here? Send the children away? (*With deep emotion*) Mr. Holger, all you will gain by it will be to make the three of us frightfully unhappy. And besides—after the loss they have just suffered—this, too! Oh, you cannot do such a thing!

HOLGER. Can't I? I'm going to do it at once. No matter how much it hurts me to say "no" to you—but you force me to do it.

RACHEL. Every time I ask you very hard for something, I get a "no." And every time you say that it hurts you.

HOLGER. I shouldn't respect you as highly as I do if you were different from what you are. I hope you will grant me the same compliment—Miss Sang!

(HOLGER *goes out.* RACHEL *drops down on a chair and begins to cry. Somebody is heard knocking at the big window.* RACHEL *goes over to the window, her face brightening as she moves.*)

RACHEL. Do you want me to open—? (*The moment she gets the window open, she cries out*) No, no, no! (*She shrinks back.*)

CREDO (*Eighteen years old; comes with a leap through the window*). Good morning, Rachel!

SPERA (*In her sixteenth year; enters in the same manner*). Good morning, good morning!

(*All three embrace enthusiastically.*)

CREDO. What did he say to make you sorry?

RACHEL. Oh, you noticed——?

BOTH. Of course, we noticed.

RACHEL. It was about you, of course—something about you!

CREDO. He won't let us see you?

SPERA. It won't do him any good.

RACHEL. Worse than that. He wants to send you away. Away from me!

BOTH. He wants to send us away, you say?

RACHEL (*Deeply stirred*). So that you cannot see me at all.

(*Both children embrace her*).

CREDO. He'll never be able to do it!

SPERA. We'll never obey him in that!

CREDO. Oh, why haven't we learned to fly yet?

SPERA. If he stops our mail, we'll use pigeons. And we'll keep a diary for you to read.

RACHEL. Yes, yes!

CREDO. And you who can afford it, you'll come to us often, won't you?

RACHEL. Will I come—? Yes, wherever you are!

(*They embrace again.*)

CREDO. I'll invent something that makes the voice clearer than the phonograph does now. That doesn't give you the voice itself, but just a kind of shadow of it. I have been making a study of it, and I think I know where the trouble lies.— And then you'll sit in your own room, Rachel, and hear us talk to you. You'll feel that we are always about you, Rachel, Rachel!

RACHEL. I'll send you telegrams and letters every day, you may be sure.

CREDO. Until he understands how useless it is to separate us.

SPERA. And perhaps lets us come together again—what d'you think?

RACHEL. Something new and wonderful has come into my life with you two.— I can no longer exist without you.

BOTH. Nor we without you.

CREDO. You are the only one we can go to with everything.

SPERA. Do you know why we came just now?

RACHEL. No.

SPERA. That toy of Credo's—

RACHEL. Does it fly?

SPERA. Yes, all around the room, way up under the ceiling.

CREDO. I have got it!

SPERA. I assure you: round and round

and round, without bumping into anything.

CREDO. I have discovered how to steer it, you know—I have got it!

RACHEL. But isn't this something entirely new?

CREDO. It's something that will grow, I tell you. Just wait!

RACHEL. So now you can make the circle in which it moves as wide or as narrow as you want?

CREDO. Exactly!

SPERA. All he has to do is to set it as he wants it.

RACHEL. Can't I come and see it?

SPERA. That's why we came, you know: just because we wanted you to see it.

CREDO. We came to bring you along with us.

RACHEL. But I don't know if that would be right now——

(*A bell is heard ringing at the main entrance outside.*)

RACHEL. Nobody must find you here.

SPERA (*Leaping out through the window*). Goodbye for a while!

CREDO (*Taking a long start and clearing the window with a flying leap*). Hurrah for the finest woman on earth!

(*A knock is heard at the door.*)

RACHEL. Come in!

(ELIAS *enters.*)

RACHEL (*Running to meet him*). Elias—at last!

ELIAS (*meeting her half-way*). Rachel! —oh, Rachel!

(*They stand for a few moments with their arms about each other.*)

RACHEL (*Stroking his hair*). How pale you look, Elias! And worn out! What is it?

ELIAS (*Smiling*). The time's so big, and our strength so small.

RACHEL. How long it is since we saw each other!

ELIAS. For the same reason. I didn't have the strength.

RACHEL. I can see that you have overworked.

ELIAS. Yes, I can't even have the nights to myself.

RACHEL. Not even the nights?

ELIAS. And we don't get enough to eat.

RACHEL. But, dear—what's the use of *that?*

ELIAS. We must practice self-sacrifice, says Bratt. And he is right. But the effect of it has been somewhat unexpected.

RACHEL. Why don't you sleep nights?

ELIAS. So this is where you are to live, Rachel?—This is what he has given *you* —while he's refusing us everything.

RACHEL. He has given it to the hospital. It is to be used for the convalescents.

ELIAS (*Going around, looking the place over*). This he has done now—as if there were nothing else that made any demands on him! Are you to live here, Rachel—in this room here?

RACHEL. Yes, and sleep in the room next to it—the one you passed coming in.

ELIAS. You have chosen peace for your share, Rachel.

RACHEL. Not exactly peace, Elias. There is a great deal of responsibility, and a great deal to do.

ELIAS. I know it, Rachel, I know it. All I meant was—I cannot understand how anybody can live as he was living in this big house—how anybody dares, while so many others— Have you heard about Maren Haug and her two children——?

RACHEL. Yes, yes, I keep track of everything.—Oh, Elias, if you knew how my thoughts have been with you these last days!

ELIAS. Perhaps that's why I have felt more homesick than ever before—more even than at the time father and mother still lived, and we were in the city.

RACHEL. That's because you are not

happy.—Tell me, Elias: have you any faith in the strike?

ELIAS (*After a glance at his sister*). Have you?

(RACHEL *shakes her head.*)

ELIAS (*Shakes his head in the same way*). It will end in the worst defeat ever heard of. Maren Haug read the future. Oh—she is not the only one who won't survive it.

RACHEL. How it has made you suffer, Elias! I can see it.

ELIAS. The people in the city, Rachel, have another kind of conscience than ours. Something else is needed to wake them up.

RACHEL. Can Bratt see it coming, too?

(ELIAS *shakes his head.*)

RACHEL. Since when have *you* seen it?

ELIAS. Since I began to stay away from both of you—from him as well as from you.

RACHEL (*Disturbed*). You have not been seeing Bratt either?

ELIAS. I haven't had a talk with him until today.

RACHEL. Was it about——?

ELIAS. No.—But don't let us talk of this now! Let us go back for a little while to what used to be, Rachel.

RACHEL. Oh, I understand.

ELIAS. Sit down. I want to sit beside you. Let us talk of the old things we used to love. I am homesick, as I have told you.

RACHEL. Suppose we go back there, Elias? A trip to our old home? To visit our childhood once more. The fiord, the steep and naked mountainsides, the pale light of the nights, the parsonage with the long stretch of shore in front of it. The landslide must be covered with grass now. And many other things also. What a trip that would be! Nature would be the same—a little melancholy, but faithful, and magnificent in its wildness. And our memories— Reindeer as tall as

father and mother— Elias, let's go home —now you are free—and so overworked —Oh, Elias!

ELIAS. I am not free, Rachel.

RACHEL. I call it free when you are unable to do anything.

ELIAS. Well, *that* isn't quite certain.

RACHEL. Oh, help them with money, yes—but you can do that through Bratt just as well. Oh, Elias—let us go!

ELIAS. There is something in that, Rachel.

RACHEL. It would make you well.

ELIAS. I'll answer you tomorrow.

RACHEL. Think if we could have another look at all the places where we used to play!

ELIAS. It's to those places my thoughts always go when I am homesick.

RACHEL. Do you remember how people used to say that they never saw one of us alone, but always the two of us together, and always hand in hand?

ELIAS. And that we were always talking our heads off—so that they could hear us from far off.

RACHEL. And what a lot of queer notions you had—all the strange things that would come into your mind, Elias!

ELIAS. But it was you who ruled—yes, it was! It's a fact, you have always been the one who ruled, until we separated awhile ago.

RACHEL. Do you remember the eiders —how tame they grew?

ELIAS. I remember every single nest.

RACHEL. How we used to look after them!

ELIAS. And protect them and bring them food. And the first time the mother bird took the little ones swimming—we were looking on in the boat!

RACHEL. And father was with us—just as much of a child as either one of us.

ELIAS. It was he who set us going. It was always some word from him that started us on all we undertook and all we thought of. Heaven and earth were not separated then. The miracles formed the rainbow that joined them. Our eyes were looking straight into paradise——

RACHEL. And we saw father and mother among the angels. Or rather, the angels had come down to them—we really believed it!

ELIAS. Wasn't the Lord himself talking to us? Whatever it was, it came from Him. Good weather and bad, thunder and lightning, the flowers, and all else that was bestowed on us. It came straight from Him. And when we prayed, it was face to face with Him. And we seemed to see Him, too, in the sea, in the mountains, in the sky. All of it *was* Him.

RACHEL. And do you remember when the bells were ringing—how we used to think that angels flew away with the sound of them, to ask the people to come to church?

ELIAS. Oh, Rachel, those who have lived through such things become exiles ever afterward.

RACHEL. Exiles ever afterward—yes, you are right.

ELIAS. Nothing is good enough after that.—No sooner had we left home than it was all over. Coldness and emptiness—and then the doubts. But I can tell you now, in plain words, what remains when all the rest is gone:—the craving for the boundless.

RACHEL. In you, perhaps—but I flee from it. Do you remember when father and mother died, and everything went to pieces, then you fled from it, too?

ELIAS. Yes, then we huddled close to each other. We didn't dare to believe—not even what we saw with our own eyes.

RACHEL. We were afraid of people.

ELIAS. Yes, do you remember——?

RACHEL. Most of all afraid that the sight of us might make them talk ill of father and mother.

ELIAS. Whom they didn't understand at all. But then, when our inheritance came, after Aunt Hanna had died, do you remember how we plunged back into the boundless at once?

RACHEL. Yes, you are right. Then it seemed at once as if all bounds had been wiped out.

ELIAS. That was the time we looked up Bratt. In his company that feeling grew, and it has been growing ever since.

RACHEL. In you, yes. But not in me. To me it comes with a sort of sacred horror, but not with any happiness.

ELIAS. It is of no use fleeing, Rachel. It is in us and about us.

RACHEL. The earth can find its way through boundless space—why not we, too?

ELIAS. Do you know, Rachel, that at times I feel as if I had wings? And no bounds—nothing to check me.

RACHEL. Death checks everything, Elias.

ELIAS (*Rising*). No, not even death—especially not death!

RACHEL (*Rising*). What do you mean?

ELIAS (*Firmly*). That what we want to live must pass through death.

RACHEL. Through death——?

ELIAS. If you want to resurrect life, you must die for it. Christianity took its life from the Cross. Our country lives because of those who have died for it. There is no renewal except through death.

RACHEL. Is that to be applied here——? You want the workmen to die for their cause?

ELIAS. If they could do *that,* then their cause would be saved. Then they would win at once.

RACHEL. A revolution, in other words——?

ELIAS. The workmen in a revolution! Good Lord!— What day is it today? Monday. Well, that means Sunday doesn't come tomorrow. There is a whole week to Sunday. And in that week some mighty hard work will have to be done.

RACHEL (*Stepping close to him*). There is only one way of working, Elias: by example—by good example!

ELIAS (*Walking away from her*). If you could only guess how true that is. (*Coming close to her again*) To show them how to leap across all bounds, don't you see? To give them an example of that!

RACHEL. Across the bounds of life itself——?

ELIAS. First one across—then another. Isn't that the way things always begin? Then ten, a hundred, thousands—for it will need thousands before the millions will fall in line to take the leap, too. But after that there can be no resistance any longer. Then Sunday will be here. Then we shall have alleluias, triumph, "Praise ye the Lord!"—First comes the Baptist; then Jesus and the Twelve; then the Seventy; then the many hundreds, the many thousands, and lastly everybody, whosoever it may be! The life of resurrection cannot be bought in any other way.

RACHEL. Men have a lot of resistance in them. They hold back for all they are worth; hold on to what they have already gained. If they didn't, life wouldn't stay in its proper course, as does the earth.

ELIAS. But stronger than the rest are those who want the New. The eternal flame—the force that bursts all bounds—you find it in the pioneers. It is on them everything depends. The greater their courage, the greater will be their following!

RACHEL. Into death——?

ELIAS. *There is no other way!* And why? Because people will not believe fully in anyone but him who dares to take that way. But let him take that final step—into the beyond—and he will be believed.—Look around you: do you find anybody in whom they believe fully now? Of course, those that are close to

Bratt believe in him. But how about those that are further off? They are the very ones that need to be converted. But they don't even turn their heads. They don't care to hear what he has to say. He may get up what we call a "movement" —not even then do they turn around. No, they leave it to the police!

RACHEL. Yes, you are right. That's the way it is.

ELIAS. But when you talk to them from the other side of life, *then they turn!* From there every word comes with so much greater force—for in there the echo is so wonderful. The great ones have to go there to get a hearing. There the speaker's platform has been reared by life, and from it the laws are proclaimed in tones that make them heard throughout the world—even by those that are hardest of hearing.

RACHEL. But it's dreadful to believe in that.

ELIAS. Dreadful?

RACHEL. I mean that dreadful things may come out of it.

ELIAS. Nothing can be more dreadful than what we already have, Rachel. What I proclaim is the religion of martyrdom.

RACHEL. That's it. Of course, there is something big about it.

ELIAS. More than that: once it has taken hold of you, there exists no other religion—none at all!

RACHEL. It's since you came to see this, that you have lost faith in the strike?

ELIAS. I have done everything in my power to push the strike—you can be sure of that.

RACHEL. I don't doubt it, Elias. (*Putting her arms around his neck*) But I am afraid on your behalf. That place down there is not the right one for you.

ELIAS. There is no other place where I should like to be.

RACHEL (*Still with her arms around his neck*). But come home with me now—at once! Please—at once! Just to breathe the air of the sea, Elias! You can be sure that on the sea you won't think and feel as you do down there. The journey homeward too—all the different moods it will make you pass through. You remember how it used to be, don't you?

ELIAS (*Who has been gazing steadily into her face all the time*). In spite of all changes, you haven't changed in the least, Rachel. I think you could begin right now to take care of the eiders again.

RACHEL. Yes, if *you* were with me!

ELIAS. Let me have a real look at you——

RACHEL. Elias!

ELIAS (*Drawing her still closer*). You're like the eider-down. When we were picking it, we used always to wonder how the young birds could tear themselves away from it—do you remember?

RACHEL. Yes. And yet they would go very, very far away from it.

ELIAS. Yes, they did go very far away. (*Almost in a whisper*) Goodbye, Rachel!

RACHEL. Are you going already?

ELIAS. I must—but I feel as if I couldn't take my arms away from you.

RACHEL. Hold me fast instead!

ELIAS. There is one thing in this life that we two never had.

RACHEL. Don't let us talk of it. What we have is so much greater.

ELIAS. And yet, in the midst of what is greatest, there are moments when we do nothing but long for what we never had.

RACHEL. Moments of tender dreams!

ELIAS. Moments of tender dreams!! (*Kissing her*) In you I kiss all those wondrous things that have been denied me. And then I kiss yourself—*just* you! (*Giving her a long kiss*) Goodbye, Rachel!

RACHEL. Tomorrow, then?

ELIAS. You'll hear from me tomorrow.

RACHEL. You'll come yourself, of course?

ELIAS. If I can.—Dear little Eider-down!

(*He embraces her, kisses her once more, and goes toward the door; there he stops for a moment.*)

RACHEL. What is it, Elias?

(ELIAS *makes a gesture with one hand as if brushing aside something.*)

(RACHEL *is still standing on the same spot, with her eyes on the doorway, when a knock at the window is heard. She wakes up and turns around. Then she goes to the window and opens it.*)

SPERA (*Leaping in through the window as before*). Who was that, Rachel?

CREDO (*Coming in after his sister*). It was your brother, wasn't it?

RACHEL. Yes.

SPERA. He must be weighed down by some great sorrow.

RACHEL. Could you see that?

CREDO. Indeed! What is it he wants?

SPERA. Something big?

CREDO. Where is he going?

SPERA. Somewhere very far away, isn't he?

RACHEL. We are going together.

BOTH. Where? When?

RACHEL. To our home in the North-land. Perhaps tomorrow——

CREDO. But why did he say goodbye to you then?

SPERA. As if he were never going to see you again?

RACHEL. Did he?—No, you misunderstood! He acts like that when he is unhappy—always. He just won't let go.

(*A door-bell rings.* CREDO *and* SPERA *disappear through the window again, and* RACHEL *closes it after them. Then a knock is heard at the door.*)

RACHEL. Come!

BRATT (*Enters, breathless and distracted*). Isn't he here?

RACHEL You mean my brother? (*Eagerly*) Has something happened?

BRATT. Hasn't he been here?

RACHEL. Yes—didn't you meet him?

BRATT. He *has* been here—as I thought. What did he say? What has he in mind?

RACHEL. What does he intend to do, you mean?

BRATT. I can see that you don't know —that you didn't talk of it.

RACHEL. No—he will be back here tomorrow.

BRATT (*Quickly*). Tomorrow!

RACHEL. Or he'll send me word.

BRATT. What could he mean by that? (*Nearer to her*) Did he mention *me*, Rachel?

RACHEL. No—well, perhaps— I think he spoke of you quite casually.

BRATT. Only casually. (*With decision*) Then he is hiding something.

RACHEL. He said that you hadn't seen each other for a long while—until today.

BRATT. Did he also say that I had seen him and not recognized him? Tell me, did he? Which would mean that he had been disguised.

RACHEL (*Smiling*). Elias? I can never believe it.

BRATT. He was never at home at night.

RACHEL. Yes, so he told me—that he didn't sleep, I mean.— But, for Heaven's sake, Bratt, what is it?

BRATT. I can't tell all at once. And you would probably not understand me, as I have nothing definite to go by—no clear expression, no tangible act.

RACHEL. But if you don't——

BRATT. Yes, yes, it's just as certain nevertheless.— O that I should once more have to—! Wait a minute, please; I'll try to explain. That's why I came here, of course.— And he and I who have been such friends, Rachel! What hasn't he been to me——!

RACHEL. But that isn't over, is it?

BRATT. There is somebody who has taken him away from me!

RACHEL. What do you say?

BRATT. I didn't understand. How could I possibly understand? Seeing it was

Elias. Not until we met again today— then I saw it at once! And the more he said, the more clearly I saw it.

RACHEL. I don't know yet what it is!

BRATT. There is somebody who has taken him away from me! It's as sure as that fall comes after summer, and death after fall.— By stirring his imagination. By starting his impetuous craving for achievement into more and more violent vibrations. Under such circumstances, how could be possibly feel satisfied among us? He was yearning to achieve something tremendous—all at once, with one blow.

RACHEL (*Alarmed*). What could *that* be?

BRATT. Elias is so easily led astray—he is so quick to believe——

RACHEL. Yes, indeed. But who could——

BRATT. Somebody who has made the strike seem very petty to him—a mere mistake, or something still worse. So that Elias became horrified and was seized with dreadful remorse. Then the misery he had to see became unendurable to him. That's the way it must have happened.— So he wished to make up for what had been lost—to make up by means of something that would draw the eyes of the whole world to our misery— something entirely new, something never heard of before. That's how it must have happened.

RACHEL (*More and more frightened*). But what—what?

BRATT. Wait! You'll misunderstand him if I don't explain myself first. For the fault isn't his.— To me he didn't say a word—although the responsibility, the fault was as much mine as his—not a word of reproach. He wanted to take it all on himself—by enormous sacrifices. Now he has given us his entire fortune.

RACHEL. His entire fortune—Elias?

BRATT. Something he said made me suspect it. Now I know. It is true! He has given us everything he possessed. He had one thousand crowns left yesterday—this he gave us today—all at once.

RACHEL (*In a tone that shows her admiration*). He shall lack for nothing!

BRATT. Oh, it isn't that! But in that way he has entirely misled us. He has been sending us these sums from east and west and north and south, until we were made to believe in a wide-spread public sympathy. But tomorrow it will be all over. Beginning with tomorrow, we shall only have enough to meet the barest necessity—and in a little while we shall not even have that much. Nothing but unspeakable misery!

RACHEL. My poor friend!

BRATT. You may well say that, for the blame is mine. You mustn't put it on him. Nobody can put it on him. That's why I *must* explain myself.

RACHEL. I am listening.

BRATT. A while ago I had reached my highest point of faith in myself—where my feeling told me: "God is on our side!" My sense of power sprang from the reliance placed in me by the others—and nothing surpasses such a feeling. Then came Elias—and before I knew what was happening he had taken the ground from under my feet.

RACHEL. Dear friend!

BRATT. But how can a man who has gone through what I have gone through —how can it be possible for him to believe a second time? And to believe still more strongly because of his earlier mistake? That's where the trouble lies. And in this there is no mistake! (*He hides his face.*)

RACHEL. My dear, dear friend!

BRATT (*Looking sharply at her*). Now and then I have encountered a face that seemed to ask: "Can *you* find the right road? Can *you* lead others along that road?"

(RACHEL *shrinks back.*)

BRATT (*Following her*). Tell me now: that was the doubt in your mind, wasn't it?

RACHEL. Yes.

BRATT. And that's why you didn't stay with me?

RACHEL. Yes.

BRATT (*Goes up close to her, she drawing back from him*). I don't help people. I lead them astray. Instead of guiding, I misguide. I always achieve the opposite of what I want. All I can do is to overreach myself—make a mess of it—and bring all to despair. Isn't that so? There can be only one end to it: my downfall, with the curses of thousands following me.

RACHEL (*Going up to him*). If anything should happen—I think so much of you—have from the very first——

BRATT. Yet you wouldn't stay with me?

RACHEL. You are a big man, and an honest man. But you take all my strength away from me.

BRATT. There you have said it yourself!

RACHEL. Yes, you carry me beyond what is clear to myself.

BRATT. There you see!

RACHEL. It's a part of your nature. You can't help it.

BRATT. A man of no matter how forceful nature—if his mind had been sown with sensible thoughts from childhood up, and if he had learned to watch and grasp real life instead of spending his time wool-gathering in another world— do you think he would lead anybody astray?

RACHEL. No.

BRATT. Here we come tumbling headlong out of the millennium—ready to save the world. But while we were straying abroad, the world has turned into a pretty tough problem—one that *our* brains are far from prepared for.— That's the thought that struck me while I was scrambling up the hill a moment ago.—

Either our fancy is extravagant, or else our will. So there is always something in us that carries us beyond our power. We, who have seen people go to heaven in golden chariots; who have seen angels in the sky and devils surrounded by eternal fire; who have been hungering for miracles—how could we possibly have the kind of brains needed to deal with real life? Oh, no!— We are to be pitied, Rachel! We are always miscalculating the distance in front of us. We are always starting out haphazardly. Our consciences can be no reliable guides to us, for they have never been at home on earth or in the present. We are always striving for Utopias, for the boundless——

RACHEL. For the boundless——?

BRATT. Now you understand?

RACHEL. Elias——?

BRATT. Of course.— I have lured him on too far. I failed to understand that a nature like his should *never* have been dragged into a thing like this.

RACHEL. Never!

BRATT. Now he is plunging himself and us into that which knows of no bounds. Soon something dreadful is going to happen. When he gave all he had, he did it with the thought of giving himself, too.

RACHEL. Himself, too? Elias——?

BRATT. With the thought of sacrificing himself in order that he might carry hundreds of the others along with him to destruction. He must have been planning it for a long time, and now it is about to happen. Do you understand——?

RACHEL. No.

BRATT. DON'T YOU UNDERSTAND——?

(RACHEL *utters a cry and falls down senseless.*)

BRATT. Yes, it's better so! If I could only drop down beside you, never to wake again! (*He kneels at her side, bending over her.*)

CURTAIN

ACT III

An immense hall. A raised throne-like chair occupies the center of the left wall, flanked on both sides by seats with richly carved and very tall backs that are fastened to the walls. The same kind of seats are along the other two walls, while, for this special occasion, a large number of chairs have been scattered over the floor.

In the rear are two huge, arched windows that do not break the line of seats. Doors in the same style as the windows appear on both sides close to the rear corners. The ceiling is of wood, with deeply sunk panels and beautifully carved. The walls are hung with draperies, coats of arms, and flags, and between these are placed fresh green branches.

HOLGER *is seated on the throne, with a small table in front of him. The seats and the chairs are filled with delegates representing the factory owners throughout the country. Other delegates are constantly passing in and out through the two doorways. Each time the discussion gets more heated they swarm in from both sides, only to disappear again after a while. Servants in medieval costumes carry around tall tankards filled with various kinds of drinks, which they serve in goblets and tumblers.*

ANKER (*He is standing on a dais just in front of the throne; on the dais is a small table for the speaker, and a larger one at which two secretaries are seated*). Once, on a very memorable occasion, someone remarked that "Beelzebub cannot cast out Beelzebub." I have made this my creed in the present case. We must not set evil against evil. For in that way we can never bring out what is good in people. And if we cannot bring out what is good, we have nothing whatever to build on. And then there is no future before us. (*He steps down in the midst of general silence.*)

HOLGER. Mr. Mo has the floor.

MO (*Ascends the platform, while a number of delegates come hurrying in from the side rooms*). On behalf of the fourteen—mind you: *fourteen*—factory owners in my city, I have the honor to express concurrence in Mr. Holger's plan. And we do this most heartily. (*Cries of "Hear"*) If the workmen organize against us, then we organize against them. (*"Hear"*) We give our support to the entire plan and to all its separate clauses.— I must say that Mr. Anker's speech has greatly surprised me. (*Cries of "Us, too"*) I think every factory owner ought to see the advantage of having all the factories governed by some central body to which they may turn for guidance in times of danger. And everyone ought to understand the advantage of having every conflict with the workmen placed under the jurisdiction of this central body—serving at once as supreme court and highest executive. What we lose in freedom we gain in security. Most heartily do we subscribe to this plan. Let the workmen find out that, if they make trouble, they'll run up against a power that is not hampered by any kind of consideration. That will make them meek, I think—while it will make us more respected than we have ever been. As soon as we can get the factory owners of another country to form a similar organization, we'll join hands with them. And in the end we shall have an organization covering all civilized countries. Holger's plan is a splendid one. And I (*turning toward* ANKER) have no fear whatever of the consequences. The expression used by Mr. Anker—that this is "to place a small minority of mankind in opposition to its vast majority"—is totally misleading. For mankind is, after all, made up of something else than factory owners and factory hands. There can hardly be any

question as to which side offers the greater advantage to all the other people. (*"Hear, hear"*) We and the other people —there you have the state. The state belongs to us, as it has always done and always will. With all my heart I concur.

(*Repeated cries of "Hear, hear, hear" are followed by an outburst of applause and general conversation as* MO *steps down from the dais*)

HOLGER. Mr. John Sverd has the floor.

A DELEGATE. Question!

SEVERAL OTHERS. Question! Question!

ALMOST ALL. Question!

SVERD (*Mounting the dais, places a portfolio on the table in front of him*). You don't need to be so explicit, my dear friends, I know fairly well how the land lies. As a chemist, you see, I am accustomed to analyze things. (*Laughter*) If nevertheless I stand here, it's merely because I have promised my colleagues— those whom I have the honor of representing—to place their opinions before you.

A DELEGATE. Which have been dictated by yourself!

ANOTHER DELEGATE. Dictator!

SVERD. If I exercise any dictatorship, it must be one of "persuasion."

MO. And now you're going to try it on us?

SVERD (*Good-humoredly*). With your gracious permission—so I will. For I happen to have at my disposal an argument which no man of brains can resist.

SEVERAL. Well, well!

SVERD. I'll hand it out at once. As this honorable gathering probably knows, our factories are located in the country. And the workmen in these factories have already obtained almost everything that is in dispute here now!

SEVERAL (*Interrupting him*). Oh, yes, in the country! That's another story!

A DELEGATE (*At the top of his voice*). Smaller conditions—and everything new!

MO. Show us your books!

SVERD (*Pointing to the portfolio*). I bring with me certified copies of our balances during the last few years. We are getting along—in a modest way, but we are getting along.

SEVERAL. In a modest way, yes.

SVERD. Yes, we are content with moderate profits—and perhaps that's the main difference between us and you gentlemen.

SEVERAL. Well, well!

A DELEGATE. Stick to your own business, please!

SVERD. And I can tell you another thing. All our workmen are members of Bratt's union, and they take Sang's paper. You bet they do! And neither the hills above us nor the falls beside us have had their complexions spoiled on that account. And now I have saved the worst to end with: we factory owners ourselves are members of Bratt's union and subser——

A MAJORITY OF THE DELEGATES (*In a violent outburst*). Damn his cheek! What have you got to do here? Socialist! Anarchist! Get out! Shut up!

SVERD. I fear there are not quite so many men of brains present as I thought!

(*This calls forth laughter from some and protests from others.*)

MO (*Shouting at the top of his voice*). Yes, that's like your impudence!

A DELEGATE (*Also shouting*). How about your own head? Don't you belong to the Numskull family?

SVERD. If I do, I have a lot of relatives here. (*Laughter*) I think a great deal of that family and hope it thinks enough of me to let me criticize Mr. Holger's plan briefly. What I want to say first of all is that a union of factory owners covering the whole country—or the whole world even—is possible only if you get all the factory owners with you.

MO. Well, there'll be no trouble about that!

A DELEGATE. They'll be *made* to join us.

ANKER. No pressure!

SEVERAL. Yes, pressure is just the thing!

(*An outburst of talking follows.*)

SVERD. Mr. President!

(HOLGER *makes no sign of hearing him.*)

ANKER (*Shouting*). But suppose the banks should stand by the others?

SEVERAL. They won't dare! We'd make them pay for it!

SVERD. But perhaps the retail dealers——?

MANY DELEGATES. Yes, let 'em try!

SVERD. It means we shall have to have two more unions: one of bankers and one of retail dealers.

MO. We'll boycott the bankers and undersell the dealers.

SVERD. There, now—that's another use for the defense fund! And then you'll have to fight the whole Liberal Party. Whereby the whole thing will be turned into politics.

MO. What else is it now?

SVERD. Mo, this is something entirely new! A union of factory owners that has a compulsory membership and uses force against the workmen, that boycotts the banks and goes to war with the retail dealers—this is a novelty, indeed!

ANKER. That will never succeed—not in all eternity!

MANY (*Angrily*). It *shall* succeed!

SVERD (*Quickly*). Grant that it succeeds! That it succeeds splendidly! You control the employers, the workmen, the market—which means that indirectly you control both local and national authorities. What will be the outcome? That sooner or later you gentlemen overreach yourselves—so much power being a direct temptation to that sort of thing—whereupon we'll have an uprising more fierce in its bitterness than any of the religious wars waged by our ancestors. Will that be progress, do you think? No retrogression—that's what it means: a backsliding to savagery that will lead to the destruction of our machinery, the burning of our finished products, the killing of our foremen. We have already had a taste of it—for the fight is on at the outposts.

ANKER. That's true!

SVERD. And what kind of a war will it be? On whom do you think the burden of it will fall? On both sides! On the employers as well as on the workmen! It would be much more convenient for both sides to stay at home and merely send word to each other that, at a certain stroke of the clock, they would—on either side—set fire to all they had, and then take care that the flames spread to the whole city in which they lived, thus paralyzing the country they should serve!

(*Against their own will, a number of delegates are moved to applause.*)

MO. Tell *that* to the workmen!

SVERD. Both sides have to be told that they are plunging headlong into what is impossible and unnatural. Back of it must lie some unreasoning racial instinct —something akin to what turns us toward the supernatural in our search for poetry and greatness. But I tell you, the day will come when man discovers that there is more of greatness and poetry in what is natural and possible—however insignificant it may seem at times—than in all the supernaturalism we have ever had, from the oldest sun-myth down to the latest sermon preached about it. And if both parties to this conflict could only stick to plain reality, what do you think they would discover? That the enemy which they both fight has nothing in common with either of them. That he is thriving on their strife, because it places both of them more securely in his clutch. I am thinking of the capitalist.

A SHRILL TENOR VOICE. You'd better leave the capitalist alone!

SVERD. My dear sir—why in the world should I leave the capitalist alone? Especially as we all know that in a young country like ours almost everybody has to operate with borrowed money and would like very much to avoid doing so. But the capitalist——

SHRILL TENOR VOICE. Leave the capitalist alone!

SVERD (*Imitating the voice of the interrupter*). Is he sacred, perhaps? (*Laughter.*)

MO. I am quite of the same opinion. These endless, useless complaints against the capitalist——

SVERD (*Taking the word of MO's mouth*). Complaints against the capitalist, you say?

SHRILL TENOR VOICE. Leave the capitalist alone! (*Everybody roars with laughter.*)

SVERD. Mr. President, won't you please stop these annoying interruptions?

(*When HOLGER pays no attention to the request, the laughter is renewed and is mingled with applause.*)

SVERD. This means that you refuse me freedom of speech. It means that neither the president nor the meeting will grant me freedom of speech. (*Cries of "Hear" and laughter*) This was just what I expected, and for that reason I brought with me a stenographer.

(*His words provoke a storm of protest.*)

ALL. That isn't allowed! The proceedings are secret! Nothing must be reported!

SVERD. Nothing but publicity will help where the right of debate is denied. (*At the top of his voice*) I brought a phonograph, too.

(*Putting his portfolio under his arm, he steps smilingly from the dais.*)

ALL. Mephisto! Charlatan! Just what we expected! And *you* talk of freedom!

HOLGER (*In a voice that rises above the din*). Mr. Ketil has the floor.

(*This announcement is greeted with applause and cries of "Bravo."*)

KETIL (*Who has been standing in the rear of the hall, calls to* SVERD, *who is seen leaving with two men, one of whom carries a small box*). Are you going?

SVERD (*Gayly*). Yes.

KETIL. But I was just going to reply to what you said.

SVERD. Oh, there are plenty left who will enjoy it.

(*He bows and goes out while the laughter provoked by his reply is still lasting.*)

KETIL (*Mounting the dais*). We have just been told how dreadful it would be for us to do what the workmen have been doing right along.

SEVERAL. Hear, hear!

KETIL. We learned long ago that we had no right to take the initiative in our dealings with the workmen. But that we have just as little right to follow their lead, that's something new. (*Signs of merriment*) There is only one thing we can do: obey the workmen. Everything else is dangerous. Consequently: let's raise their wages—so they can spend a little more on drink. (*Laughter and cries of "Hear, hear"*) I need hardly tell you that the workmen must share in the profits—especially when there are none to share. (*General merriment*) It follows, of course, that we must give them a voice in running the business—which, I am sure, will make the banks much more anxious to grant us credit. (*Merriment*) Just now, when the competition is more keen than ever, we are to surrender both profits and control—which will lead us to a fine end, I am sure! (*Wild applause*) What can property in private hands mean but slavery to all the rest? No, indeed— property for nobody, and poverty for all: that's the ideal! (*Tremendous outburst of approval*) Freedom cannot exist side by side with the power of money. Poverty and freedom: there's the ideal for you! (*Applause as before*) Mr. Anker, who is a God-fearing man, spoke most touchingly about the vices of wealth—that is, about the vices of those who are wealthy or hope to become so. And we heard of sloth, and prodigality, and luxury, and immorality, and lust of power, and brutal contempt for other people. These are the vices that generally go with wealth. How much better, then, are the vices of the workmen! For I suppose, if such a mean thought be at all permissible, that they have theirs as well. Filthiness, slovenliness, slavishness, envy, drunkenness, thievishness, brawling, and a murder now and then—nay, in these days, when anarchism is rampant among them, massmurder. I can't say that I care very much for any of these vices, whether they belong to ourselves or to the other side. But if it be that each side must have its own, why speak only of those that go with wealth? Is it because the vices of the workmen are so much more repulsive? (*Laughter and applause*) Or can it really be the opinion of Mr. Anker—who is a God-fearing man—that these vices will be disposed of by letting the workmen share in the profits? Does he mean that profit-sharing is a cause of repentance— to them as well as to us? (*Strong approval*) To me that kind of rant—I hope you'll pardon the term!—to me it seems rather weak-minded. (*Laughter*) Like all the rant about morality we have to hear whenever we want to do anything worth while, anything really effective. As I see it, the main trouble lies just in our morality. (*Roars of laughter*) The danger of which we have heard so much here is just that we always are so dreadfully moral. (*Tumultuous applause and cries of "That's right"*) It prevents us from defending the existing order, the state, the country—all that we possess and want to pass on to our children—from defending it in such a manner that they are made to realize and remember that here is something NOT TO BE TAMPERED WITH. And until this is done, we'll never have peace.

(*As* KETIL *steps down he is given an ovation. Before it is over, most of those present are on their feet, talking eagerly.*)

HOLGER (*When the hubbub quiets down a little*). Well, now—Mr. Anker wants to be heard again.

A DELEGATE. Oh, have we got to have more of Anker?

MANY. We don't want any more of Anker!

ANOTHER DELEGATE. We have had enough of that anchor! (*Laughter.*)

THIRD DELEGATE. Let's try another.

FOURTH DELEGATE. No more anchoring! Question!

MANY. Question!

ANKER (*Who in the meantime has ascended the dais*). No, I think you'll have to have another try at my anchor first. (*Laughter*) The other one seemed inclined to drag, I should say—although it went down with a big splash. (*Cries of "Well, well"; many delegates go out, talking more or less loudly as they leave*) The new time, the new order that is coming—whether we want it or not—means just that there shall be neither great wealth nor great poverty. There is something half-way between those two, and that is what is coming. And as we get nearer to it by degrees, the vices characterizing both wealth and poverty will drop away. This is what we ought to realize in time—and by doing so we'll avoid these incessant dreadful conflicts. A previous speaker remarked that there must be something the matter with us because we so rarely take hold in a proper way. He seemed to think that we were caught in something that is beyond our power. No matter what that something may be—I am sure it exists. To me

our extravagant war budget, our enormous administrative expenses, our wasteful private living, are very serious symptoms: the life we live is beyond our power. But for this fact, anarchism would be impossible. The lack of responsibility, the utter lack of moral stamina, displayed by our men of means in their wasting of millions, as if there were nobody in the country but themselves and those serving their pleasures: that's also anarchism—not a whit less brutal—and a rebellion against the laws of God and man. It is like crying to all the rest: "You, too—do just what you please!"

KETIL (*Rising*). Mr. President.

(*As* HOLGER *is seen to note down his name, a ripple of pleasant anticipation passes through the assembly.*)

ANKER. The same is true of literature of that literature which appeals to the wealthy and well-to-do—to the so-called "educated" classes. When it shows the same spirit—when it preaches unrestrained individualism—when it tears down everything and urges the violation of law and good manners alike—then it is a form of anarchism as much as that which hurls dynamite to kill.

A DELEGATE. Mr. President, I think we are getting too far away from the question before us.

MANY. Order! Order!

SEVERAL. Question! Question!

(*A number of other delegates stream in from the side rooms and join in the cry of "Question."*)

ANKER. There is no one in the world who has the right to do what he pleases with his own.

A DELEGATE. You bet we have!

ANKER. Indeed, we have not! Above us there are both written and unwritten laws. And I fear that you will break both, and especially the unwritten ones, if you try to enforce the conditions prescribed for the workmen in Mr. Holger's plan.

SEVERAL (*Talking simultaneously*). Oh, you can't frighten us! We are not at all scared!

ANKER. I find those conditions revolting—a breach against written as well as unwritten law. And I am sure there are many here who agree with me. (*He stops.*)

HOLGER (*Rising*). I think the time has come to find out.

GENERAL OUTCRY. Yes, yes!

(*All that have been in the side rooms come hurrying into the hall.*)

HOLGER. Will those who agree with Mr. Anker please signify that fact. (*Silence*) Will they please speak up, I mean. (*Silence; then laughter.*)

A DELEGATE (*At last, in a timid voice*). I agree with Mr. Anker.

(*A roar of laughter greets his words.*)

HOLGER. One man—that's all!

(*The delegates yell and stamp on the floor.*)

ANKER. If that's so, I must apologize for taking up the time of the meeting.

(*He goes toward the door, followed by the one delegate who agreed with him.*)

A DELEGATE. Good luck!

ANKER (*In the doorway*). That's more than I dare to wish you! (*He disappears.*)

HOLGER. The question has been called for.

MANY. Yes, yes!

HOLGER. Then you don't want to hear Mr. Ketil first?

EVERYBODY. Oh, yes, yes! (*Applause.*)

HOLGER. But there is one speaker before Mr. Ketil—Mr. Blom. (*Silence.*)

(BLOM *rises—a serious man, elegantly dressed in black. He has not taken any part whatsoever in the various demonstrations. But he has been seen from time to time trying to catch* HOLGER's *attention, not succeeding until a few moments before* KETIL *demanded the floor.*)

HOLGER. I suppose you are are also in favor of the motion before us?

BLOM. I am.

HOLGER. Mr. Blom has the floor.

BLOM (*Mounting the dais*). May I ask for a glass of water?

HOLGER (*Looking around; many delegates do the same*). What has become of the servants?

(*Several delegates hurry to the side doors to look for servants.*)

MO. Here's one! (*He beckons, and a servant appears.*)

BLOM. Bring me a glass of water— iced. (*The servant leaves*) Our country has already lost millions—millions. The annual profits of our factories are already swallowed up. And more than that.

A DELEGATE. And more than that.

BLOM (*Politely*). And more than that. For this reason the light-hearted—not to say flippant—tone characterizing these proceedings has offended me very much.

A DELEGATE. Very much.

BLOM (*Politely*). Very much. We shall not weather the crisis just started—just started—without self-control and discipline.

A DELEGATE. And discipline.

BLOM (*Politely*). And discipline. (*Laughter*) When we possess self-control and discipline, then, and only then, can we hope to have with us—on our side— that power——

(*The* SERVANT *has in the meantime returned with a magnificent pitcher and an equally magnificent goblet on a tray; he pours water into the goblet and offers it to* BLOM.)

BLOM. Which is the greatest of all— namely—— (*He takes the goblet and drinks.*)

A DELEGATE. Namely——?

SECOND DELEGATE. The army.

THIRD DELEGATE. The king.

FOURTH DELEGATE. The voters.

FIFTH DELEGATE. The ladies. (*Laughter.*)

SIXTH DELEGATE. The cash. (*More laughter.*)

BLOM (*Putting down the goblet*). I mean the Church.

SEVERAL. Aw—the Church!

BLOM. The Church. Only by self-control and discipline can we get the Church with us.

A DELEGATE. With us.

BLOM (*Politely*). With us.

ANOTHER DELEGATE (*Seated very far back*). What the devil do we want with the Church when it can't make the workmen behave?

SEVERAL. Hear, hear!

A THIRD DELEGATE. What have we got it for, anyhow?

BLOM (*Unmoved*). The Church does not side with the workmen. We can see that—see that. But neither does the Church side with us, because we lack the order and discipline we want to enforce on the workmen—on the workmen—and which we want the Church to help us enforce.

A DELEGATE. To help us enforce.

BLOM (*Politely*). To help us enforce. I agree entirely with the proposed plan. But unless we obtain the support of the Church, the carrying out of it will be impossible to us.

A DELEGATE. Impossible to us.

BLOM (*Politely*). Impossible to us. That's my opinion. (*He steps down.*)

HOLGER. Mr. Ketil has the floor.

(*General applause. Everybody pushes forward to hear better.*)

KETIL (*Mounting the dais during the applause*). Well, well—it's *we*, then, that lack discipline! (*Laughter and cries of "Hear, hear"*) And the Church, poor thing, is standing there, not knowing what to do—not daring to help us because we lack order and discipline. (*Laughter and cries of "Hear, hear"*) So that's the reason why the Church has always been helping those that had the power? And we must suppose that all who ever held power have also had self-control and discipline! (*Signs of general satisfaction*) Let us then by all means get hold of the power, so that we, too, can be sure of the Church! (*A storm of approval follows*) And of the workmen also! When the French Government shot down ten thousand of them at Paris—including all the worst mischiefmakers—there came peace for many years. A little bloodletting now and then has its uses. (*Laughter; cries of "Hear, hear"; talk among the delegates*) I understand they are soon going to have another one down there. (*Laughter*) I don't think anything of that kind is needed here. But it depends on ourselves. If we seize the power today and show that we mean to keep the social body in good health, even if it takes a bloodletting to do so, then I think we may escape it—but not otherwise. (*Loud cries of "Hear"*) Somebody said here a while ago that we were to blame for the anarchism of the others—that we were anarchists ourselves—and that the anarchism on both sides was wrecking the national welfare. Perhaps. But if you consider what some fool of a millionaire, or—to mention a still worse fool—some son of a millionaire (*Laughter*) wastes in the course of several years: what does it matter in comparison with what a strike can waste in a few weeks? Nay—if you turn to England, or, still more, to America—in a few days, when, as frequently happens, the striking workmen destroy machinery, burn millions' worth of property, bring every form of business to a standstill, and upset the markets all over the world? With that kind of human beasts—always lying in wait within the workmen, no matter how peaceful they may seem—we are to share the control of our business and the profits which guarantee that control. And having to deal with such people, we are supposed to hesitate about seizing the power and using it for the good of all! (*Loud applause*) Not only do I cast my own vote for every point of Mr. Holger's plan, but I demand that we adopt it unanimously.

(*He steps down in the middle of a tempestuous ovation, all except* BLOM *rising to their feet.*)

A DELEGATE. Let's carry it by acclamation!

EVERYBODY. Yes, yes! (*Applause.*)

MO. Three cheers for Holger—our great leader! Hurrah!

(*All present join in, including* BLOM, *who has now risen.*)

ANKER (*Appearing suddenly in the doorway with the man who followed him out*). Beg your pardon, Mr. President, but we can't get out.

HOLGER. Can't get out?

ANKER. All the doors are locked.

HOLGER. But the doorkeeper—eh?

ANKER. The doorkeeper isn't there.

HOLGER. What's that? What has become of the servants? Eh?

ANKER. We couldn't find any servants. (*Signs of general anxiety.*)

MO. But one of them was here a moment ago.

(*Several delegates rush to the doorways.*)

A DELEGATE. There he is now. (*He beckons.*)

(*The* SERVANT *enters.*)

HOLGER. One of the extra servants. (*To the* SERVANT) See that these gentlemen get out. (*The* SERVANT *looks at his watch before he goes out with* ANKER *and the other delegates*) And try to find the doorkeeper. Eh?—You need not be disturbed, gentlemen. I have caused the doors to be locked in order to provide against intruders. The police are outside. And I suppose the servants are getting ready for the dinner.

SEVERAL (*In tones of relief*). Oh, that's it!

HOLGER. This interruption has prevented me from expressing my gratitude as spontaneously as I could have wished —my gratitude for this splendid tribute —and also for the confidence you have shown me by the adoption of my plan. You may be sure that I shall not disappoint you. I thank you also for helping me to break up that constitutional debate into which we found ourselves plunged so unexpectedly. (*Laughter*) The tendency to play at parliament, in season and out, is one of the scourges of our time. Every idea is talked to death; every higher aim is dragged down. But I suppose that what has its origin in a choice exercised by mediocrity can hardly act otherwise. (*Cries of "Hear, hear"*) Please be seated, gentlemen (*A few sit down, a majority remain standing*) The action we have taken here now I regard as decisive. As I see it, it is a great event and it has been the chief aim of my life. (*Cries of "Hear"*) Shortly before I had the honor of bidding you welcome, I had a conference with the workmen, at which I had once more to hear that they, and not we, have built the factories—that they are making the money we are living on. And we know, of course, that the same is true of the state: they have built it, and they are maintaining it. All we do is to live by their efforts.—But the truth is, that at no time or place have the efforts of scattered workers achieved anything like that. They have never been able to reach beyond their own needs—beyond the earning of bare necessities. Only the co-ordination of such efforts could achieve something more by uniting great numbers in the pursuit of a common goal. This work of co-ordination used to rest principally on the big landowners and the great guilds. Those were the men of power that built our societies. The warriors were partly a help and partly a hindrance. The same holds true of the priests—they sometimes helped and sometimes hindered. But we are the heirs both of the nobility and the guilds. In our own day we stand for this work of co-ordination. We are now the founders of great fortunes. It is by us that city and country alike are built up; it is through us the workmen gain a living; and from us springs that prosperity which finds something to spare for the arts and sciences. (*Tumultuous and prolonged enthusiasm*) As long as the greater part of the wealth remains controlled by *us,* so long will all that is born out of it continue to be rich in individuality, originality, and variety. Everyone consults his own taste, and everybody finds it suited. But imagine in our place a single authority, be it that of community or state! Only one producer, only one purchaser, and, of course, only one taste. And also, of course, only one standard of value. That would be outright Hell! Then, all the year around, this earthly life would be reduced to one long Sunday afternoon of boredom. (*Laughter*) In the end the nations would then grow so much alike that we could hardly tell whether we were living in this ant-heap or in that—except possibly by our manner of growling at each other. (*Laughter*) Although I suppose in the end that difference would be wiped out, too—eh? (*More laughter*) When they call out to us from the other side that the will of the majority must rule, and that *they* are the majority, then we reply: the insects are also in a majority. (*Cries of "Hear, hear"*) If such a majority should come into power here—by the ballot or any other means—a majority, that would mean, without the traditions of a ruling class, without its nobility of mind and passion for beauty, without its age-tested love of order in big things and small—then, quietly but firmly, we would give the word: "Guns to the fore!"

(*The entire gathering is on its feet in a moment, shouting, applauding, and crowding up about* HOLGER.)

HOLGER. And now, gentlemen, the banquet will begin! (*He turns around to push a button; as he does so, the first of three guns is fired outside, while at the same moment an orchestra begins to play a lively march composed especially for the occasion*) I'll take the liberty of leading the way.

(*He steps down from the throne and offers his arm to* KETIL; *behind them the rest begin to fall in, two abreast.*)

ANKER (*Appears again with his companion midway between the two doors*). We cannot get out. (*Everybody stops to listen*) We are even unable now to get below this floor. We have tried both stairways.

HOLGER. Burst open the doors then!

ANKER. We could tell that the doors were fastened with heavy bars—on the outside.

HOLGER (*Leaving* KETIL). What does this mean? Where is that servant?

ANKER. He disappeared.

(*The delegates begin to show apprehension.*)

MO. There he is now. (*Pointing toward one of the side rooms.*)

HOLGER (*In a commanding voice*). Come here!

(*The* SERVANT *approaches.*)

SEVERAL. What does all this mean? What is it?

HOLGER (*With a silencing gesture*). If you please! (*Takes the* SERVANT *by the arm and leads him down to the foreground*) Explain! What does all this mean?

MANY DELEGATES (*Crowding around the man*). Yes, what does it mean?

SERVANT. Let go! (HOLGER *drops his hold*) You want to know what it means?

EVERYBODY. Yes.

(*The* SERVANT *mounts the dais.*)

SEVERAL. Well, he's going to make a speech!

SERVANT. You want to know what it means?

EVERYBODY. Yes!

SERVANT. We are locked in——

HOLGER. But the doorkeeper, the servants——?

SERVANT. They have left.

HOLGER. Of their own will? Or under compulsion?

SERVANT. Both. Those that wanted to go took care that the rest did. Now there is no one left. (*Panic-stricken silence prevails.*)

MANY. But the police? (*They begin to stir about uneasily*) The police! Call the police!

(*A couple of delegates lead the way and many follow them to the big windows, which are thrown open, several leaning out to look for the police.*)

A DELEGATE. No police are in sight!

SEVERAL. We can't see any. There are none outside!

MANY. What? Are we locked in? (*They surge toward the windows.*)

MO (*Coming forward and shouting at the top of his voice*). Explain! There are no police there—not one outside!

(*The delegates crowd around the* SERVANT *again.*)

KETIL. Have you fixed the police too?

SERVANT. Yes, the police lines have been moved further off.

HOLGER. Was that done in my name?

SERVANT. It was.

DELEGATES (*Packed together in the foreground*). That's a devilish trick! What's up? What's going to happen? We're betrayed! What can be done?

MO (*Mounting a chair*). Keep quiet, everybody! (*To the* SERVANT) What's going to happen? (*All stop talking, with the result that the lively strain of the march is heard the better*) Can't anybody stop that foolish music?

SEVERAL. Stop the music!

EVERYBODY. Stop the music!

BLOM (*Leans out of the window, shouting*). The music must stop! Stop it!

(*Everybody listens expectantly, but the music continues with undiminished vigor.*)

MO (*Desperately*). Can't anybody make it stop?

HOLGER. You'll have to send somebody up to the roof—that's where the orchestra is.

KETIL. It has been done already.

(*New pause, during which the music goes on as before.*)

MO. It goes right on! For Heaven's sake, go, some of you!

(*Three or four delegates rush out.*)

SERVANT (*To* BLOM, *who has come forward again*). And such poor music at that!

BLOM. No, I don't think so! I don't think so. But the whole thing is dreadful. (*The music stops.*)

MO. At last!

SEVERAL (*With evident relief*). That's better!

MO (*To the* SERVANT). Will you tell us now: what does it mean? (*A breathless pause ensues.*)

SERVANT. You have been summoned hence.

(*The same deep silence prevails again.*)

MO (*After a long while, almost in a whisper*). By whom?

SERVANT. By Maren Haug—the woman we buried yesterday. She wants you to join her. (*Deep silence again.*)

MO (*All the time remaining on the chair*). What—what does that mean?

SERVANT. When this place was built, electric wires were laid from the rooms down to the old mining gallery that runs right beneath us. That gallery has been cleared, and during the last few nights it has been loaded. (*Silence as before.*)

HOLGER (*Who so far hasn't made a movement*). Who's in charge of the job?

SERVANT. The man who laid the wires.

HOLGER. Is he here now?

SERVANT. No, he has more to do afterward.

MO (*Bursting out*). Who are you?

SERVANT. What does it matter? I am not looking for immortality.

MO. Kill the fellow! (*Leaps from the chair.*)

MANY (*Trying to get at the* SERVANT). You scoundrel! Assassin!

HOLGER (*Stepping in between*). No, no! Wait! Wait, I tell you! (*When comparative quiet has been restored*) I want to speak to this man alone. (*To the* SERVANT) Will you come down here and let me talk with you?

SERVANT (*After a glance at his watch*). You'll have to be brief.

(*He steps down and goes to* HOLGER; *both come further down the stage,* HOLGER *motioning those around them to withdraw.*)

HOLGER. What do you want for letting us out? Go as high as you like. Ask any guarantee you choose. How do you want the money paid out?—You can leave here on a special steamer this very evening.—Why don't you answer?

SERVANT (*Goes over to the throne and mounts the platform on which it stands*). Now I am master here! It's under my command you'll have to make this trip! And you'd better hold fast when it begins to roll.

(*General alarm and whispering among the delegates.*)

KETIL. A question to our master—if it so please him?

SERVANT (*With his watch in his hand*). Yes—but quick.

KETIL. What's the good of all this?

SERVANT. Of the—ascension?

KETIL. Yes. What's the use of it?

SERVANT. Advertising.

SEVERAL (*Repeating in whispers*). Advertising?

KETIL. I dare say this advertisement will cost *you* a lot more than us.

SERVANT. Oh, others will follow. It's the numbers that will do it. Like so many shining stars you're going to proclaim our cause! And I hope you appreciate the undeserved honor of your glorious ending!

HOLGER. And now's the time?

SERVANT. Now is the time. Most noble fellow stars—attention! (*He starts toward the rear.*)

HOLGER. Well, *you'll* give no signal!

(*He pulls out a revolver and fires four shots in quick succession at the* SERVANT.)

SERVANT (*As the shots ring out, takes a few steps backward, putting his hand first to his heart, and then to his abdomen; at last he clasps his head with both hands*). That's good!

(*He reels forward and falls at the feet of* HOLGER, *who has been following him. All rush forward to have a look at the prostrate body. Some mount the speaker's dais, others climb up on the throne, while others get up on chairs to look over the heads of those in front of them.*

At that moment the MAN IN BROWN *appears suddenly beside the body.*)

MAN IN BROWN. Ha-ha-ha-ha-ha-ha!

(*He crouches down and slaps his knees as he hops around like a bird; then he runs like a flash toward the right, while* HOLGER *fires two shots after him.*)

MO (*In utter panic*). Are there others?

EVERYBODY. There are others! There are others! What will happen now? (*They run around aimlessly.*)

MO (*Who has been running toward the windows*). Ssh! Ssh!

A DELEGATE. What is it?

MO. Ssh, ssh! I think some one is calling outside——

(*He leans out of one of the windows, all of which are open.*)

MANY (*Eagerly*). Is there anybody to help us? (*They rush wildly toward the windows.*)

MO. Ssh, I tell you! It's a woman. She's standing on the other side of the moat. Listen! Can't you see her?

A DELEGATE. She's signaling to us.

MO. Keep quiet now! (*Silence.*)

A WOMAN'S VOICE (*Though barely heard, its horror-stricken tone can be distinguished*). Come out of there! They have mined the ground under the Castle!

SERVANT. Rachel!

HOLGER (*Still standing beside him, says in a low voice*). Is he alive?

SEVERAL (*Calling out*). We can't get out!

MO. One at a time. (*Shouting*) We can't get out! Send somebody to open for us!

MANY. Send somebody to open for us!

(*Most of those that have remained behind hurry to the windows to get a look.*)

MO. Ssh! Keep quiet. (*Silence.*)

WOMAN'S VOICE. Nobody can get there! The drawbridge is raised!

SERVANT. Rachel.

HOLGER (*Who has remained immovable, says almost in a whisper*). Can he be her brother?

DELEGATES (*Sweeping backward from the windows again and talking all together*). The drawbridge is raised! We're locked in and trapped! What can be done? Are there no ropes to slide down—no ladders?

A DELEGATE (*Shouting above the din*). Are there no ropes we can slide down on to get hold of ladders?

HOLGER. I am afraid not. Everything is new here.

MO. Why in the world did you bring us here?

A DELEGATE. It's a murder-trap, that's what it is!

SEVERAL. You shouldn't have brought us here! It's your fault!

MANY. If anything happens to us, it's your fault!

MO. Your boundless vanity and arrogance are to blame for this!

ALMOST EVERYBODY. It's dreadful! It's up to you to get us out! You saw last year that the place was dangerous! We relied on you! Why don't you do something?

HOLGER (*Calmly*). Gentlemen, try to be a little more calm! Bear in mind that the explosion cannot wreck the whole castle. And bear in mind, too, that the man who was to give the signal is lying here.

(*At these words the* SERVANT *makes an effort to raise himself.*)

A DELEGATE (*Shouts*). He's alive!

SEVERAL. Is he alive?

(*Again the crowd closes around the* SERVANT, *who is barely able to raise his head.*)

A DELEGATE. Ssh! He's trying to say something!

SERVANT. I—I am not alone. (*He sinks back again.*)

ANOTHER DELEGATE (*In a whisper*). Where are the others?

SEVERAL (*In low tones*). Where are the others? Where do you think the explosion will take place?

A DELEGATE. Right here, of course!

OTHER DELEGATES. Yes, of course, right here!

MANY. Right here! Of course, it must be right here!

MO (*Bursting into wild laughter*). Why didn't I think of that before? Ha-ha-ha-ha!

(*He runs to one of the windows and flings himself out before anybody has time to stop him.*)

SEVERAL (*Run to the windows, but draw back in horror*). Killed! Smashed against the stone pavement! (*They repeat this to others, who didn't hear at first.*)

OTHERS. Horrible! What's to become of us?

(*Another delegate wants to throw himself out of the window, and when the rest try to stop him a fight ensues.*)

HOLGER (*In commanding tones*). Take care! Despair is contagious!

SEVERAL (*To the rest*). Yes, it's contagious! You'd better take care!

HOLGER. Why don't you try to meet the inevitable with dignity? All of us

have to meet death once. And our death will do more for order in this country than any one of us could achieve in the longest of lifetimes. For you may be sure that the power will never pass into the hands of people who resort to such methods. Remember that! And let us die happy for that reason! Our death will fill our fellow citizens with just that resentment and courage which alone can save our country now. Long live our country!

ALL. Long live our country!

(*Quiet has barely returned, when the frightful laughter of the* MAN IN BROWN *is heard from the right.*)

A DELEGATE. Oh, it's *him*, of course! (*Runs in the direction of the laughter.*)

SEVERAL. Yes, it must be him. (*Run out.*)

MANY. It's him! Catch him! (*Run out.*)

ALL. It's him! Catch him! Kill him!

(*All except* HOLGER, ANKER, *and* KETIL *rush out wildly,* BLOM *walking out after the rest.*)

KETIL (*To* HOLGER). They don't know what they are doing any longer.

HOLGER (*Who has been following the wild rout with his eyes*). Yes, they are trying to run away from it—of course!

ANKER (*Gently*). Friends, there is nothing left for us now but to trust in the mercy of God.

KETIL. Well, go ahead, old chap! As for me, I am an old sailor and have looked death in the eye before.

(ANKER *kneels down at the left and begins to pray.*)

HOLGER (*Walks back and forth; as he passes the body of the* SERVANT *he says*). He's dead now, that fellow. (*All three keep silent for a while.*)

KETIL. There isn't any way out of this?

HOLGER (*Absently and without stoping*). None at all.

KETIL. No, I thought so—not when a massive thing like this begins to go—

Well, now I'll sit down here and not make another move—come what may!

ANKER (*Turning his head toward* KETIL). But don't put on airs about it. Dear friend—why don't you come and pray for your soul instead?

KETIL. Not much use, I fear. I guess the soul is what it is. It can't change as quick as all that. And if anybody should be waiting for it on the other side—well, I imagine he won't let himself be fooled by what little I could say now.

(*The laughter of the* MAN IN BROWN *is heard right above them, followed immediately by the cries and clatter of his pursuers.*)

HOLGER (*Stops and listens for a while; then he goes slowly up to* KETIL). And for the sake of that pack of cowards——!

KETIL. Yes, they are not much good.

HOLGER. I have known it all the time. But as long as they would take orders—eh?

KETIL. Yes—they were good for that—very good. But let them only get scared——

HOLGER. Then they run like dogs from a whipping. I can see that now.

KETIL. Yes, we need better stuff than that.

HOLGER (*After a while*). I should have liked to live a little longer!

ANKER (*Turning his face toward the other two*). Let us pray for our children! It'll be so hard on them to begin with. Let us pray that God may console them, and that there may not be so much evil in their time as there has been in ours. Let us pray for that!

(*The laughter is now heard from the left, not far off; then the yelling and shouting of the pursuing crowd, coming nearer and nearer, until the whole pack bursts into the hall, crossing it from left to right.* BLOM *walks after the rest.*)

HOLGER (*Who follows the crowd with his eyes as long as anybody remains in sight*). One mob or the other——

KETIL. No—strong men, that's what we need.

HOLGER. One will be enough. And he'll come!

ANKER. Hurry up now and pray with me—pray God to help the righteous so that they may bring light and peace to those who are suffering. God save our country! God——

(*A deep rumbling noise is heard; then wild human cries quickly cut off.* KETIL, *with the chair on which he sits, is lifted from the floor and disappears.* HOLGER *falls and disappears also. Clouds of dust envelop everything in an obscuring mist.* ANKER *remains barely visible for a while longer—it looks as if he were passing right through the wall. But to the very last his voice can be heard.*)

ANKER. God save our country! God save——

CURTAIN

ACT IV

Under the trees of a big park. Wooden seats are built around some of the trunks. Faint strains of gently melancholy music are heard before the curtain rises and continue to be heard through the act—a distant chorus, as it were.

RACHEL *enters slowly, followed by* HALDEN. *During the ensuing scene* RACHEL *remains standing or walking around.* HALDEN *leans against a tree most of the time, but now and then he sits down for a few moments.*

RACHEL. Thank you! (*She looks around*) How fortunate it is that I have this park. Within doors the sorrow breaks me down—I have had a bad night. Out here I can stand up under it. These walks, with nothing but the sky above, and the spring weather—oh, it feels good!

HALDEN. There is consolation in nature.

RACHEL (*Looking at him*). Yes, but nature does not try to rob us of our sorrow, as do human beings. It only lets us feel its own imperishable power, and reminds us of what lives on. (*Softly, as if to herself*) Lives on.

HALDEN. That's just the point at issue. Your sorrow must become absorbed in that which points ahead.

RACHEL. It's what my sorrow cannot do. And I don't want it to.—Please don't get impatient: don't you see that I am winning him back to myself through my sorrow? I couldn't keep up with him while he was alive—and so I let him get away from me that last evening because I didn't understand him. He was a man of faith who preached no creed except that embodied in his own deeds. Faith is action. But one without faith finds it so hard to understand him who has it. And so I let him get away from me. It's something I can never forgive myself, something I shall never cease to regret. It stabs and claws at my flesh; it fills the air around me with sobs and screams. Sometimes I seem to share his agony where he lies buried in the ruins; at other times I am passing by his side through a hailstorm of curses poured upon him by hundreds of thousands ranged in endless rows.—And it is not *him* they hit. He knew in advance that very few could grasp what he was doing. It only made his mandate more compelling. In that way only could his action rise to sacrifice. So great was his pride toward his fellow men; so great his humility toward the cause he served. I feel certain that he scorned to explain himself even to those he had to lead into death. He was too modest to do so.—No lash or blow can reach to him—but me—to me they reach. How could I be so mistaken? How could my love for him so fail to sharpen my perception?

HALDEN. What is to become of you? You must resist.

RACHEL. What is to become of me? If I can sleep at night, my suffering begins anew in the morning, and if I *cannot* sleep—than I shall die. Nor can I weep! The tears are there—yet I cannot weep. But I like it better so, for thus I win him back to me again.

HALDEN. If he were alive, he would say: "Don't waste any sorrow on me, but give it to——"

RACHEL (*Interrupting*). So he would! He was like that! I thank you for those words! As he lived, so he died—for others! But *I* can find no place for all those others. Although now the fate of those he died for is worse than ever, I can find no place for them—I have no place for anyone but him.—Oh, when I think of the man who lured him on to this.—It has been written that whoso shall offend one of the little ones, it were better for him that a millstone were hanged about his neck and that he were drowned in the depth of the sea. But what of him who leads astray the yearning of another man for noble deeds— what should be done to him?

HALDEN. Oh, I suppose both of them meant to do good, to save somebody else by their deed——

RACHEL (*Interrupting again*). The idea that anybody could be saved in such a way! By first being made cruel enough to desire other people's destruction! What are people to be saved from? Or if evil is to be suppressed by the sowing of still more evil, how can goodness get a chance to grow?

HALDEN. Suppose what has happened should arouse the conscience of the people?

RACHEL. Why, that's what he was saying—his very words, I think— Arouse the conscience of the people? After all

these thousands of years that we have been subject to the influence of the family and of religion, can it be possible that we are unable to arouse people's conscience except by— O ye silent and exalted witnesses, who hear without answering and see without reflecting what you see, why don't you show me how to reach the upward road? For in the middle of all this misery there *is* no road that leads upward—nothing but an endless circling around the same spot, by which I perish!

HALDEN. Upward means forward.

RACHEL. But there is no forward in this! We have been thrown back into sheer barbarism! Once more all faith in a happy future has been wiped out. Just ask a few questions around here! The worst feature of such a mad outburst of evil is not the death of some or the sorrow of others: it is that all courage is frightened out of the world. Mercy has fled, and all are crying for vengeance. Justice, kindness, forbearance, all our angels of light have fled away. The air is filled with fragments of mutilated corpses, and armed men are springing out of the ground. All others are in hiding—I can't dress a patient's wound without having to remember—I cannot hear a moan without getting sick at heart. And then the knowledge that no matter what I do, it won't help—it won't help!

HALDEN. No, it won't help! That's what tormented him.

RACHEL. And was that a reason for scattering his torment broadcast over all of us? For robbing everybody of what courage they had? Could it be possible to inflict a worse wound on mankind? What is death itself compared with a life without the courage to live it? When I look at that one man who was saved—when I see him in his chair, lame and wordless— he who possessed limitless courage—and when I see the workmen follow him around begging for mercy—those men who once thought they could crush him—! And then the sun, the spring—ever since that dreadful night—nothing but fine weather, night and day—a stretch of it the like of which I cannot recall. Is it not as if nature itself were crying out to us: "Shame! Shame! You sprinkle my leaves with blood, and mingle death-cries with my song. You darken the air for me with your gruesome complaints." That's what it is saying to us. "You are soiling the spring for me. Your diseases and your evil thoughts are crouching in the woods and on the greenswards. Everywhere a stink of misery is following you like that of rotting waters." That's what it is telling us. "Your greed and your envy are a pair of sisters who have fought each other since they were born"—that's what it says. "Only my highest mountain peaks, only my sandy wastes and icy deserts, have not seen those sisters; but every other part of the earth has been filled by them with blood and brutal bawling. In the middle of eternal glory mankind has invented Hell and manages to keep it filled. And men, who should stand for perfection, harbor among them what is worthless and foul."—At last I have found a voice! Until now I have done nothing but listen, and help, and have kept silent, and fled from everything.—But I knew that out here my sorrow would find words.

HALDEN. It must be great indeed to make you so unjust.

RACHEL. But it is relief nevertheless—almost like crying.—But you are right: sorrow is an egoist. Others do not exist, or they are only in the way. I am abusing your kindness.

HALDEN. Don't talk like that!

RACHEL. But in those few words of yours there was something that—that—Oh, I hate those calculations on a large scale. They overlook what is human, although in this alone salvation lies. I fear

whatever is inhuman.—Isn't it horrible to think of? With me Elias had already suffered all a man can stand of the inhumanity of the miracle. And on top of it he must needs fall victim to the inhumanity of theories—! Now I am coming to see how it happened. It is not enough to say that somebody made a wrong use of his passion for self-sacrifice. That would not be enough to explain such a choice on his part. No, something more was needed. They got hold of his worship for everything of supernatural dimensions. He was like his father: both had a childish fondness for that kind of thing. The dreams of idlers had in him become a religion. He could not perceive the salvation that lies in furnishing peace and light for the toil of the millions. He could see it only in great characters, in commanding wills, in monstrous happenings. That's why he gave away his big fortune as he did—to die the death of a Samson! That's why he did it all secretly, silently. That seemed to him the noblest way of all.—Yes, they must have filled his imagination with the idea of something surpassing all that had been counted greatest before. Thus it was carried beyond what is human. There were no boundaries to be crossed in such a case. Someone must have observed how easily the passion for the superhuman can be led astray, and then made use of this fact. It was like handing a razor to a child with the words: "Put it in your mouth."

HALDEN. But it cannot possibly have happened like that.

RACHEL. I am not condemning anybody. What right has the sister of Elias Sang to condemn anybody? But tell me, Mr. Halden: when goodness uses dynamite, what is then to be called good, and what evil? The greatest thing about goodness is that it creates. Out of its own it adds joy, and perhaps strength as well, to other wills. But how can it take away life? What a horrible fate Elias had to meet: to fall into the hands of such a monster!—I was standing on the ramparts when that enormous structure blew up. I was standing beside Bratt. We were thrown to the ground, and when he got up again his reason was gone. If I hadn't had him to care for at once, the same thing would have happened to me. Do you think Elias could have done it if he had caught sight of us two standing there?—His face that last evening, as he was leaving me, was like a cry of distress! Now I understand why. Can you imagine anything more cruel than a power within ourselves that goads us on to that which our whole nature resists? How can happiness be possible on this earth until our reasoning faculties become so spontaneous that no one can use us like that?— Oh, the pain within me!—Oh, that I could weep myself free from it!—If he were here, that man who has done all this—if he could hear how I am crying out lest my sorrow choke me—do you think that through my wail he would hear the wailing of thousands of others? —But were he standing here—I shouldn't speak a harsh word to him. All human beings live as if surrounded by a cloud of smoke. They do not see. We are brought up to be what we are.—Oh, I am not accusing anybody. But God, whom we are to understand better the further we proceed—there is something in the brightness of this day, in its everlasting wholesomeness and beauty, that tells me—God must be present in all that we suffer from what is unnatural, irrational, and inhuman. The more numerous and frequent and loud our complaints become, the more deeply will God make himself felt.—Thus, brother, you have also been of service in your death. Not as that man of dread made you believe— but by calling forth suffering and opening the gates of sorrow. No circumstance is wholly our own until touched by sorrow;

no ideal until sorrow has breathed upon it; no insight until the eyes of sorrow have met ours. Our mind is like a room full of visitors until sorrow steps across the threshold, be it with harsh or gentle tread—then the room becomes our own; then we are left by ourselves!—O Elias, Elias, only now do I understand you as you deserved to be understood! From now on I shall never leave you again— nor that for which you died. Our sufferings shall purge it; our tears shall glimmer through it like flames and render it sacred to thousands.—My wishes outstrip my powers. My strength is gone. Once more I am thrust back into impotence. Even sorrow demands strength.

HALDEN. There they are bringing Holger.

RACHEL (*Going toward the left to meet him*). Poor fellow, he has had his morning tour.

(HALDEN *places himself at the left so that he cannot be seen by* HOLGER, *who is carried by servants in a comfortable and luxurious armchair. Other servants follow behind.* HOLGER's *head is wrapped in bandages; his right hand is paralyzed.*)

RACHEL (*Holding* HOLGER's *left hand*). He wants to rest awhile here.

(*The* SERVANTS *put down the chair.*)

HOLGER (*Who has tried to raise his right hand*). I am always forgetting that my right hand is useless. I wanted to make the servants——

RACHEL (*After bending over him, to the* SERVANTS). Please step aside a little.

(*The* SERVANTS *leave.*)

HOLGER (*In a low voice*). I have something to say to you.

RACHEL. What is it, dear friend?

HOLGER. When they had dug me out— and it was found that I was the only survivor, you asked—to be allowed to nurse me.

RACHEL. Yes.

HOLGER. And so—I couldn't help being brought here—and became your first patient in the house and the park I had just handed over to you.

RACHEL (*On her knees beside him*). Does it trouble you, dear friend? Is it troubling you in any way?

HOLGER. No—but—I have been too ill to tell you——

RACHEL. What? (*Long silence.*)

HOLGER. Has your brother's body been found?

RACHEL. Yes—dreadfully mangled——

HOLGER. Nothing to show, then—how he died——?

RACHEL (*With sharpened attention*). Didn't he die in the same way as the rest?

HOLGER. He spoke to us—told us a signal would be sent to the galleries below—and then he was shot down——

RACHEL (*Drawing back*). He was shot down——?

HOLGER. I didn't know him.

RACHEL (*Rising with a quick movement*). You shot him?

HOLGER. I didn't know him. I wasn't aware—that he was your brother. But I am afraid—had I known him—I should have shot him just the same.

RACHEL (*In a whisper*). Oh, it's horrible, horrible!

HOLGER. He died splendidly.—Just after he had been hit he said: "That's good!"

RACHEL. Oh, how he must have been suffering——!

HOLGER. He heard your voice outside. And so he spoke your name— You called to us twice, and both times he spoke your name.

RACHEL. Elias, Elias——!

HOLGER. Are you going to cast me off?

RACHEL (*Throwing herself on her knees beside him*). No, no! (*At that moment she bursts into tears*) Oh, now I can cry—now I can cry! And I say as he did: that's good! (*She is shaken by sobs; finally she rises to her feet again*) Elias,

Elias, you kept your own pain hidden from me—but now you have relieved me of mine! (*She breaks into sobs again.*)

HOLGER. Come—come and take me away.

(*The* SERVANTS *hurry up to him and carry him out to the right, moving very slowly.*

HANS BRAA *and* ASPELUND *enter from the left and follow after* HOLGER. *They are seen exchanging a few words with each other while crossing the stage.*)

RACHEL (*Without noticing the workmen*). So he spoke my name! I don't understand—but since I learned that—— (*She begins to weep again; sits down.*)

(HALDEN *comes forward. For a moment he stands looking down at her. Then he kneels solemnly before her and raises both arms toward heaven until both his hands meet palm to palm.*

RACHEL *doesn't notice him at once but when she does so she turns instinctively away.*)

HALDEN. You were right.

RACHEL (*Almost inaudibly*). In what——?

HALDEN. And I yield to you.

RACHEL (*Still in a low voice*). What do you mean?

HALDEN. More than you think. (*He rises to his feet and stands very erect.*)

(RACHEL *looks hard at him. Just then* BRATT's *voice is heard and he becomes visible in the background.*

HALDEN *makes a deprecatory gesture with one hand and goes out to the left.*)

BRATT (*As if speaking to somebody walking beside him*). S-o!—Really, you think so?—Well, indeed!

RACHEL (*Following* HALDEN *with her eyes*). There was something— But I can't make out the rest.—Oh, is that you, Bratt?

BRATT (*Looking ill and speaking in a low, dragging voice*). Yes—and Mr. Lasalle. May I introduce: Miss Sang—

Mr. Lasalle. (*He bows first to one side, then to the other.*)

RACHEL. But you have introduced him to me so many times.

BRATT. Perhaps I have. But it wasn't you I had in mind. It was Mr. Holger, Junior. Was it not he that stood here a moment ago?

RACHEL. Holger, Junior?

BRATT. Yes, that fellow with the electric wires.

RACHEL (*Leaping to her feet; in a whisper*). What are you saying——?

BRATT (*Stepping back*). You frighten me.

RACHEL. Who was it that stood here, you say?

BRATT. That stood—that stood——?

RACHEL. That stood here—who was it?

BRATT. Well—? Yes, who was it? There are times when I can't——

RACHEL (*Going closer, but speaking very gently*). Who was it that was standing here?

BRATT. Will you permit me to ask Mr. Lasalle?

RACHEL. Yes, do!

BRATT (*Bowing slightly toward the right*). Pardon me, Mr. Lasalle, but who was it—who was it first started the work on the ruins?

RACHEL. Oh—I see! (*She sits down.*)

BRATT (*Nearer to her*). For now ruins are quite the fashion, I understand?

RACHEL. Are you still going up to the ruins of the Castle every day?

BRATT. Yes—it was there it disappeared, you see.

RACHEL. How are you today?

BRATT. Yes.—Oh, yes, thank you.—If it were not for this thing that disappeared —and that I can't find again. (*He stands staring, a little downward and a little to the left, with his left cheek resting in his left hand*) That thing I looked for so many years. And now I can't remember what it is. Isn't that awful?

RACHEL (*Rises, caresses him gently, and straightens out his dress*). Now, my dear Bratt, you'll be all right here with me.

BRATT. Yes, I am all right.—If it were not for this thing I can't get hold of.

RACHEL. But I am sure Mr. Lasalle will help you.

BRATT. Mr. Lasalle says we have to search the ruins.

RACHEL. Yes, of course, it was there it disappeared.

BRATT. It was there it disappeared.

RACHEL. Well, go over there now.

BRATT. Yes.—If you care, Mr. Lasalle—? Oh!—Yes.—Goodbye! (*He goes out, seeming to listen to somebody beside him*) Do you think so? I assure you that I am looking all the time, but I can't find it. And I had taken so much trouble with it——

(*The last words are heard from the outside, as he disappears to the left.*

A SERVANT *appears following* BRATT.)

RACHEL (*To the* SERVANT). He mustn't be allowed to leave the place. (*The* SERVANT *goes out to the left*) I haven't the strength to divide myself. And I wouldn't if I could.—Come back to me, you thoughts of my grief! Come to me, my black doves, and close me in!—Elias! —I should have been to you what mother was to father. She had the courage and the consecration. I didn't have enough, and so you complained of me in your last moments. For to call me then, when life was leaving you, was like a call to all that then was passing out of your reach unfinished, to all that in which you had not succeeded—and you gave it my name! That's the reason why your eyes are pursuing me: I see them as they were when, with the breathing of that complaint, the light went out of them.— There you lay deserted by all, while your life was ebbing away, and my name on your lips was the last glimpse of the waning shore.—And I feel as if for me, too, life was passing out of sight, and I stood here utterly alone, calling to you.

(*She walks a few steps as if held by some vision; then she sits down.*

The music, audible all the time, assumes now a brighter color, more suited to what follows.

CREDO *and* SPERA *enter quickly. As they catch sight of* RACHEL, *they halt. Then they steal up to her slowly, one from either side of the tree at which she is sitting. And finally they kneel beside her, one on either side.*)

RACHEL. You here? (*She draws them to her*) And I didn't even remember you existed! Thank you for coming—thank you! (*She breaks into tears as she takes her arms away from them; they wait quietly*) Did you have permission to come?

CREDO *and* SPERA. Yes.

SPERA (*Cautiously*). We came here to see uncle?

CREDO (*In the same way*). And as we had come——

SPERA. Just now——

CREDO. He said that after this——

BOTH. We might stay here with you.

RACHEL. Did he say *that*?

SPERA *and* CREDO. Yes. He said that now he was going to build for us *here*.

RACHEL. Oh—this is the first glimpse of daylight!

SPERA. He said that everything should be arranged——

BOTH. As you want it.

RACHEL (*Drawing them to her again*). My own friends! (*Silence.*)

SPERA (*Cautiously, as before*). Oh, we haven't talked of anything but you these days.

CREDO (*In the same way*). And of what we wanted to tell you—if we had a chance.

SPERA. For we were afraid that you couldn't stand talking to anybody——

CREDO. That you were suffering too much.

RACHEL. It has been hard. (*She cries again.*)

(CREDO *and* SPERA *wait with their arms folded about her.*)

SPERA (*Softly*). We know that we cannot be to you what *he* was. But we will try.

CREDO (*In the same way*). We'll try to be just as you want us. We'll share with you everything that happens to us.

SPERA. That's what we used to do when father and mother lived.

CREDO. We'll discover so many new things together.

RACHEL. No, there is no longer any future for me!

BOTH. But you have us!

SPERA. You have *our* future!

RACHEL. *You* have the whole world before you.

SPERA. And how about you? You who are giving so many a share in the future?

CREDO. You are so kind to everybody.

SPERA. To everybody within reach.

RACHEL. Oh, I can't even see them. I have tried, but I can't bear it. And even if I could, what would be the use?

SPERA. Of making people well and happy?

CREDO. There is nothing finer on the earth!

SPERA. You should have heard father speak of it!

CREDO. Of conquering what he called "the racial pessimism."

RACHEL (*Becoming attentive*). The racial pessimism?

CREDO (*Cautiously*). Yes, that thing to which your brother succumbed.

RACHEL (*To herself*). Racial pessimism.

SPERA (*With the same care*). Which has grown to such an extent lately. It is awful to hear people talk now.

RACHEL. What a strange word! What did your father have to say about it?

CREDO. It was to him our worst misfortune—what we ought to fight against first of all.

SPERA. And it was to *that* fight he wanted us to devote our lives.

RACHEL. But how did he want you to fight it?

BOTH. By means of inventions,

SPERA. First of all, in that way.

CREDO. He began to teach us when we were little children.

SPERA. Credo knows just what is needed.

CREDO. Yes, I do. This is what I am working at every day.

RACHEL. But how can inventions——?

CREDO. Make men more content? By making it cheaper for them to live—and easier.

SPERA. So that a few square yards of ground will give food enough for a man.

RACHEL. Would that be possible?

CREDO. When our clothes can be made out of leaves and straw; when we can make silk without silkworms and wool without sheep; when our houses can be built for one-twentieth of what they cost now and heated for nothing—don't you think that will make a difference?

SPERA. And then the railroads, Credo!

CREDO. When we can bore through rock as cheaply as through ordinary soil; when we get rails made of cheaper material than iron; when we can get the iron out of the ore more easily than now; when we get a motive power costing next to nothing—then the railroads will be like streets, on which travel is free. Then it will be as if we had abolished distance.

SPERA. And the air-ships, Credo.

CREDO. Oh, you know all about that, Rachel—that we'll soon be able to sail the air as we are sailing the sea now?

SPERA. Credo will work it out, I tell you!

CREDO. Traveling must cost a trifle only and life must be made interesting.

SPERA. People must cease to go hungry, to live in cold and darkness and ugliness, to go around in nasty clothes. That comes first—afterward we can take up other things.

CREDO. Tell what you mean to do, Spera.

SPERA. No, you first!

CREDO. I'll start Young People's Leagues.

RACHEL. What——?

CREDO. Young People's Leagues—all over the country. I'll get hold of the brightest, you know. I'll begin with the schools—for at school they must start learning how to live for each other. Each school will choose some one thing to work for, and then there will be other things for which several schools work in common. And there must also be something for which all the schools in the country work together. Do you see? And it won't end there. We'll do the same thing with the day-laborers, the skilled workmen, the sailors, the clerks, the university students—there must be something each group works for, and something else that all the groups work in common for. Isn't that right? There must be rivalry about it, and pride in what they get done. And, finally, there must be something that every organization in the whole country helps with.—Now it's your turn, Spera.

SPERA (*Timidly*). I want to learn how to speak in public. If I can, I shall try to tell the women that they, too, must have something to live for—from the time they begin going to school. For instance, two or three might join together in taking care of a smaller girl—and she would be *theirs,* don't you know?

RACHEL. Oh, let me kiss that sweet little mouth! (*Kisses* SPERA) The mere fact that such dreams exist—I suppose that's in itself a promise of never-ending renewal.

CREDO. All that we have to suffer now, what is it in comparison with what people used to suffer in the past?

SPERA. Yet they pushed ahead. And we are only just beginning now.

RACHEL. Oh, you darling!

CREDO. Do you know what father used to say? Think only, he would say, when all those are set free who are now employed in making war—when they begin to work with the rest. What new inventions we'll have then! And what prosperity!

SPERA. And then he said——

CREDO (*Waving her aside*). And then he said, that even that was nothing compared with what would happen when all men took up their home on earth once more.

SPERA. Heaven is here! In all that we do, don't you know? That's where heaven is!

CREDO. And in the future, and in what we do for the future—there's heaven!

RACHEL. There is a longing in everybody——

CREDO. For something better! It proves that more happiness is in store for us here! Don't you think so?

RACHEL. When you talk like that, I can see *him!*

CREDO. Do you know—about us and father and mother——?

SPERA. We have, so to speak, to do the work they left behind.

RACHEL. You mean that I should be doing his—I, who——

CREDO. But, Rachel—just *because* you have suffered so terribly!

RACHEL. You think——?

SPERA. Oh, tell her about what came after the "iron age" of which the ancients used to talk.

CREDO. No, about Antichrist, rather!

SPERA. Well, that's the same.

CREDO. Men have always known that, when their discouragement and despair reached their utmost, then the renewal was at hand—then they got strength enough for it—only then!

SPERA. Every strong race has had a feeling of it.

CREDO. Their poetry has prophesied about it.

SPERA (*Cautiously*). Soon you will come to feel it, too.

RACHEL (*Rising*). I'll go to Holger at once, to thank him for this happiness!

(CREDO and SPERA *rise also.*)

CREDO. All three of us will go!

SPERA (*Nestling close to* RACHEL *and speaking very tenderly*). All four of us will go!

RACHEL (*Kissing her*). Thank you!— All four of us!—And do you know what we'll do besides?

CREDO. No.

SPERA. What?

RACHEL. We'll ask him to see the workmen.

BOTH. Yes, yes!

RACHEL. For someone must begin to forgive.

BOTH (*Repeating in low tones*). Yes, someone must begin to forgive.

(*They go out together to the right.*
The music, which has been hovering about them all the time, follows them like a greeting out of the future.)

CURTAIN

THE LIFE AND WORKS OF BJÖRNSTJERNE BJÖRNSON

By ALFRED JOLIVET

The son of a Norwegian minister, Björnstjerne Björnson, born at Kvikne, Norway, in 1832, spent his childhood among Norway's peasantry, in the beautiful country at Naesset where he learned to farm the land and to love and know its people. When he was only eleven he was sent to school at Molde where he read Sturleson, the stories of Asbjörnson and those of Walter Scott. He went to Christiania (Oslo) to study in his seventeenth year and there began his career as a writer. While still a student, he became a literary critic for the newspaper *Morgenbladet* in 1854, and he contributed articles and criticism to other papers as well. In 1857 he wrote his first historical play, *Mellem slagene (Between the Battles)*. This was followed in rapid succession by several provincial tales, *Synnöre Solbakken (Sunny Hill, 1857), Arne (1858), and En glad gut (A Happy Boy, 1860).*

With *Sunny Hill*, a new type of prose made its appearance in Norway, one that shows the influence of the sagas, of the Norse tales that were being collected and published at the time, as well as the tales of Hans Christian Andersen. Björnson succeeded in mixing and combining these ingredients, becoming the creator of a truly Norwegian prose.

Arne is more complex, somewhat autobiographical, with a poet-hero who is keenly aware of the creative force within him. *A Happy Boy* is an even simpler tale, with the hero the son of a poor day laborer who finds his lowly station in life intolerable. Subsequently, he marries the granddaughter of a rich peasant, in spite of the grandfather's violent opposition. The Norwegian peasant's rise up the social ladder was one of Björnson's favorite subjects; though at the outset his hero is arrogant, even conceited and unreasonable in his reactions, he gradually overcomes his failings and deserves the happiness he finally achieves.

Björnson has been reproached with idealizing the peasants in his books—official reports of the day on conditions of health and morality in rural Norway are full of distressing facts, no trace of which is to be found in Björnson's idylls. But Björnson, as Norway's greatest lyric poet, told tales of country life that were suffused with lyricism and, at moments of deep emotion, his characters abandoned prose and their agitation found its natural expression in lyrical form. This in no way meant that he departed from the truth by idealizing Norwegian country life, for no one knew it better than he did; he transposed it without distorting it.

Björnson's historical dramas make up a series that runs parallel to his prose tales of country life. At an early age Björnson had become interested in the drama, and after the publication of *Between the Battles* in 1857 he was put in charge of the Norwegian theater established in Bergen by Ole Bull. During the next few years Björnson wrote several historical dramas and his development, in many ways, resembled that of Ibsen's, who had been his friend at school. During the late 1850s, both contributed to a revival of interest in the Middle Ages, taking the old sagas and stories and expanding and enlarging them. Björnson fought stubbornly and successfully for the Norwegian theater to rid itself of the last traces of Danish influence. In 1865 he was made director of the Christiania Theater, at a time when not only the plays performed but also their casts were Danish, and the public put up with it. Björnson reacted violently against this state of affairs and succeeded in having plays staged in a Norwegian theater performed in Norwegian.

Björnson peopled his stage with the heroes of Norway's glorious history in the Middle Ages. He wanted to restore its patent of nobility to the nation which had just regained its independence. In *Kong Sverre* (1861), he brought to life the great figure of King Snorre, who dared to defy the power of Rome. He wrote a play about King Sigurd Jorsalfar, *Sigurd Jorsalfar* (1872), who set out on a crusade and through whom the heroism of the Norwegian warriors became known as far away as Jerusalem.

But his most outstanding historical work is the trilogy dealing with *Sigurd Slembe* (Sigurd the Bad, 1862), the man born to be king but robbed of the throne by intrigue and usurpation—a man whose strength of character and will

power are epitomized in his consciousness of a mission to be carried out. However, as often happens in Björnson's works, Sigurd Slembe tries to realize his rightful ambition by wrongful means, by murder. And by this violation of moral law, he oversteps man's proper bounds and brings about his own destruction.

After this trilogy, Björnson wrote a play called *Maria Stuart i Shotland* (Mary Stuart of Scotland, 1864). Here Björnson wanted to bring to life again the spirit of the Renaissance and the setting in which it took place.

Björnson owed his fame as a writer to his lyrics and plays, but he never completely abandoned prose narrative. His tales of peasant life, written parallel with his dramas, have also remained famous. *Fiskerjenten* (*The Fisher Lass,* 1868) represents his transition from the short story to the novel; more specifically, it marked a change in Björnson's narrative style. Here the action proceeds at an extremely swift pace, with unexpected changes of mood, full of a swirl of incidents and a flood of emotions.

Just as the tales of country life are suffused with lyricism, so too the historical plays contain many lyrics, often of some length. This is the very core of Björnson's genius—the ability to produce an immediate impression which wells up spontaneously and in which the music of the words and the beautiful images express the various aspects of sensibility.

Contemporary events now began to affect Björnson painfully, and moved him to pour out his feelings in lyrical form. He was deeply shocked and distressed when Germany went to war with Denmark in 1864 and defeated her. He was bound to Denmark by ties of friendship and gratitude. In Copenhagen he had found richer, more advanced art forms than in Norway, as well as subtler, more cultured criticism and, in a short time, a more knowledgeable, more receptive audience for himself. In addition to these personal reasons, he believed in Scandinavian solidarity, envisioning a spiritual union of the three Northern countries to safeguard the independence and originality of each one of them. For him, this meant that in case of danger the three countries should make common cause.

Now the Danish frontier, the outpost of Scandinavianism, was in danger. As early as 1863, when Frederick VII died, Björnson made an appeal to Sweden; but neither Norway nor Sweden went to the aid of the Danes. The defeat moved Björnson to express his feelings in despairing poems. He wrote of the fall of Dybböl in these words: "White and red, such gay hues, are the colors of blood and death. The flag falls like a wounded seagull; the cross it bears is the cross of grief which its nation bears on its shoulders."

As we know, for Ibsen this tragedy meant the bankruptcy of an ideal, and caused him to despise his fellowmen and to engage in harsh self-scrutiny. Björnson was too much of an optimist to lose hope; by 1872 his attitude had changed and, in the course of a speech which he made in Copenhagen, he stated that the future of the northern countries lay, not with France or Russia, but with Germany and that the only means of recovering Schleswig was by conciliation and reconciliation. These words caused a great stir; Ibsen castigated them in a famous poem.

Björnson passionately followed the course of events. He was the outstanding example of a deeply committed poet and his whole life was a fight—a good fight. For the sake of Norway's dignity, he stood out against, not the mere influence of Denmark now, but Danish hegemony in the matter of the theater; for the complete independence of his country he fought several battles against Swedish claims. These activities required almost incessant work as a journalist and lecturer.

Meanwhile he was soon to fulfill his ambition of giving Norway dramatic literature that could stand comparison with the drama of the large nations. He had in mind, in particular, middle-class plays of the type that had been evolved in France. On several occasions he had written to friends that his historical plays were written only for practice, to prepare him for the work of which he dreamed. Earlier, it is true, he had written a play which dealt with a misunderstanding between husband and wife which finally has a happy ending. This charming play, which is reminiscent of Musset here and there, did not actually come to grips with contemporary reality, but only discussed some of its aspects.

In 1874 Björnson wrote and produced his first two great contemporary plays one after the other—*Redaktoren* (*The Editor*) and *En fallit* (*The Bankrupt*). There is genuine realism in these plays, and an accurate, subtle description of newspaper life (he took his opponent Friele, the editor of *Morgenbladet,* as his model for the editor) and of the business world. We also find in these plays the general concern of the day with the discussion of problems, but their leading idea is that sincerity is the sine qua non of a happy, useful life. *The Bankrupt,* which was a tremendous popular success, presents the conversion of a merchant who thinks he can escape disaster by a tissue of lies; the last act describes, perhaps too complacently and unctuously, the peace of mind with which the full confession of his errors is rewarded.

In 1875, Björnson bought a farm at Aulestad where he went to live a patriarchal life. But before long the fancied idyll brought him only irritation and spiritual poverty—irritation caused by provincial narrowmindedness and the void that lies beneath religious bigotry. Björnson was shocked by this, and to fill the vacuum left by his own departing faith, he immersed himself in books. He read a tremendous amount—critical works on the Bible, works on education by English philosophers, and others on evolution, which interested him even more. To his optimistic mind evolution was necessarily synonymous with progress. A new faith took the place of the old one as a result of a natural impulse of his mind and, above all, the enthusiasm which was part of his make-up.

Then in 1877, Björnson wrote another of his tales, "Magnhild," a short story about an orphan girl who learns of the hardships of peasant life. Also that same year, he produced a play called *Kongen* (*The King*), an attack on the existing political system which sets the king apart in unnatural, unhuman isolation. This, incidentally, is not one of his best plays.

Björnson left Norway in 1882 and spent five years abroad. During this time, in line with the moralizing purpose of *The Bankrupt* and *The King*, Björnson wrote *En hanske* (A Gauntlet, 1883) one of his most controversial plays. He maintained that a young man getting married can and should be required to have led as perfectly chaste a life as his bride. For this Björnson was attacked not only by authors like Brandes and Strindberg, but by the whole of the young Norwegian naturalist school. He stood his ground fearlessly and toured the Northern countries, delivering a lecture on "Monogamy and Polygamy" which became famous.

In that same year, 1883, his new religious ideas moved him to write a play which is perhaps the most poignant work in Norwegian literature, *Over oevne, annet stykke* (*Beyond Human Might*). This is a drama of religious ecstasy which transports us beyond the ordinary circumstances of life to the regions of the supernatural at the cost of extreme spiritual tension. Björnson very skillfully

chose as his setting a region of northern Norway where the natural features have a gigantic, supernatural quality. Björnson felt that in this setting he could present the phenomenon of miracles with some degree of verisimilitude. This is, in fact, the theme of the play. Pastor Sang, the hero, is fearless in the face of danger, his courage suffused with evangelical gentleness. He resolves to try to cure his wife, who has been paralyzed for years, by the power of his prayers alone. Cautious clergymen and the local people alike await divine intervention with absolute confidence. Their growing exaltation, as it were, reflects the prayers of Sang, alone in his church, face to face with his God. At last the sick woman stands up and takes a few steps toward her husband, but suddenly falls down dead. Sang collapses too, killed by his first doubt.

Björnson seemed to want to deny the possibility of miracles and perhaps, following from this, the actual soundness of Christian dogma. But as a matter of fact, the major interest of this play lies in the scenes describing mystical exaltation—hence a belief in miracles—which give it a quality that can only be called sublime.

During the following years, he wrote several novels. The first was *Det flager i byen og på havnen* (*The Heritage of the Kurts*, 1884). The action of this extensive novel takes place in and around a school for girls, and Björnson surpassed himself in his description of their artless, merry, lively, sometimes passionate natures. What should they be taught about life to protect and encourage them? What are the proper views on education and how should it be reformed? In spite of the misfortune that befalls one of the heroines, morality and good will triumph in the end.

In his next novel, *På Guds veie* (In God's Way), Björnson took up the problem of freedom of religious thought again. He contrasts healthy, natural morality (what we might call the optimistic principle of evolution) with the unhealthy, narrowmindedness of pietism, which ruins human values. The conclusion is that wherever good folk are busy at work, they are living in God's way.

Björnson continued to write for the theater, and in 1895 he wrote another play with the same title, *Over oevne, annet stykke* (Beyond Human Might). In this play Björnson gave prominent parts to Pastor Sang's children, Elias and Rachel, showing that Elias was possessed by the same driving force as his father, a force which now impels him to overstep human bounds. For the first time Björnson speaks of the fate of the workers and their relationship with their employers. With great forcefulness he describes the wretchedness and despair caused by a strike which was certainly justified. The employers appear very unattractive, with their leader declaring for ruthless resistance to his workers. Elias also goes beyond man's natural limits by responding to the employers' callousness with a desperate action. He dynamites the hall where they are holding a meeting and is blown up with them, having stayed there in disguise to give the signal to set off the explosive. In spite of some powerful scenes, this play is not comparable with the first one he wrote under the same title.

But in 1898 Björnson had a play performed which is certainly one of his most moving works, *Paul Lange og Tora Parsberg*. It is based on a real occurrence which had shocked and distressed him. Ole Richter, a fine politician and a friend of Björnson's, had been compromised because of the misuse of his powers as minister of state, unauthorized by the head of the Cabinet, in the matter of a joint Swedish and Norwegian foreign ministry. The accusation was untrue, as Richter wrote to Björnson under the seal of secrecy, and Björnson felt it was his duty as a friend to publicize the contents of this letter. Richter declared that Björnson had no valid reason for doing so. It was an impossible situation which caused a scandal. Richter committed suicide on June 15, 1888. He served as Björnson's model for Paul Lange, the principal character in the play. The scene in which he is confronted with his political enemies and exposed to their attacks is an extraordinarily powerful one. The play is, indeed, a moving tribute to the friend for whose death Björnson felt responsible. Some people blamed him for praising weakness in this play, but he replied that the men whose thoughts are intent on the future and who seek to mold it are highly strung and often impressionable and for this reason they are thought to be weak. But the greatest men are found among their ranks.

In 1902, Björnson celebrated his seventieth birthday. In the following year the Swedish Academy awarded him the Nobel Prize. He was given a tremendous reception in Stockholm and, in the course of the traditional banquet, he delivered a speech full of information about himself, his aims, and his examples. This was in 1903. The separation of Norway from the joint Swedish-Norwegian monarchy was to take place two years later and the situation was tense. There were those who did not fail to say that Björnson had sold himself to the Swedes in exchange for the Nobel Prize. In actual fact, Björnson never changed his views about relations between Norway and Sweden—he wanted them to be on an absolutely equal footing. If they were not, it would be better to dissolve the Union, but he hoped that this could come about by mutual agreement, without going to war, of course, and with no violence of any kind. Union with Sweden would have to be replaced by an alliance to which Denmark could become a party. "There is only one course to be adopted

—that of fairly and squarely giving us the status and rights of a sister nation. If the Swedish flag-wavers cannot bring themselves to do so, we shall separate from them, only to come together again in an alliance afterwards, of course."

In 1906, at the age of 74, he wrote his last novel, *Mary*. It is one of his best prose works, astonishing in its charm, the powerfulness of the scenes he depicts, and in its wealth of accurate psychological detail. It is the story of the childhood and adolescence of Mary, a member of a wealthy family, which is described in great detail up to the time when she meets two young men who want to marry her. She chooses the wrong one—but before the marriage has taken place, having given herself to him, she realizes that she has chosen a man who does not deserve her love, and is saved by the one she had rejected. As is often the case in Björnson's works, it is when the two sexes come face to face that his characters' true, innermost self is revealed and his heroines—this applied particularly to Mary—become fully self-aware at the same time as their fate is taking shape.

In his last play, *Nar den ny vin blom-strer* (*When the New Wine Blooms,* 1909), written a year before he died, Björnson is in an optimistically cheerful mood as he sounds the praises of love rekindled in an old man's heart by a young girl, resulting in a return to married life by an estranged couple.

Early in June, 1909, when Björnson was taking a cure at Larvik, he had a stroke which left him paralyzed in one arm. He could not be moved to Aulestad until August. After returning there he had a very serious relapse.

It was decided to take him to Paris for electrical treatment, but this did not improve his condition. For five and a half months he struggled with death, and on April 26, 1910, he died.

His coffin was taken by rail to Copenhagen, where a crowd in silent mourning escorted it to the harbor. Draped in the Norwegian flag, it was transferred to the battleship *Norge* while a Danish band played the Norwegian national anthem. On its arrival at Christiania, a sovereign's twenty-one gun salute was fired from Akershus fortress. And the imposing ceremonial of his funeral proceeded, with the participation of a whole nation united in sorrow.

Alfred Jolivet is honorary professor of Scandinavian languages and literature at the Sorbonne.

Translated by Annie Jackson.

THE 1903 PRIZE

By GUNNAR AHLSTRÖM

THE FIRST TWO Nobel Prizes, those of 1901 and 1902, were given to candidates with very substantial claims. Sully-Prudhomme (1901) had been proposed in a semi-official move by the Acadèmie Française, and a similar petition by the Prussian Academy of Science had nominated Theodor Mommsen the next year. Still, in 1903 the Swedish Academy remained a novice as a distributor of international honors, and it listened earnestly to the advice of the more venerable academies with long experience in these matters. But the Nobel Prize was becoming accepted. In the press outside Sweden, expressions of approval and esteem became more and more numerous. It was in this atmosphere of growing goodwill that the candidates for the 1903 Prize were welcomed. Certain candidates reappeared, new names were launched, and international institutions drew up lists. Carducci's name was discussed, Gaston Paris was put forward, and Frédéric Mistral was mentioned repeatedly. Fourteen members of the Madrid Academy reached an agreement to propose José Echegaray, and Sully-Prudhomme devoted a few flattering sentences to François Coppée, sending along a list of his eighty published volumes with the recommendation. The Anglo-Saxon contribution appeared less massive, and took the shape of a poetic work of Tennyson's time bearing the alluring and lugubrious title *The Epic of Hades*. The author, Algernon Charles Swinburne, was Oxford's choice, proposed by his admirers and friends at Corpus Christi and Jesus colleges.

Tolstoy's prophetic features continued to loom on the academic horizon like a reproach. "This year I shall write down the name which I wrote last year," said Ludovic Halévy in the autumn of 1902. The great Berthelot, withdrawing his vote from Zola, now proposed the same candidate because "His humanitarian works are known throughout the world." A letter from a new correspondent, who was later to become a Prizewinner, arrived with a similar message. It read as follows:

> Sirs,
>
> I have the honor to propose as a selection for the 1903 Nobel Prize:
>
> first, Leo Tolstoy;
> second, Georg Brandes;
> third, Maurice Maeterlinck.
>
> I beg to remain, yours etc.,
>
> Anatole France.

European public opinion has gradually forgotten Georg Brandes but in Scandinavian literature he remains one of the towering figures of the beginning of our era. In his great work, *The Main Trends of Nineteenth-Century Literature,* he had put forward a view of literature which was colored by Positivism, was anti-theological and politically disruptive. By forming an alliance between the teachings of Hippolyte Taine (whose friend and disciple he was), Ernest Renan and John Stuart Mill and the views of Heinrich Heine and German liberalism, he ignited an incendiary flame. An idealist of this stamp could hardly arouse the sympathies of the conservative Swedish Academy. But his candidacy recalled the fact that the Scandinavian countries could avail themselves of distinguished achievements which deserved recognition now that France and Germany had, quite rightly, received their tribute. This being the case, in the domain of world literature it was Norway who took first place. And indeed the final choice was between Ibsen and Björnstjerne Björnson, with a preference for the latter. Rumors from Christiania said that Ibsen was showing alarming signs of old age. Björnson inspired more confidence and his vitality seemed inexhaustible. But there were difficulties in his case, of another kind.

Norway had been united with Sweden as a result of the tumult following the Napoleonic wars. Bernadotte, that son of the Revolution, had let himself be influenced by the fallacious theory of "natural frontiers." That Scandinavian peninsula which formed but one unit on the map ought also quite naturally to form one political unit, owing allegiance to a single sovereignty—namely, his own. This geographical realism came to be proved false by the events of the following century. The Norwegians' own feelings of independence developed with the same rhythm as the general nationalist aspirations of the period, and Björnson was their literary champion. He had composed the moving national anthem and expressed the popular wish to be dissoci-

ated from the Union: "This pact, with its suffocating miasmas—we hate it, we curse it." The Swedes and their King were severely criticized and any form of cooperation was resented as a humiliation. It was not far from 1905, the year in which the Union was to be abolished in a spirit of peaceful generosity to which Sweden greatly contributed.

The world of today, which has survived blows of a very different kind of violence, will perhaps smile at the spectacle of these minuscule antagonisms. A lyrical Garibaldi rises up in the midst of this parody of tumult, leading an army of beautiful poems into battle from out of the depths of the Norwegian valleys, like a rustic Gambetta steeped in high principles. It was Björnstjerne Björnson himself in person, and his wife Caroline, the majestic "we," who actually took part in international controversies; a corpulent, square-shouldered Viking with a passionate generous heart who, with his spectacles on his forehead, and a manuscript in his pocket, was always ready to mount the barricades of eloquence. From there he would send forth his lightning, whether it was a question of internationalism or Germanism, of republic or monarchy, of the theologians' doctrine of Hell or of the Church's belief in miracles, of feminism or socialism, of sexual morality or of polygamy, of oppressed Armenians or of haughty Czars.

Wherever Björnson was to be found, there the storm raged. His latest skirmish had taken place in Paris, where he had gone to attend the performance of a play of his in 1901. The play had not been received as he had hoped, and in an interview he had indignantly described the French as "the Chinese of Europe," with minds closed to all international trends.

Conservative, conventional Sweden looked on Björnson as a swashbuckler and a chauvinistic braggart who "gobbled up Swedes" at every meal. But the reading public admired him, considering him a great poet, and a novelist and dramatist who knew how to demolish the barriers standing between ancient and modern literature. To political liberals he appeared to be a good democrat and a valuable support to those whose aim was, through joint effort, to settle the Swedish-Norwegian dispute and put the matter onto a sound basis. The initiates also knew that his feelings toward Sweden were more complicated than his battle cries led one to believe and that in reality he loved and respected the country, to which he owed enrichening impressions and great friendships ever since the days of his youth. But people judged by appearances, and the situation was delicate.

"It is not without hesitation that I utter the name of Björnson," declared the Swedish university professor who was the first to propose him as a candidate in 1901. "Without any doubt one must know how to overcome one's personal feelings and pay homage to him, particularly when this homage comes from official Sweden."

But the situation had improved since then. Björnson's seventieth birthday was celebrated on December 8, 1902, and he spoke to representatives of the Swedish press of the friendship which should reign between sister nations. Everything tended to convince the Swedish Academy that the attention of the world of literature was concentrated on Björnson. Having been convinced, it took action, and unanimously announced its decision, which was at once communicated to the illustrious laureate.

"It is with deep emotion that this evening we read your letter, which brings us this great unexpected message," Björnson wrote to the Permanent Secretary, Dr. af Wirsén. "I take this opportunity to thank you for the kind words you have chosen with which to inform me of the news which is so welcome to us. I shall be honored to attend in Stockholm on the 10th of December."

This last point was important. The two preceding Nobel celebrations had had to take place without the laureates in literature. Björnson was going to be the first. He immediately started to prepare his speech.

At last the glorious day came, and with it that perilous moment when the rabid republican was to bow to the old sovereign, Oscar II, King of Sweden and Norway. A newspaper described the atmosphere: "With one movement the whole assembly rose amid thunderous applause, in which the royal family joined. Pale with emotion, the poet stood still, but Dr. af Wirsén took him by the hand and walked toward the King. Many eyes filled with tears at this moment. The King moved forward to meet him cordially, and shook his hand at great length while leaning toward him to speak a few words. Then the royal hands gave the signal for applause and the thunder broke out louder than ever."

Translated by Camilla Sykes.

Pearl S. Buck

1938

"For her rich and truly epic description

of peasant life in China and for her

biographical masterpieces"

Illustrated by FRANÇOISE ADNET

PRESENTATION ADDRESS

By PER HALLSTRÖM

PERMANENT SECRETARY
OF THE SWEDISH ACADEMY

PEARL BUCK once told how she had found her mission as interpreter to the West of the nature and being of China. She did not turn to it as a literary specialty at all; it came to her naturally.

"It is people that have always afforded me my greatest pleasure and interest," she said, "and as I live among Chinese, it has been the Chinese people. When I am asked what sort of people they are, I cannot answer. They are not this or that, they are just people. I can no more define them than I can define my own relatives and kinsmen. I am too near to them and I have lived too intimately with them for that."

She has been among the people of China in all their vicissitudes, in good years and in famine years, in the bloody tumults of revolutions and in the delirium of utopias. She has associated with the educated classes and with primordially primitive peasants, who had hardly seen a Western face before they saw hers. Often she has been in deadly peril, a stranger who never thought of herself as a stranger; on the whole, her outlook retained its profound and warm humanity. With pure objectivity she has breathed life into her knowledge and given us the peasant epic which has made her world-famous, *The Good Earth* (1931).

As her hero she took a man who led the same existence as his forefathers had during countless centuries, and who possessed the same primitive soul. His virtues spring from one single root: affinity with the earth, which yields its crops in return for a man's labors.

Wang Lung is created from the same stuff as the yellow-brown earth in the fields, and with a kind of pious joy he bestows upon it every ounce of his energy. The two belong to each other in origin, and they will become one again with the death he will meet with tranquility. His work is also a duty done, and thus his conscience is at rest. Since dishonesty avails nothing in his pursuits, he has become honest. This is the sum total of his moral conceptions, and equally few are his religious ones, which are almost entirely comprehended in the cult of ancestor-worship.

He knows that man's life is a gleam of light between two darknesses; from the one behind him runs the chain of forefathers from father to son, and the chain must not be broken by him, if he is not to lose his dim hope of survival in a surmised, unknown region. For then would expire a spark of the life-fire of the race, which each individual man has to care for.

And thus the story begins with Wang Lung's marriage and his dreams of sons in the house. Of his wife, O'Lan, he does not dream, for—as is proper and fitting—he has never seen her. She is a slave at the great house in the neighboring town and cheap to buy, since she is said to be ugly. For that reason she has probably been left alone by the young sons of the house, and to this the bridegroom attaches great value.

Their life together is happy, for the wife proves to be an excellent helpmate, and the children soon make their appearance. She satisfies all the demands laid upon her, and she has no claims of her own. Behind her mute eyes is hidden a mute soul. She is all submission, but wise and prompt in action; a wife also in her paucity of words, springing from a philosophy of life learned in a hard school.

Success attends the two. They are able to set aside a little money, and Wang Lung's great passion, next to parenthood, his longing for more ground to cultivate, may now venture forth from subconsciousness. He is able to buy more fields, and everything promises happiness and increase.

Then comes a blow from the hand of fate; a drought descends upon the district. The good earth is changed into yellow, whirling dust. By selling land they could avert starvation, but that would be to bolt and lock the door to the future. Neither of them wishes to do that, so they set forth in company with the growing army of beggars to a city in the south, to live on the crumbs from the rich man's table.

O'Lan had made the journey once before in her childhood, when the end of it was that she was sold to save her parents and brothers.

Thanks to her experience, they accommodate themselves to the new life. Wang Lung toils as a beast of burden and the others beg with an acquired aptitude. Autumn and winter pass. With the spring, their yearning for their own land and its tilling becomes unendurable, but they have no money for the journey.

Then again fate intervenes—as natural a fate in China as drought and plague and flood. War, which is ever present somewhere in that great country, and the ways of which are as inscrutable as those of the powers of the air, stalks across the city and makes chaos of law and order. The poor plunder the homes of the rich.

Wang Lung goes with the mob without any definite motives, for his peasant soul revolts at deeds of violence, but by pure chance a handful of gold coins is almost forced into his hand. Now he can go home and begin the spring work on his rain-soaked soil. More than that, he can buy new fields; he is rich and happy.

He becomes still richer, though ultimately not happier, through the plunder acquired by O'Lan. From her days of slavery she knows something about hiding places in palaces, and she discovers a handful of precious stones. She takes them nearly as unpremeditatedly as a magpie steals glittering things, and hides them as instinctively. When her husband discovers them in her bosom, his whole world is transformed. He buys farm after farm. He becomes the leading man in the district, no longer peasant but lord, and his character changes color. Simplicity and harmony with the earth vanish. In their place comes, slowly but surely, a curse for the desertion.

Wang Lung no longer has any real peace in his lordly leisure, with a young concubine in the house and O'Lan pushed into a dark corner, to die there when she has worn herself out.

The sons are not attractive figures. The eldest devotes himself to an empty life of indulgence, the second is swallowed up by greed for gold as a merchant and usurer. The youngest becomes one of the war lords who drain the unhappy country. Around them the Middle Empire is torn asunder in the tumult of new creation, which has become so agonizing in our days.

The trilogy does not carry us so far, however; it concludes with a sort of reconciliation between the third generation and the good earth. One of Wang Lung's grandsons, a man educated in the West, returns to the family estate and applies the knowledge he has acquired to the improvement of the conditions of work and life among the peasants.

The rest of the family live without roots in that conflict between old and new which Pearl Buck has described in other works—mostly in the tone of tragedy.

Of the many problems in this novel, the most serious and somber one is the position of the Chinese woman. From the very beginning it is on this point that the writer's sympathy emerges most strongly, and amid the calm of the epic work it constantly makes itself felt. An early episode in the work gives the most poignant expression of what a Chinese woman has been worth since time immemorial. It is given with impressive emphasis, and also with a touch of humor which is naturally rare in this book. In a moment of happiness, with his little first-born son dressed in fine clothes on his arm, and seeing the future bright before him, Wang Lung is on the point of breaking into boastful words but restrains himself in sudden terror. There, under the open sky, he had almost challenged the invisible spirits and drawn their evil glances upon himself. He tries to avert the menace by hiding his son under his coat and saying in a loud voice, "What a pity that our child is a girl, which no one wants, and is pitted with smallpox into the bargin! Let us pray that it may die!" And O'Lan joins in the comedy and acquiesces—probably without thinking at all.

In reality the spirits need not waste their glances on a girl child. Its lot is hard enough in any case. It is Pearl Buck's female characters which make the strongest impression. There is O'Lan with her few words, which carry all the more weight. Her whole life is portrayed in equally scant but telling lines.

Quite a different figure is the chief character in the novel *The Mother* (1934). She is not referred to by any other designation, as if to indicate that her whole destiny is expressed in that word. She is, however, vividly individualized, a brave, energetic, strong character, of a more modern type than O'Lan's, perhaps, and without her slave temperament. The husband soon deserts his home, but she keeps it together for her children. The whole story ends in sorrow, but not in defeat. The mother cannot be crushed, not even when her younger son is beheaded as a revolutionary, and she has to seek a stranger's grave to weep at, for he has none. Just then a grandson is born, and she again has someone to love and sacrifice herself for.

The mother is the most finished of Pearl Buck's Chinese female figures, and the book is one of her best. But in character descriptions and the storyteller's art she is at her best in the two biographies of her parents, *The Exile* (1936) and *Fighting Angel* (1936). These should be called classics in the fullest sense of the word; they will endure, for they are full of life. In this respect the models from which the portraits are drawn are of great significance.

One seldom feels any great sense of gratitude for the company proffered in contemporary novels, and it is gladly forgotten. The characters have no great wealth of qualities, and the writer puts forth all his powers to lessen them, often by a persistent analysis with foregone results.

Here, however, one encounters two consummate characters, living unselfish lives of action, free from brooding and vacillation. They are profoundly unlike each other, and the fact that they are thrown together in a common struggle in a hard and strange world often leads to great tragedy—but not to defeat: they stand erect even to the very last. There is a spirit of heroism in both stories.

The mother, Carie, is richly gifted, brave and warm, of a solid nature, harmonious amid ever-straining forces. She is tested to the utmost in sorrows and dangers; she loses many children because of the harshness of the conditions of life, and at times a terrible death threatens her in those troubled times. It is almost as hard for her to witness the never-ending suffering around her. She does what she can to mitigate it, and that is not a little, but no power is sufficient for such a task.

Even inwardly she passes through a hard and unceasing struggle. In her calling, and with her nature, she needs more than the conviction of faith. It is not enough for her that she has dedicated herself to God; she must also feel that the sacrifice has been accepted. But the sign of this, for which she begs and prays, never comes. She is compelled to persist in an untiring endeavor to find God and to content herself with trying to be good without divine help.

However, she preserves her spiritual health, her love for the life which has shown her so much that is terrible, and her eye for the beauty the world has to offer; she even retains her happiness and her humor. She resembles a fresh fountain springing from the heart of life.

The daughter tells her story with rare and lively perspicuity. The biography is precise in regard to the course of events, but creative imagination plays its part in the various episodes and in the description of the inner life of the character. Nothing is falsified, for this imagination is intuitive and true.

The language has vivid spontaneity; it is clear and suffused with a tender and soulful humor. There is, however, a flaw in the story. The daughter's devotion to her mother makes it impossible for her to do justice to her father. In his family life his limitations were obvious, limitations sharp and at times painful. As a preacher and soldier of Christ he was without blemish, in many respects even a great character; but he ought to have lived his life alone, free of the familial duties he hardly found time to notice, duties which in any case weighed lightly with him against his all-absorbing calling. Thus he was of little help to his wife, and in her biography he could not be fully understood.

This was accomplished, however, in another book, whose title is the key to his life and being: *Fighting Angel*. Andrew did not possess his wife's richly composite nature; his was narrow but deep, and as bright as a gleaming sword. He devoted every thought to his goal of opening the way to salvation for the heathens. Everything was insignificant compared to that. What Carie prayed for in vain, communion with God, he possessed wholly and unshakably in the firm conceptions of his Biblical faith. With this faith he walked like a conqueror, further than any other in the immense heathen country; he endured all hardships without noticing them; and he encountered threats and dangers in the same manner. For the poor, blind, strange brown people he felt tenderness and love. Among them his stern nature broke into blossom. When he had won their souls to a confession of faith, he did not doubt the genuineness of the confession; with the naiveté of a child, he accepted it as good. The door to God, always denied them before, had been opened to them, and to weigh them and judge them was now in the hands of Him who knows best. They had been given their possibility of salvation, and for Andrew it was urgent to give this possiblity to all he could reach in that immense country, where thousands were dying every hour. His enthusiasm burned, and his work had something of genius in its magnitude and depth.

He strained his forces to the utmost in never-ending action, and the repose he allowed himself was the mystic's abandonment to the infinite amid ardent prayers. The whole of his life was a flame which rose straight and high, in spite of all storms; it could not be judged by ordinary conceptions. The daughter, whose portrait conceals none of his repellent features, maintained pure reverence before the nobility of the whole. One is profoundly thankful for both these perfectly executed pictures— each in its way so rare.

By awarding this year's Prize to Pearl Buck for the notable works which pave the way to a human sympathy passing over widely separated racial boundaries and for the studies of human ideals which are a great and living art of portraiture, the Swedish Academy feels that it acts in harmony and accord with the aim of Alfred Nobel's dreams for the future.

Mrs. Walsh, I have attempted a short survey of your work, indeed hardly necessary here, where the audience is so well acquainted with your remarkable books.

I hope, though, that I have been able to give some idea of their trend, toward opening a faraway and foreign world to deeper human insight and sympathy within our Western sphere—a grand and difficult task, requiring all your idealism and greatheartedness to fulfill as you have done.

May I now ask you to receive from the hands of His Majesty the King the Nobel Prize for Literature, conferred upon you by the Swedish Academy.

ACCEPTANCE SPEECH

By PEARL S. BUCK

IT IS NOT POSSIBLE for me to express all that I feel of appreciation for what has been said and given to me. I accept, for myself, with the conviction of having received far beyond what I have been able to give in my books. I can only hope that the many books which I have yet to write will be in some measure a worthier acknowledgment than I can make tonight. And, indeed, I can accept only in the same spirit in which I think this gift was originally given—that it is a prize not so much for what has been done, as for the future. Whatever I write in the future must, I think, be always benefited and strengthened when I remember this day.

I accept, too, for my country, the United States of America. We are a people still young and we know that we have not yet come to the fullest of our powers. This award, given to an American, strengthens not only one, but the whole body of American writers, who are encouraged and heartened by such generous recognition. And I should like to say, too, that in my country it is important that this award has been given to a woman. You who have already so recognized your own Selma Lagerlöf, and have long recognized women in other fields, cannot perhaps wholly understand what it means in many countries that it is a woman who stands here at this moment. But I speak not only for writers and for women, but for all Americans, for we all share in this.

I should not be truly myself if I did not, in my own wholly unofficial way, speak also of the people of China, whose life has for so many years been my life also, whose life, indeed, must always be a part of my life. The minds of my own country and of China, my foster country, are alike in many ways, but above all, alike in our common love of freedom. And today more than ever, this is true, now when China's whole being is engaged in the greatest of all struggles, the struggle for freedom. I have never admired China more than I do now, when I see her uniting as she has never before, against the enemy who threatens her freedom. With this determination for freedom, which is in so profound a sense the essential quality in her nature, I know that she is *unconquerable*. Freedom—it is today more than ever the most precious human possession. We—Sweden and the United States—we have it still. My country is young—but it greets you with a peculiar fellowship, you whose earth is ancient and free.

FIGHTING ANGEL

By PEARL S. BUCK

ANGEL—one of an order of spiritual beings, attendants and messengers
of God, usually spoken of as employed by him in ordering the affairs
of the universe, and particularly of mankind. They are commonly
regarded as bodiless intelligences.

—Century Dictionary.

"Who maketh his angels spirits
And his ministers a flame of fire."
—The Epistle to the Hebrews.

1

You might have seen him walking along
the street of any little Chinese village or
market town, a tall, slender, slightly
stooping American. At one time in his
life he wore Chinese clothes. I have a
picture of him thus, seated upon a stiff
carved Chinese chair, his large American
feet planted before him in huge Chinese
shoes, those shoes which made the Chinese women laugh behind their hands
when they cut the soles, and which made
many a passerby stop and stare as he
strode by in dust or upon cobblestones.
He even smiled himself, a little painfully,
when open jokes were shouted as he
passed. But the Chinese shoes, the long
Chinese robe, the little round black Chinese hat with its red button—none of
these made him in the least Chinese. No
one could possibly mistake him. The
spare, big-boned frame, the big, thin del-

icate hands, the nobly shaped head with
its large features, the big nose, the jutting
lower jaw, the extraordinary, pellucid,
child-blue eyes, the reddish fair skin and
slightly curly dark hair—these were
purely and simply American.

But he wandered about China for
more than half a century. He went there
young, and there he died, an old man, his
hair snow white, but his eyes still child-
blue. In those days of his old age I said
to him, "I wish you would write down
what your life has been for us to read."
For he had traveled the country north
and south, east and west, in city and
country. He had had adventures enough
to fill books and had been in danger of
his life again and again. He had seen the
Chinese people as few white men ever
have—in the most intimate moments of
their own lives, in their homes, at marriage feasts, in sickness and in death. He
had seen them as a nation in the cycle of

their times—he had seen the reign of emperors and the fall of empire, revolution and the rise of a republic and revolution again.

So he wrote down the story of his life as it seemed to him when he was seventy years old. He spent his spare time throughout a whole summer writing it. I used to hear his old typewriter tapping uncertainly during hot afternoon hours when everybody else was sleeping, or in the early dawn, because, having had as a boy to rise early on a farm in West Virginia, he could never sleep late. It was more than a physical inability—it was spiritual. "Arise, my soul, for it is day! The night cometh when no man can work." The night—the night! He remembered always the shortness of life. "As for man, his days are as grass: as a flower of the field, so he flourisheth. For the wind passeth over it, and it is gone; and the place thereof shall know it no more."

But when it was finished the story of all his years made only twenty-five pages. Into twenty-five pages he had put all that seemed important to him of his life. I read it through in an hour. It was the story of his soul, his unchanging soul. Once he mentioned the fact of his marriage to Carie, his wife. Once he listed the children he had had with her, but in the listing he forgot entirely a little son who lived to be five years old and who was Carie's favorite child, and he made no comment on any of them.

But the omission told as much as anything. For indeed the story was the story not of man or woman or child but of one soul and its march through time to its appointed end. For this soul there was birth, predestined, a duty to be done and it was done, and there was heaven at the end—that was the whole story. There was nothing of the lives of people in it, no merriment of feasts, no joy of love, no tales of death. There was not one

word of any of the incredible dangers through which he had often passed. There was nothing in it of empire or emperors or revolutions or of all the stir of changing human times. There was no reflection upon the minds and manners of men or any subtlety of philosophies. The tale was told as simply as the sun rises out of dawn, marches swiftly across the firmament, to set in its own glory.

So others told me his story—his brothers and sisters, Carie, and his son. I heard the talk of people among whom he lived and worked. Most of all, I knew him myself as one among my earliest memories, as one in whose house I spent my childhood, as one who in the last ten years of his life came and lived with me under my roof, and looked to me for care and comfort in his age. In spite of this, for years after he died I could not see what he was. His outlines remained ghostly to me, even when he ate at my table, most of all when he was ill and I tended him. It was only when I came back to the country that had made him and sent him forth that I saw him clear at last. For he was born in America, and he was the child of generations of Americans. No country except America could have produced him exactly as he was.

I do not know the old and precise history of his family and I have not asked because it does not matter. Some time before the American Revolution they came from somewhere in Germany, for the sake of religious freedom. I do not know just when except that I know it was in time for one of his ancestors to be a courier to George Washington, and for two others to fight loyally under Washington's command. I say it does not matter because it is not as an individual that he is significant. If his life has any meaning for others than himself it is as a manifestation of a certain spirit in his country and his time. For he was a spirit, and a spirit made by that blind certainty,

that pure intolerance, that zeal for mission, that contempt of man and earth, that high confidence in heaven, which our forefathers bequeathed to us.

The first words which he remembered spoken were words which he never forgot as long as he lived. They remained not so much words as wounds, unhealed. He could not have been more than seven years old. It was a summer's day, in June, a beautiful day, and the afternoon was clear and warm. He was sitting on the steps of the porch of the big farmhouse that was his home. He had been in the orchard looking for a sweet June apple, when he heard the sound of wheels, and looking through the trees he saw a stout, kind neighbor woman coming to visit his mother.

He had always liked Mrs. Pettibrew. He liked her easy cheerful flow of talk, larded with stories, and her rich sudden gusts of laughter, although he was desperately shy, and never answered her questions with more than a smile, strained from him against his will. But he wanted to be near her because she liked everybody and was always jolly. So he had waited until she was seated on the porch and his mother had brought the baby out in her arms and settled herself in the rocking chair to nurse him. Then he sidled around the house and sat very quietly, listening to them, munching his apple. He would not appear interested in them, for after all they were women.

"Howdy, Andy!" Mrs. Pettibrew shouted.

"Howdy," he whispered, his eyes downcast.

"Speak out, Andrew!" his mother ordered him.

They both looked at him. He felt hot all over. He knew, because his older brothers and sisters often told him, that his face easily went as red as cockscomb. He could not have spoken if he would—

his mouth was so dry. The apple he had bitten was like dust upon his tongue. He scuffed his bony big toe in the grass miserably. The two women stared at him.

His mother said, worrying, "I declare, I don't know what makes the boy so scary."

"He don't hardly seem like yours, Deborah," Mrs. Pettibrew said solemnly. "He don't even look like yours. I don't know where he gets those light eyes and that red hair. Hiram especially is as handsome a boy as ever I saw—but all your nine children are big and handsome and a sight for sore eyes, except Andy. But then—most families have a runt in 'em."

And this was kind Mrs. Pettibrew! His heart began swelling in him like a balloon. It would burst and he would begin to cry. He wanted to run away and he could not. He sat, his mouth full of dry apple, scuffing his toe back and forth in the grass, caught in agony. His mother released him. She said, kindly enough, "Well, he isn't so handsome, maybe, but he's awfully good, Andy is. None of the others is as good as he is. I always say likely he'll be a preacher, too, like Dave is and like Isaac talks to be—and if he is, he'll be the best of them."

"Well, of course it's better to be good than pretty," Mrs. Pettibrew said heartily. "Say, Deborah, before I forget—I heard a new recipe for quince preserves. . . ."

They forgot him. He could get up now and walk away. The tightness about his heart loosened a little and he could breathe again. He could walk away pretending he had not heard. They went on talking about the quinces, not knowing any more than he did what they had done. They had, that June day, in a farmhouse in the West Virginia hills, set his feet on the path that was to lead him across plains and seas to a foreign country, to spend his years there, to lie at last

in a distant grave, his body dust in foreign earth, because his face was not
beautiful. All his life he was good. It was
better to be good than pretty. "For what
is a man profited, if he shall gain the
whole world, and lose his own soul?"
Goodness was best. On that day he made
up his mind he would always be good.

But then there was a tradition of goodness in his family. He could remember
his grandmother, sitting beside the fire.
The family in her youth had come from
Pennsylvania to Virginia. They were all
Presbyterians, but not she. She had been
born and reared a Mennonite, and to the
end of her life she wore her little, dark,
close-fitting Mennonite bonnet and held
to her rigorous Mennonite faith. She had
never been to what she called "a pleasur-
ing." Church on the Sabbath, twice,
prayer-meeting on Wednesday until she
was old, prayers twice every day—this
was the routine of the house which she
helped to maintain. She sat in the chim-
ney-place, disallowing all other life.

She had, besides religion, a great belief
in ghosts. I used to wonder at a strange
timidity in Andrew, and even sometimes
in my childhood to be a little ashamed of
it. It was not that he was in the least a
coward when any necessity was concerned. That is, for the sake of his duty
he could and did act in complete disregard of his life. No, it was a childlike
timidity, a dislike, for instance, of going
upstairs alone in the dark, a reluctance to
get up in the night to investigate a noise.
I have seen him return half a dozen times
to see if a door were locked. "I got to
thinking about it until I couldn't be
sure," he would confess, smiling half
shamefaced.

One day, when he was an old man, he
dropped the secret unconsciously, for he
never consciously revealed himself to
anyone. Someone began, half playfully,
one evening about the fire, to tell a ghost
story. He could not bear it. He got up
and went away. Afterwards he told me
alone, always with that half-shamed smile,
"The old folks used to tell ghost stories
at home until I didn't dare to go to bed.
But of course I had to. They weren't just
stories, either—they said they were true."

The old grandmother believed them.
Sitting in her corner, very old, it was impossible for her to discern the cleaving
line between flesh and ghost. So many
who had been with her in the flesh were
changed to eternal spirits. Soon she, too,
would be changed. It was nature to believe that spirits came back to places they
had known and loved . . . she, too,
would come back. The small boy, sitting
unobtrusively among his heartier brothers and sisters, listened and never forgot.

But that house was full of belief in
spirits. God was a spirit and God was
forever in that house. And the Devil was
a spirit, and where God was the Devil
was also. They were inseparable—enemies, but inseparable. He grew up familiar with them both. Morning and
night he sat and heard his father reading
from the Bible the story of the war between these two. Year after year his
father plodded straight through that
story, for it was his boast to read the
Bible through every year. Religion—the
house was full of it, too. There were
seven sons and six of them were ministers. Religion was their meat and their
excitement, their mental food and their
emotional pleasure. They quarreled over
it as men quarrel over politics. Within its
confines they made their personal quarrels.

For it was a quarrelsome family, this
family. Father and mother were quarrelsome together. The man was a big, domineering, square-jawed landowner. He
had a passion for land. He kept them all
poor buying more and more land, and he
implanted in every son he had such a
hatred for the land that not one of them

was willing to farm it after him. I remember that Andrew would not even take the slightest interest in any of Carie's gardens. She felt it a hurt, but I knew he could not help it. I saw him an overworked boy, starving for books, hungry for school, loathing the land and tied to it until he was twenty-one. Only at twenty-one was he free, and then he rode away on the horse his father gave to each of his sons when they came to their majority. He rode away to belated college, to retrieve the years which seemed to him wasted. He never took up spade or hoe again, not for flower or vegetable, not even for Carie's garden.

But until they were all twenty-one they had to work under the man on the land, and his wife and his two daughters had to work in the dairies and the kitchen. The father owned a few Negroes, but he disliked owning them. Besides, he had his sons and his daughters. He drove them all, a big, domineering, thundering fellow, reading the Bible aloud to them night and morning, commanding them. "Honor thy father and thy mother"—although it did not matter so much about the mother. He domineered over them all cheerfully enough, for he had a shrewd sense of humor. He domineered over the whole community. He was head of the school board and he chose the teachers for the one-room school, and when they came, he sheltered them in his big unpainted rambling house, where half a dozen extra people could be fed without noticing it. It was at his house the preachers lodged when they came circuit-riding to the little Presbyterian church, for he domineered over the church, too. Sometimes a preacher made him angry with his preaching and twice, at least, he turned Methodist for short periods purely as a matter of discipline to a refractory preacher. Later he was to suffer for introducing this method of revolt. For Deborah, his wife, after one of their

violent quarrels, joined the Methodist church and stayed in it. He never forgave her, not only for the revolt but because it deprived him of a tool against the Presbyterians when he needed it. And of his seven Presbyterian sons, one, Christopher, in the madness of his rebellious youth, joined the Methodist church and remained in it, stubborn, obdurate, as all this family were stubborn and obdurate —"the preachingest family in Greenbrier County," a local newspaper reporter called them when he was writing of them half a century later, "with dissenting blood as strong as lye."

When I was sent home to America to college, I made my first acquaintance with them all. They were, most of them, white-haired by that time, an amazing array of tall, passionate, angry men, not one of them under six feet, every one of them with the same shining bright blue eyes and dry humor and intolerant mind. The quarrel between them was as hot as ever, so hot indeed, that it had become a byword in the county, a cause for shame and laughter, and it had all been argued even in the newspapers. The five Presbyterian preachers quarreled among themselves on many matters, for there was endless material for quarreling—over the period of creation in Genesis and the interpretation of the minor prophets and Song of Solomon, and predestination and the second coming of Christ; and failing these, there then could always be quarreling over the division of the land, the sale of the old farmhouse and its ancient handmade furniture, and whether or not Becky's husband was treating her properly. But they always banded together against the Methodist—although Andrew by then had long been waging his own missionary wars. "Poor Chris," they called the Methodist, striving furiously to pity him for his misguidance.

But when I saw "poor Chris" it was

hard to pity him. He was a presiding elder in his chosen church, as rabid and intolerant as any of them, and as bitterly sure of his own theology as the sole road to salvation. It added difficulty that he was very successful and that he had no notion of his pitiable condition, and that he was big and confident and completely arrogant. To hear him roar out the Beatitudes on a Sunday morning, hurling them like cannon balls at his congregation, to see his brows beetle over his bright blue eyes as he shouted, "Blessed are the meek . . ." to hear him insist, "Blessed are the poor in spirit . . ." was a thing to hear and see.

Yes, Andrew grew up in an embattled atmosphere, the atmosphere of a militant religion. But he never quite equaled his brothers in looks or assurance. He was tall, but he stooped a little. He had not the others' full prideful gaze. Girls never looked at him as they did at black-haired Hiram, who strummed a guitar and never quite paid back the money he borrowed to go to college, or as they did at cautious John who prudently married early a rich oldish widow and withdrew from the family religious war and went to the state legislature instead, or as they did, for that matter, at any of the others. Girls did not, indeed, look at Andrew at all because he never forgot what Mrs. Pettibrew had said. Those unforgotten words kept him secretly shy all his life. He withdrew further and further into passionate personal religion. But under his shy, remote exterior all the stubborn fire burned. He was no whit behind any of them there. Indeed, he was the hotter in his goodness, because there was no worldliness in him to ease it.

It was not from Andrew that I heard the story of that terrific family. Indeed, I remember only one tale he ever told me of them. Once when I was a very small girl I pressed him for a story, not really hoping for much. Carie was my great

source, but she was busy at that moment with a new baby. Andrew had come in from an evangelistic trip, and in a moment of unwonted ease, he took me on his knee before the fire. It was a knee, I remember, a little bony beneath my short skirts, for he was always spare, having great scorn for anyone who was fat. If a fellow missionary developed a paunch Andrew was at once indignant and suspicious of him—"He's eating too much," he would exclaim, "he's getting lazy." It was the great indictment, next to an unsound theology. On this occasion, perched upon his ridgy knee, I inquired, "Do you know just one story?" I stared into his very clear, not unkindly eyes. "Not one out of the Bible," I amended hastily. "I know all those." He was taken aback—clearly he had been raking over the Old Testament in his mind. "Let me see," he said ruminating. "Maybe when you were a little boy?" I suggested, to be helpful. I waited for what seemed a long time. He could not, apparently, remember much about having been a little boy. But at last he thought of something.

"Once my father had some pigs," he began solemnly, remembering, staring into the fire, "and those pigs would keep squeezing through the fence of the orchard where they were supposed to stay to eat the windfalls. They kept getting into the front yard. Well, my father was a short-tempered man. He grew very angry. He'd rush out and chase them back no matter what he was doing, but pretty soon they'd be in again. One day he got so angry he couldn't stand it. He raced after them clear to the fence and they ran as hard as they could and squeezed in just ahead of him—that is, all but one. The last one was fatter than the others and he stuck. My father whipped out his pocket-knife and cut off his tail."

I stared at Andrew, astonished. "What did he do that for?" I asked.

"Just to teach him a lesson," he answered, smiling a little.

But I remained grave. "What lesson?" I inquired further.

He gave one of his unexpected restrained laughs. "Maybe not to get so fat," he said.

Later I was to hear many tales of that intrepid man, father of Andrew. People feared him and liked him, laughed at him and trusted him. Rampaging and angry, enormously stubborn, he was endlessly kind to his poor neighbors and utterly ruthless to his family. Once he went around the corner of one of his big barns and discovered a poverty-stricken fellow standing by a knot-hole, holding a large sack into which was pouring a steady stream of wheat. When he saw Andrew's father, he ran. Andrew's father said nothing at all. He took the man's place, and stood holding the bag, his eyes twinkling. After a while a voice came from within the barn, "Ain't it about full?"

"It's just about full, I reckon," he answered amiably.

There was dead silence within the barn. He knotted the mouth of the sack and heaved it to his great shoulders and went inside and discovered a cringing, waiting figure.

"There—take it," he said, flinging the sack at the man, recognizing a poor neighbor, a tenant farmer. "Next time come and ask me and I'll give it to you!"

I never saw Andrew's father and mother, but I have their tintypes. His father has a square indomitable face with the most arrogant eyes I have ever seen. Only a man sure of God and of his own soul can have such eyes as those. I have never seen them in other human faces.

But the woman is his match. Her jaw is no whit less strongly turned than his, and if her eyes have not that gleam of God in them, they have the calmness of the Devil. No wonder God and the Devil were such realities in that turbulent home! Someone told me—not Andrew—that when Deborah was sixty years old she not only turned Methodist for good and all, but she decided she had worked enough and that she would never work again. She changed completely with this decision. From being the incessantly busy, capable, managing mother of the big household, turning out cheeses and pies and cakes and loaves of bread, for she was a notable cook, she became a woman of complete leisure. She never so much as made her own bed again. She sat on the wide porch of the farmhouse all day long on pleasant days, rocking placidly, and in bad weather she sat by the sitting-room window that looked out on the road. She took walks by herself, a tall, always slender, upright figure. She went to her Methodist church alone except when Christopher was home.

Her family were amazed, and her husband was almost beside himself with rage. But she lived them all down and for nearly thirty-five years maintained her complete leisure while perforce she was waited upon by one after the other of them. She became a center for the women of the neighborhood to visit. Once, all unplanned, twenty-two women met there to spend the day, and a dozen was nothing uncommon. They sat on the porch or in the sitting-room, gossiping, strengthening one another. If God was pre-eminent in that house, it was only by a very narrow margin.

But it is Andrew's story I am telling and none of these others matter, because they mattered so little to him. They gave him his body and soul, they kept God and the Devil hot about him, and it is true that in certain large ways they shaped him. He learned his creed from them, the creed not only of his theology but of his place in creation as a man. In that house bursting with its seven great sons, roaring with the thunder of the quarrel between man and woman, he

[165]

heard it often shouted aloud that the Bible said man was head of the woman. It had to be shouted often to that indomitable old woman, eternally in her rocking chair. It made no impression on her, but it made a deep impression on her seven sons. Carie told me once that of those seven great boys, grown young men when she first saw them, not one would have thought of going upstairs to bed unless one of the two sisters lighted a candle and went ahead of them, one after the other. What a procession it was— David, Isaac, Hiram, John, Christopher, Andrew and Franklin! And the sisters were Rebecca and Mary, tall women as their brothers were tall, subdued, smoldering, forbidden by their father to marry in their youth because he and his sons had need of their services, marrying at late last men too humble for them. Of this furious seed, out of this turbulent soil, Andrew was born.

2

The story should begin when Andrew left home at twenty-one, because Andrew himself always began his life there, counting as worthless the years when he had to do nothing but the labor of his hands to feed nothing but human bodies. And no one seems to remember much about him as a child or a boy. Somebody said once, an old woman who had been a neighbor for a while, "That boy always had the hands of an old man—they said he was born with old hands." And there is only one thing to be told of his adolescence, because that is all I really know, except that I heard rumors of a subdued puckish humor in him, a sort of humor which indeed he kept all his life. I used to think it tinged with cruelty sometimes, although I am sure it was not meant to be so. But I met once an old

man who knew him as a child, who went to the one-room school with him in the few winter months when they were not busy on the big farm. The old man spat tobacco juice and grinned when he told it. "That Andrew!" he observed. "When he was a boy he could make a face fit to bust a cat open with laughin' at him. Then when we was all hollerin' and snickerin' the teacher'd turn around mad and he'd be the only one with a sober face." Whatever the humor was, it was always firmly repressed behind a sober face and it leaked out only in dry jokes and occasional barbed thrusts. It never rollicked or burst out full and free, and because he so held it back, there was often bitterness in his joke, and his laughter was silent or at most a single "haw!" of sound.

Once I said to him, "What did you do all those years of your youth?"

His face shadowed. "I worked for my father," he answered briefly.

His sister Mary said to me once, "Pa wanted Andrew to stay on the place because he was so reliable. He was the one boy out of the lot that you could be sure would get every chore done on time and as it ought to be done. He had an awful sense of duty."

"I suppose you know he hated every bit of it," I said.

"That didn't make any difference to him," she answered vigorously. She smiled. "Nor to Pa," she added.

She was an old woman then, too fat, coarse, a little sloppy. Years of living with a man beneath her had made her careless. But when she smiled one saw the family eyes, hard, fearless, blue.

Yet those years of his early adolescence were tremendous years, for they were the years of the Civil War. Four of the sons went to fight the North. David, Hiram, Isaac, John—they marched out of the house in gray uniforms, transferring for a brief while their war against the Devil to the Yankees. Two were wounded, one was kept prisoner for a long time in a Northern prison. I never heard Andrew mention any of it except to say one day that he had disliked bean soup ever since Isaac had come back from the war and told them he had to eat it three times a day in Yankee prison. "At that," Andrew added with his wry smile, "it was so thin Isaac said he had to dive for the beans." And when the youngest and last of his children went to tell Andrew of her betrothal, he looked up from his page long enough to say with that wry look of his, "I don't know what I've done to have all three of my children marry Yankees!" Yes, there was one other memory in him—he never heard the name of Abraham Lincoln mentioned without commenting drily, always in the same words, "Lincoln was a very much overrated man." In Andrew's house I grew up never knowing that Lincoln was a national hero, or that across the sea in America children had a holiday from school on his birthday.

But wars and the times of men were of no importance in the life of Andrew. Somewhere in those adolescent years while he served his father carefully in silence and in hated waiting, he received his missionary call. I know, because that brief story he wrote of his life begins with it. So far as he was concerned here was the dawn of his life, his real birth. "At the age of sixteen," he wrote, "I received the first intimation of Divine Call to the mission field."

Afterwards, questioning him, I pieced out the story from his scanty words. It was, of course, inevitable that he should be a preacher of the gospel. It is impossible to think of any of those tall men as ministers—they were all preachers, not ministers, and so was Andrew. I suppose it was inevitable that all of them should be preachers. There were reasons for it, aside from the opportunity it gave them

to exercise personal authority over other people's minds and lives. At that time it was a calling of high social position. The preacher in a community was also the leader in other ways, and an ambitious young man wanting power could scarcely find a more satisfactory way of getting it. And these seven young men were all ambitious and power-loving.

But I have it from Andrew himself that at first he never thought of being a missionary, or indeed of leaving his home state. He had, in his curious mixture, a clinging love of home. I think it was really a part of his sense of physical timidity that made him love security and safety and shelter. If he had not been born in a religious age, he would have been a scholar, shutting himself into some warm book-lined room for life. I have seen him come back from a long hard journey on foot or donkey-back through half a Chinese province, and be almost childishly comforted with food and a cup of hot tea and a blazing fire. "It's good to be home—oh, but it's good to be home!" he would murmur to himself.

"I never left home without an inner struggle," he told me when he was an old man. But he was born with a restless, angry conscience, and I never knew him to postpone the hour of his going or shirk the most difficult or dangerous journey. He carried his scourge in his own heart. And because he was so rigorous with himself, he was unmerciful in his judgment upon lesser men. I have heard him exclaim against a fellow missionary, "He doesn't like to leave the comforts of his home—he's lazy!" If he had never been tempted himself, or if being tempted he had sometimes yielded, he might have been gentler with his fellows. But he was invincible toward weakness, as all are who are strong enough for their own temptations. For he was strong enough for the greatest conflict of his life—the conflict of his sense of duty with his strange physical timidity.

This is the story of his call. A missionary from China came to preach in the Old Stone Church in Lewisburg, West Virginia, and he told the tale of his life. Andrew, then sixteen, sat in the line of his family in the front pew, listening to the story of hazard and danger and desperate human need, and listening, he was afraid. He was so afraid that he hurried home alone, and avoided the missionary. But his father brought the tall gaunt man home to the big Sunday dinner, and there he could not be avoided. And the missionary, looking down the long line of sons, said to his father, "Out of all these sons you have begotten, will you not give one to China?"

No one answered. The father was taken aback. It was all very well to go to hear a missionary once a year or so and give him a square meal afterwards and drive him in the surrey to his next church, but it was quite another thing to give him a son.

"I don't want the boys to get such notions," Deborah said decidedly from her end of the table.

"God calls," the missionary said quietly.

"Have some more chicken and gravy," the father said hastily. "Here, Deborah—more mashed potatoes—fetch the hot bread, Becky—eat, man! We're hearty folk around here!"

Nobody answered, but terror caught Andrew's heart. Suppose God should call him to go? The food turned dry in his mouth.

Afterwards he went for days weak with terror. "I believe I lost ten pounds," he said, remembering after fifty years. He grew afraid to say his prayers lest God should call him as he prayed. He tried not to be alone lest heaven crack and God's voice come down to him, commanding him. He never felt home so

warm, so sheltering. Yet he was miserable. "I was avoiding God," he wrote when he was an old man. "I knew it, and I was miserable."

For it was a necessity to his being that he feel the channel clear between him and his God, and now, do what he would and go where he would, he felt the pursuit of God.

His mother laid hold of him one day. "What's wrong with you, Andy? You look like you're getting the jaundice!"

For a long time he would not tell her, but she clutched him firmly by the shoulder. She was still taller than he was. Finally he mumbled the truth, his eyes filling with helpless tears. "I'm afraid I'm going to get the call," he said.

"What call?" she asked. She had entirely forgotten the missionary.

"To the foreign field."

"Get out!" she said with vigor. "Your pa wouldn't hear to it! He's counting on you to take hold of the land."

I suppose nothing would infuriate Andrew more, though he has been long dead, than to know that this had anything to do with making God's call more tolerable. But certainly his soul revolted at his mother's words. He wrenched his shoulder loose from her and strode off. He would never stay on the land, call or no call. Anger swept out fear, for the moment. He went away into the woods alone and there he cried out resolutely to God. "I subdued my stubborn heart," he wrote. "I cried to God, 'Here am I—send me!' Immediately peace filled my soul. I was afraid no more. I felt myself strong. When I gave up my own will, God's power descended upon me. And God sent me."

So his life was decided. But he said nothing then. He planned his years. Five years more he must serve his father. He knew, because of the other sons ahead of him, that on his twenty-first birthday his father would give him the choice he had given each of the others, to stay at home and receive wages for the work he had until then been doing for nothing, or to receive a good horse and a hundred dollars and ride away. They had all chosen to ride away and so would he. He would tell no one, but he would ride away and go to college and to seminary and fit himself for his life. His heart beat at the thought. Books—there would at last be plenty of books. He was always starved for them, and he never had enough of school. One of the few fervent things I ever heard him say was, "I *loved* school!" Indeed, I do not believe I ever heard him use the word "love" in any other connection with himself. "God so loved the world . . ." that use I heard often enough. It was odd to hear him say, "I love . . ." I remember it, because I was being sent away to school those days, myself, and was not at all sure about loving it, and I had never thought of his loving anything except God.

On his twenty-first birthday he rode away, then, his call hot in his breast. His life was begun and he came to it starved. His story tells me he was not ready for college at once. The Civil War had interrupted all schools, and while the older sons, when they came home again and before they went away, taught the younger children, still he was very unevenly prepared. So he went for a year to Frankfort Academy—I know no more than that—and thence to Washington and Lee University, where Hiram had gone just before him.

My first knowledge of those years was when I was still a little girl. I was rummaging all the book shelves in the mission house on the hill above the Yangtze River, in a state of starvation very much like Andrew's own. All the books in the world would not have been enough for me, and in that mission house there were very, very few of the world's books. So

because Andrew was away on one of his long preaching tours, I did what I never dared to do when he was home—I went into his study to search again his shelves, not very hopefully, for I had combed them before and had read Plutarch's *Lives* and Josephus and Fox's *Martyrs*, and anything at all promising a story. This day I was so desperate I took down Geikie's *Commentary on the Bible*—and put it back again. It was worse than nothing. Then in sheer emptiness I decided to look through the drawers of his old roller-top desk. I remembered having once seen some books there when he chanced to open a drawer. But when I looked they were only his mission account books, kept in meticulous detail in his slightly wavering handwriting, for he had a sunstroke once that nearly ended him, and left him with a right hand that trembled a little when he held it to write. I opened one drawer after the other. In the bottom one I saw a heap of curious rolls of leathery paper. They were very dusty and no one had looked at them for a long time. Indeed, some of them had never been opened. I took them out, one by one, and unrolled them. Upon them were printed Latin words. I was studying Latin by then myself, and I saw his name, and always the three words, *Magna cum laude*.

"What do they mean?" I went to ask Carie.

She was in her bedroom, darning swiftly, a big sock stretched over her hand. Those spare bony feet of his, walking miles every day on their mission, over city stones and cobbled roads and across dusty footpaths, kept her sewing basket always piled high. Pride came over her face like a light. "Your father was graduated from the university with honors in every subject," she said. Years afterwards when I went to college I was inclined to be hurt when he said nothing to a report card which I felt was distinguished by

A's. But if he said nothing it was because he expected no less of his child, and indeed, expected something rather better than he ever got from her, I am afraid. I once to my astonishment received a mark of 99 for geometry, a subject in which I was never at my best. "A good mark," he said reservedly and added at once, "a hundred would have been better."

He was desperately poor in college. I can imagine him, tall, already slightly stooped but with the lofty bearing of great dignity which he always had. It was there already, because his fellow students were afraid of him and none of them seemed very near him, and that was to be true of people all his life. He was very nearsighted, too, and did not know it, nor had anyone ever paid enough heed to him to find it out. He sat in the front seat if he could, and when he could not, he copied what was written on the board from one of his fellows. He could not recognize people unless they passed near enough to touch him, and so he never learned to look at faces or to be observant of anything around him and he was driven the further in upon himself. Later when one of his professors suggested glasses his delight was simply that now he could see better to read. He had no social life at the university, partly because he was poor and wanted only to buy more books, and partly because he did not want society. He wanted only to get the meat out of his books. Hiram, the handsome, could go to parties and strum his guitar and call on pretty girls, but Andrew did none of these things. And yet he was tremblingly happy. He got up earlier than ever, with an enormous sense of luxury because there were no cows to be milked, no chores to be done. He could follow his single desire, his books. He would excel them all there. Hiram could never approach him; none of them could, not even David, gifted almost to the point of genius in languages.

I know, for Andrew told me, that he was too poor to afford eleven dollars a month for board in the mess hall, and that he and Hiram lived in one room in the old wooden dormitory, and cut cord wood in winter and stacked it in one corner of their room and cooked scanty meals of mush and potatoes over the same fire that warmed them. He told me this because it seemed to him incredible that a girl could spend so much, forty years later, at college. Listening, she had not the heart to tell him that what he gave her, thinking it generous, was not enough to pay for her food and room, even. She sat silent, and after he was gone, went away and found herself a job of teaching in a night school. But for Andrew the times had not changed. He never lived in time but in eternity.

I know no more of his college life except that he was graduated, bright with honors and warmed with unwonted public attention, and except this one thing, which remained to him a tragedy all his life, even when he was an old man.

The night after his graduation, when he was to leave the next day, a fire broke out in the ramshackle wooden dormitory. Hiram had been graduated a year before. Andrew was alone, and being young and wearied with excitement and triumph, he slept heavily. Only at the last moment was he wakened by thick smoke and a terrible heat. The house was on fire. He fumbled his way to the stairs which were already blazing, and ran down to safety. They collapsed behind him. No one was burned, since nearly everyone was already gone. But he stood watching the flimsy building blaze and dim and drop to ash in such agony as I do believe he never felt again. His books, in which his life was bound, which he had bought so hardly, one by one, were gone.

He went home again, penniless. Everything was the same. His father received him with rough welcome, with scanty well-meaning sympathy. Books! Well, wasn't he done with them? Was he ready to settle down to real work now? Wages were ready. But he was not ready. It seemed impossible to begin again that dull physical round. He dreaded the labor which absorbed the powers of the brain as a useless by-product and left the numb bodily fatigue which could only be assuaged by sleep. He chanced upon an advertisement in a religious paper. "Wanted: A young man to sell Bibles." It struck him at once that to sell Bibles was to do more than merely sell a book—it was to spread wide the word of God. So he answered the advertisement and a package of Bibles arrived and he set out on foot to go from house to house.

"I do not know," he wrote years later in that abridgment of his life, "where the fault lay, but I sold only one copy. Whether the people were very hard of heart or whether I was not fortunate in my address, I do not know. I only know that God did not bless my endeavor."

The truth is of course that anyone less like a salesman than Andrew was never created, and I suppose it takes salesmanship also to sell the Bible. I can imagine him approaching a house in a misery of shyness. I can imagine a hearty housewife opening her door in the early morning in the thick of after-breakfast work to discover a tall, stooped, blushing young man upon her threshold, inarticulately holding forth a book.

"Madam, I am selling Bibles. I do not know—"

"We've got a Bible," she doubtless replied with vigor. After all, of course every house had a Bible. Wasn't it a Christian country? She slammed the door and plunged her hands into the dishpan —a Bible, of all things!

"I concluded at the end of a month," Andrew wrote, "that God had not called me to the task of selling anything."

So he went back to his father, not knowing what else to do, and his father, chuckling a little, paid him generously enough, although to Andrew no pay was enough for work he hated.

All his years at college he had kept secret within himself his determination to be a missionary. And how Andrew could keep his own counsel! He could hold a dear plan inside himself for years and shape every end to it, and everyone to it. Years later this secrecy was a torment to Carie, an exasperation to his fellow missionaries. Andrew had early discovered that the most successful means of doing what he liked was to do it without telling anyone what he was doing. But as the summer wore away it was necessary that he tell his father and mother that he was going to seminary in the autumn to fit himself to be a missionary. He had saved his wages, every penny. In the lavishness of the food upon the table what he ate was never missed. And his brother John had by then married his rich widow and had promised to help him with a loan. David, too, then preaching in a little town in the next county, was sympathetic.

He told his parents, and was instantly met with terrific opposition from his father.

"Tomfoolery!" the stormy old man roared, shaking his shaggy white hair back from his forehead. "Go and preach, if you have to—though I'll say six sons out of seven is what I call too much of a good thing. But to go gallivantin' to foreign countries is beyond any man's call."

"Not beyond God's call," said Andrew. He was by all odds the most stubborn man I ever knew when God called him to a thing. So I know his father's anger and roaring only set him harder in his own way. Whatever his mother might have said, left to herself, no one can tell. But when she heard the old man's verdict, she was immediately mild out of contrariness.

"*I* don't care, Andy," she said, rocking back and forth. "You do as you have a mind to—there's only one thing I ask of you as my son. Promise me, Andrew."

In his relief and gratitude he promised her. "I certainly promise, Mother."

He had not dreamed of what her condition would be.

"You shan't go till you find a wife to go with you," she said, rocking to and fro. "I wouldn't be easy if you hadn't a wife to take care of you."

He nearly fainted. A wife! He had not thought of such a thing. He had never dreamed of marrying—a wife, when he had to live in strange dangerous countries—a woman—he didn't know a single one!

"How can I ever find a woman willing to go?" he groaned. "You might as well forbid me to go!"

"Oh, get out," his mother replied amiably. "There's always women willing to marry any two-legged thing in pants."

Andrew went away in a daze. His mother was not reassuring.

In the end it seems he put the matter up to God. I am not saying he did not make a few efforts himself. But they were futile. I do not know about them in any detail, since he always maintained the strictest silence about his failures, whatever they were, and forgot them at once. But one evening when he was a very old man he told me something. In those years I sat a while with him alone every evening, so that he might have someone to talk with if he chose. He talked more in those hours than he ever had before— not consecutive talk, but bits of incidents plucked at random out of three-quarters of a century of life. I had to do my own piecing. He said suddenly on one of those evenings, "You might have had Jennie Husted to be your mother."

"What!" I exclaimed. It was impossible

to imagine anyone except Carie for our mother. I instantly resented Jennie Husted. Who was she?

"I worried a lot in seminary because of my promise to my mother," he said, staring into the fire. "I observed many young ladies—from a distance, that is," he added quickly. "If any seemed at all possible, devout and well grounded in faith, I asked them first if they had ever considered the foreign field. It seemed prudent to ascertain their feeling on this point before I took the time and expense of proceeding further. They all replied in the negative."

"But who was Jennie Husted?" I demanded.

"My trial sermon," he proceeded in his calm fashion, disregarding interruption, "was considered very good—in fact, so good that it was published in a church paper. It was entitled, 'The Necessity of Proclaiming the Gospel to the Heathen, with Especial Reference to the Doctrine of Predestination.' After its publication, I received a letter from a Miss Jennie Husted. In it she warmly supported my views and we entered into a correspondence. Her home was in Louisville, Kentucky. In the last year of my seminary course I asked for permission to call upon her. I felt a strong premonition that God had called her to be my wife. I went all that distance to see her, under that impression. But when we met, I found I was mistaken."

"What happened?" I asked, exceedingly curious.

"I was simply mistaken," he repeated firmly, and would say no more.

"Well, at least tell me what she looked like," I pressed, bitterly disappointed.

"I do not remember," he said with great dignity.

I never knew any more than that about it. It did not seem to me, however, that Carie's place as our mother had been seriously threatened.

3

I put out of my mind entirely Carie's side of their meeting and their marriage. After all, so far as Andrew was concerned, Carie, as Carie, had very little to do with it anyway. It was providential— that is, God provided it that in the summer of his graduation from seminary when he was ready for service and held back only by his promise to his mother, a young woman should have been found who was interested, or so it appeared, in going as a missionary with him.

He had come to his brother David's house this summer, as he had the summer before, to study under his brother. David was a scholar in Sanskrit, in Hebrew, in Greek, not to mention other biblically important languages. And besides, Andrew acted as supply for neighboring churches as well as for David. It gave him practice, as well as a chance of earning a little money. And Andrew doubtless needed the practice. He could never throw off wholly that shrouding mantle of shyness. A certain secret doubt of himself as a man was always mingled with his certainty of himself as God's messenger. There was never any doubt of his divine guidance, never any doubt of his rightness. I think the truth of it is that he never could get Mrs. Pettibrew's words out of his mind. All his life he rather wistfully admired handsome and clever young men. Many handsome and clever young Chinese certainly did what they liked with him.

Still, in spite of Mrs. Pettibrew, he had turned out better than he knew. The red thatchy hair of his boyhood had miraculously turned a dark curly brown. I know it was an astonishment because the change came rather quickly so that he was teased about having dyed his hair, to his horror. Carie told me that when she first saw him his hair was undeniably red,

but the summer he proposed to her, the same summer they were married and went to China, his hair was dark. He was, she said, "Not bad-looking at all." But he kept his sandy eyebrows and his moustache was reddish, and later when he came and went among the Chinese and grew a beard, they called him "red-beard," although those who knew him nicknamed him—for everyone in China has a nickname—"The Fool about Books." Well, he was in love with books always, to the day we buried him with his little Greek New Testament, which was more a part of him than any of us ever were.

I have a picture of him the summer he married Carie. In the fashion of those days, he is seated and she is standing beside him, her hand a little awkwardly upon his shoulder. But obviously he does not know it is there. He looks out of the picture with the gaze I know so well, a gaze compounded of that obstinate jutting jaw, those childlike clear eyes, and a beautiful, saintly brow. That untroubled brow of his remained exactly the same, though he would have been eighty his next birthday had he lived until the year came round again to summer. I never knew which of those three parts of his face were more unchangeable, but I think it was his brow. It was wide and smooth, the skin transparently fair. He wore his sun helmet low over his eyes, so that the reddish-brown sunburn of his cheeks never reached his brow. In the morning, after his habitual hour of prayer alone in his study, it was marked by three strips of flaming red where he had leaned his head upon his outspread fingers. But these soon faded, leaving the smooth high brow white. He was never bald and the dark hair grew thinner and silvery. For he never suffered. He lived that extraordinary and rare thing, a completely happy life, and there was never a line upon that really noble brow.

I put relentlessly aside Carie's side of the story.

In those long evenings of his old age I asked questions of him. "What did Mother look like when you married her?" I asked him. He stared into the coal fire he loved to have burning upon the hearth in his room. He spread his hands to the blaze. They showed no trace of the youth spent upon a farm. They were a scholar's hands, rather large, very thin and finely shaped, the nails meticulously tended. but then I never saw him otherwise than neat and spotlessly clean. Never once in all our shifting poverty-stricken childhood, or in all the later years of his age, did I ever see him except freshly shaven, his stiff wing collar white, his hair brushed. He was fastidious in all his poverty. He would never own more than two suits—if he had more he gave them away to someone who needed clothing— and those suits he wore to threadbareness, but he was always fresh and clean. Wherever he went, traveling and stopping by night in little filthy Chinese inns, he never began the day without bathing himself in some fashion. And I never saw him with dirty hands.

"Your mother?" he reflected. "I don't exactly remember. She had dark hair and eyes and she was fond of singing."

"How did you propose to Mother?" I asked, too boldly.

He was embarrassed. "I wrote her a letter," he replied. He considered for a moment and then added, "It seemed to me to be the only way of putting everything clearly before her for her mature reflection."

"Mother's father didn't want her to marry you, did he?"—this to goad him a little into remembering.

He replied tranquilly. "There was some nonsense, but I wouldn't stand for it. He was a man with a temper, although a good man in his way—but very stub-born. I have little use for stubborn people."

"And then?"

"Well, we were married and came straight to China. I remember that no one told me about berths on the train and we sat up."

"I thought somebody said you bought only one ticket on the train," I said, prodding him.

"Oh, that," he said, "there was nothing to that."

"You mean it was only a story?"

"Oh, of course I bought another ticket as soon as my attention was called to it," he said.

And he laughed at himself, his dry, half-silent laugh, because he had been such an innocent about tickets and travel. The real joke of it was that he could not realize that he was never anything but an innocent about all worldly affairs. Tickets and the intricacies of travel remained a bewilderment to him, although in some fashion or another he always arrived at his destination. This he did by the simple expedient of invariably being very early at a dock or a station so that if he wandered into the wrong ship or train somebody would find him there and put him off in time for him to discover the right one. He traveled, of course, incredible distances, and by any means he could. Yet we never saw him start on a ship or a train, or indeed in any modern conveyance, without a sense of his helplessness and of anxiety and doubt of his arrival, and what amounted to a certainty that he would never get back again. Yet somehow, usually through the help of some pitying person who perceived his bewilderment, he always came back safely. He had a principle against luxury of any sort, although secretly he loved its comfort, and he would not hear of traveling first-class, nor until he was a very old man, even second-class. When trains began to be built in China he was as excited as a child and took the greatest pleasure in traveling by them over country through which he had once plodded on foot or upon a donkey. But for years he steadfastly refused to ride in any except the third-class, where the benches were narrow boards, and if we did not watch him he would even climb into a fourth-class coolie car. It was not because he was penurious for the sake of money. He was penurious for God's sake, that everything might go into that cause to which he had dedicated his life—and to which also he ruthlessly and unconsciously dedicated all those lives for which he was responsible.

His honeymoon upon a ship crossing the Pacific was spent in improving his knowledge of the Chinese language. He had begun the study months before. He ordered his life now as he always did. A certain number of hours each day were spent in the study of Chinese, a certain number on Hebrew and Greek. His Bible he always read in those languages. The great dissatisfaction of his life was with the inadequate translations of the Bible into English and later into Chinese. For all the absoluteness of his creed he was a thorough scholar, and he never regarded any translation of the Bible as the final Word of God. The final Word of God was there, locked somehow into the Hebrew and Greek originals, and it was the passion of his life to uncover the truth of the Word. The first heresy he ever uttered—and he was full of unconscious heresies which he would never acknowledge as such—was that "they" were all wrong in translating the word "day" in the first chapter of Genesis—it meant not "day" but "period"—"God created the world in seven periods," he used to say. But he put no faith whatever in scientists, in their study of man's be-

ginning—"A lot of old fellows getting excited over a few scratches in some cave or other," he would say, dismissing the lot. And Darwin he relentlessly held to be a soul possessed by Satan. "Evolution!" he would snort. "Devilution, I call it!" Yet he could listen with wistful reverence to some Biblical archaeologist recounting the uncovering of Nineveh or Tyre, and he could hear with amazing humility of belief such fantasies of fulfillments of ancient prophecies, such madness of miracles, such imaginations of resurrection and millenniums as are not to be found between the covers of any of the novels he disdained to read because they were not "true."

Into Chinese, then, he plunged with ardent enjoyment. He was, as a matter of fact, a man of genius in all languages, and he delighted in the intricacies of Chinese, in aspirate and non-aspirate, in tones—ascending, level, level on an ascent, descending, exclamatory—in all the fine shades and distinctions of meaning and constructions. He spoke Chinese as few white men ever do, with feeling, and literary precision. It came at last to be more native to him than his own tongue—he spoke it far more. Once in an American pulpit, when he went back on a furlough, he rose before a great audience to pray. As he always did, he stood a long moment in silence, to empty his mind of all except God. Then, feeling no one there except himself and God, he began to pray—and the prayer came in Chinese. Only when he was half through did he realize what he was doing. He stopped and then went on in English. But the prayer became nothing. He was conscious of others there now, and God was gone.

Indeed, few Chinese even spoke as accurately as he did, for few knew the syntax of the language as he did. There exists today a little book he once wrote on Chinese idioms, a really valuable study, written with the compression which was natural to him. And it was characteristic that when it was revised and he was urged to make an index to it, he refused to do it, saying, "It won't hurt people to look for what they are after, if they really want it."

The very precision of his knowledge, however, made his Chinese speech seem too literary, and indeed it was often beyond the comprehension of ordinary people. I remember it was a life-long complaint against Carie that she had a certain carelessness in Chinese pronunciation. "Your mother," he would say to us plaintively, "will never learn that certain words are aspirates." He would beseech her, his sensitive ear offended to agony, "Carie, I beg you, that word is aspirate—"

To which she replied robustly, "What's the odds? I can't be bothered, so long as they understand me. Besides, the common people understand me better than they do you."

It did not help the situation at all that this last remark was perfectly true.

When I look back over the eighty years of Andrew's life, I realize that the pattern of it is very simple. The first twenty-eight years were years of struggle and preparation, carried on doggedly with a very genius of stubborn persistence to that moment when he set sail for China. From that moment, for fifty years the pattern is one of simple happiness. All around me today, in every country of the world, I see people struggling for personal happiness. They struggle in a hundred ways. They put their hopes in a hundred different things—in new forms of government and social theory, in plans for public welfare, in private accumulation of wealth. None is quite free from that search for individual happiness. For however he may disguise his struggles

under noble names of causes and crusade, the bitter truth is that no perfectly happy individual takes part in any struggle. Andrew was the happiest person I have ever known and he never struggled. He went his way, serene and confident, secure in the knowledge of his own rightness. I have seen him angry at others because they obstructed the way of the Lord he trod so surely, but I never saw him puzzled or distrustful of himself. I never saw him in undignified argument with others. He took his own way with proud tranquility. There was a greatness in his clear determination.

Nor can I tolerate for a moment any mawkish notion that it was his religion that filled him with that might. Religion had nothing to do with it. Had he been a lesser mind he would have chosen a lesser god, had he been born for today he would have chosen another god, but whatever he chose would have been as much god to him. Whatever he did he would have done with that swordlike singleness of heart. As it was, born of the times and of that fighting blood, he chose the greatest god he knew, and set forth into the universe to make men acknowledge his god to be the one true God, before whom all must bow. It was a magnificent imperialism of the spirit, incredible and not to be understood except by those who have been reared in it and have grown beyond it. Most of all are those yet in it unaware of what they are.

But to Andrew spiritual imperialism was as natural as the divine right of kings was to Charles the Second. Andrew, too, had that same naïve and childlike guilelessness of the king. He would have been pained and astonished if anyone had ever told him he was arrogant and domineering. Indeed, he did not seem so, his bearing was of such gentleness and dignity, his step quiet, his voice soft, his manner always restrained and controlled except for those rare strange sudden furies, when something he kept curbed deep in him broke for a moment its leash. Everyone was afraid of him at those moments. His children were terrified when they saw that quick working of his face, the sharp upthrust of his hand. Someone would be hurt—struck—his hand or his cane flying out. It was over in a second, and it broke through less and less often as he grew older, until at last it died altogether, I think, or distilled itself into a diffused strength and no longer burst forth in anger, so that in his last years he was mellowed to his heart's core.

But in his youth there were those swift furies in him. I know now he never allowed one to escape him without shame and contrition. I do not doubt that when he let his hand drop so suddenly and left the room so quickly he was going into his study to fall upon his knees and beg God's forgiveness. But I think it never occurred to him to beg forgiveness of any man. It really did not occur to him, for he was not humanly proud. If he had seen it as his duty to ask forgiveness he would have done it eagerly. He never shirked his duty. But it seemed important to him only to have God's forgiveness, to make sure that clear deep channel between him and God was not defiled. At all costs he kept it clear and deep, and so he lived happily. For he had this happiness: he espoused early a cause in which he believed all his life without a shadow of doubt. Not even his own mind betrayed him. He had his mind in exorable control. He died, sure that he had chosen rightly, had believed wisely, and had achieved success in what he had done. There are not many to whom such happiness is given.

Being always perfectly happy he had a charm about him. He was quietly gay very often, sometimes full of jokes. I have often seen him sitting at table or in the stillness of evening after the day's work was over, when suddenly his blue eyes would brim with secret laughter and he would laugh silently. "What is it?" I always asked. Sometimes, rarely, he would tell me. But most often he would say simply, "I was thinking of something." I think he felt open laughter unbecoming. Yet sometimes when he did tell its cause he would choke and stammer with laughter. It always took us a little aback when he told us, because the thing he laughed at was often rather surprisingly simple, an incongruity of some sort. Carie smiled at him as she did at one of the younger children. This perception of the simple incongruous was as far as his humor went.

But it could be difficult at times, because if he disliked a person he did not conceal his laughter. For instance, he disliked women at best, but he especially and openly hated the large, florid, over-confident type which our Western civilization seems to have developed in such numbers. Once when he was quite an old man he sat at my table opposite a guest who was such a person. Andrew, disliking her at once, had sat in doughty silence, refusing to acknowledge her presence beyond a scant bow. She, rattling along in her voluble way, spoke of the ball she was going to attend after dinner at the American Consulate and worried as to whether or not she would "mind" dancing with the Chinese men who would be present. She had never danced with men of another race than her own. Andrew lifted his eyes from his plate alertly. I knew he hated the way she looked, her fat arms bare to the shoulder, her large bosom bursting under her tight gown. Bulk of flesh filled him with distaste to the point of rage. Now I saw his absent eyes take on their familiar mirthful, mischievous gleam. He began suddenly in that deceptive, slow, soft voice, "I should think a Chinese man could scarcely be found who—" I pressed his foot under the table, hard and quickly. The large lady's eyes glittered.

"Do have some—some coffee," I pleaded with her. "Oh, your dress is lovely," I babbled on. "That color is so becoming—just like your eyes!"

She turned toward me, flattered and effulgent. "Do you think so?"

"Yes, indeed—indeed," I cried. I kept my foot hard on Andrew's. He was stirring his cup of tea, shaking with silent laughter, forgetting everything except the picture he saw in imagination of this immense American supporting against her hugeness a slight Chinese figure in the foolishness of dancing. Afterwards when I remonstrated with him, as I dared to do in those days, he remarked calmly, "Well, the woman ought to be laughed at—she's a fool." Andrew was always very sure of himself.

"It was very unfortunate," Andrew used to say to us, "that your mother was given to seasickness. I remember she was seasick at once upon leaving the shores of America. I urged her to exert herself to control it, but she seemed determined to let it take its course. Control would have been possible in another less stubborn nature. But in her case she allowed seasickness to become aggravated so that she never really recovered."

"You don't mean she really could have helped it!" we cried, springing to Carie's defense.

"One has to make an effort," he remarked serenely. "Besides, it was most inconvenient."

So I do not imagine on that wedding journey across a stormy typhoon-ridden ocean that Andrew was a very good nurse to a seasick bride. He would of course have been very considerate in his inquiries, but he would not have known what to do for her. He was never ill himself. He ate, he told me with unconsciously pleasurable memory, his first raw oysters that night out of Golden Gate. It was so rough that the first one slid down his throat before he swallowed it, so he could not get its taste. The second one he bit firmly. "With a little pepper and catsup," he remarked gently, "I found them eatable. I believe I ate twelve, but regretted afterwards that I had not stopped at six."

"You weren't seasick?" we inquired with malice.

"Not at all," he replied. "I have never been ill on the sea. I had merely a sense of regret for a few hours, but I kept my mind on other things."

He had a constitution of steel and a digestion which nothing could disturb. It was as near as he ever came to seasickness, and he could never understand the tortures of Carie's more delicately balanced body.

But Andrew was never ill in any way. For years on his journey he ate what there was to be eaten. Hard-boiled eggs were a delicacy that Chinese farm wives set before him and he ate them. One night at home he saw hard-boiled eggs on a salad Carie had made.

"Twelve," he murmured gently. "I have eaten twelve hard-boiled eggs today."

"Andrew!" cried Carie, alarmed. "Why did you do it?"

"For Christ's sake," he said. "If I hurt the people's feelings they would not listen, and being poor, it was their best."

Once, to make conversation in a peasant home, he looked out over a field of whitely blooming buckwheat, and remarked that he liked buckwheat made into cakes. The housewife immediately hustled about and he found himself confronted with a huge plateful of thick, dry, enormous buckwheat cakes, with nothing on them. He plodded through as many of them as he could. Not then, nor any time he went to that house, did he ever shirk eating them, though he dreaded them and was dejected every time he felt it his duty to go there.

So when Carie was seasick he could not believe that if she tried she would not be better.

"An effort—" he would murmur above her distracted head.

"Oh, go away, Andrew!" she implored him. "Isn't there some book you ought to be studying?"

"Andrew has no conception—" she used to say to us over and over, under her breath. But in the next breath she begged, "You children mustn't pay attention to me. Your father's a wonderful man."

He was wonderful. He preached his first sermon in Chinese six months after his arrival. It is considered a fair feat if it is done after two years, so Andrew was a missionary prodigy. He was quite proud of himself, too, and told it many times with naïve pride, although it is only fair to say that he would always add with that subdued gleam in his blue eyes, "Of course it is another question as to whether anyone understood me or not. I never heard of any conversion as a direct result of it."

His own memories of their first landing upon Chinese shores were very unlike Carie's. She could not escape the misery of the people she saw about her. But Andrew was astonished at the comfort in which the missionaries lived.

"As soon as we landed," he said, "we were met by a delegation of older missionaries who were very glad to see me, since no new reinforcements had come for some years. We were taken to dine at Dr. Young Allen's home. The dinner was an excellent one—much too excellent for a missionary's table, I remember thinking at the time. But afterwards I heard that Dr. Young Allen engaged himself also in mercantile pursuits. He fell into these ways during the period of the Civil War when the home church was not able to continue his salary—I believe it was stoves."

"You went to sleep during dinner and Carie was ashamed," we told him, having heard Carie tell the same story.

"I don't remember anything of that," he said mildly.

"I bought my first overcoat in Shanghai," he went on. "It was an extravagance, I thought, but I was told it was essential."

Carie in the midst of all her seasickness had grown four wisdom teeth on her honeymoon and her rather small lower jaw was so crowded that she was miserable. Andrew took her to a dentist, for the only dentists in China then were in Shanghai, and waited while she had them out with no anesthetic—four great strong new teeth. Carie always had beautiful sound teeth. Once when she was sixty years old a dentist called his pupils to look and see how perfect teeth might be at her age. They gathered around her, solemn young Chinese dentists, while she obligingly opened her mouth as wide as she could. She laughed as she told it. "They stared until I felt my mouth was full of their eyes," she said. But there was a little pride in her voice—she knew she had a good body. And the wisdom teeth had deep strong roots.

Immediately after the teeth were pulled they went on the junk to go by canal to Hangchow—I had the story from Andrew, not Carie—and a hemorrhage set in before they sailed and he had to take her back to the dentist.

"It was very inconvenient," he said, "but we started again with a delay of a little under two hours. I was eager to get at my work."

4

The fascinating thing about Andrew and Carie was that from the two of them we always got entirely different stories about the same incident. They never saw the same things or felt the same way about anything, and it was as though they had not gone to the same place or seen the same people. Andrew remembered nothing of the canal journey except long conversations with the senior missionary and an immense amount of progress in the language, while Carie spent the hours on the tiny deck under a big umbrella against the sun, staring at the slowly passing banks, the fields of rice being harvested, the little villages. I know—for how often have I walked through Chinese fields in September!—that the warm windless air was resonant with the syncopated beat of flails threshing out the rice from the threshing floors of earth. I know the deep blue skies above the shorn gold fields and the flocks of white geese picking up the scattered grains of rice. It is still hot, and little children tumble in the path, naked and brown with the summer sun, to fall asleep curled in the shade at the root of a tree. For the very air is sweet and somnolent with that broken rhythmic beating of the flails.

But Andrew was alert to the mission compound.

"Everything was much better than I had dreamed," he told me once. "The houses were big and clean and the meals were excellent. I had expected to live in small mud huts. I was uncomfortable in the midst of such comforts—good food, servants, space. Your mother put up some sort of pinkish curtains in our room. I thought they were too fancy and said so."

"Did she take them down?" I asked.

"No," he said, "she always had her own notions. But I was there very little. I spent my time downstairs in the study. We began to study Chinese the morning after my arrival. We began at eight and studied until twelve, and again at one until five o'clock. Then we took a walk for exercise. There were no textbooks worth the name, so we began reading the New Testament. The teacher read a line and we repeated it after him as nearly as possible in the same tones. We did this every day except Sunday."

"Didn't you get tired?" we asked. Carie had often grown tired. There was a bed of chrysanthemums against the gray brick compound wall and she sat by the window so that when she could no longer endure the drone of the old teacher's voice she could look at the flaming heavy-headed flowers. She would not let herself look at them often—only when she was so tired she could not bear it. And then when they faded, mercifully there was a heavenly bamboo near the window, hung with heavy plumes of scarlet berries. And sometimes wild geese flew across the piece of sky that stretched above the compound.

"Tired!" exclaimed Andrew. "How could I be tired when I was doing the one thing I most wanted to do—fit myself for the Work?"

All his thoroughness inherited from his Teutonic ancestors went into that study. He dug and delved among the roots of the language. He learned the two hundred and fourteen radicals and the tones of the words, the aspirates and non-aspirates. He mastered its grammar and explored its idiom. He began the study of the Confucian classics so that from the first he would have a cultured vocabulary and mode of expression. It was characteristic of the tenacity of his mind and the singleness of his purpose that the philosophy of Confucius, so essentially that of Jesus Christ, never once appeared to him as of importance. "Confucius says some very nice things," he was wont to say calmly, "but he knew nothing of God and of course understood nothing of the wickedness of human nature and the necessity of salvation from sin through our Savior, the Lord Jesus Christ."

He was exceedingly scornful in after years of those missionary souls, more delicately balanced, who saw in the wisdom of Confucius a means of a sort of salvation, after all. "He's off the track," he would say of such a soul, with a genuine sorrowful pity.

But Andrew found cause for endless astonishment at his fellow missionaries. The people about him were as he expected them to be—unsaved. But he had not expected to find missionaries quite so human as they were. "Most of them," he said, "though good, were not very bright men." "That fellow!" he exclaimed of another. "He was lazy. He didn't want to leave the comforts of his home. He'd go to a chapel on the street once or twice a week and then wonder why the Lord didn't give him converts."

"They were very quarrelsome men," he said, remembering those early holy men of the church. "I remember how exceedingly astonished I was, when I was first sent to Soochow, to find Dr. DuBose and Dr. Davis, the only two white men in the city, one living at the north and one at the south, and never meeting or speaking to each other. When I went to see Dr. Davis and spoke of Dr. DuBose, he said, 'Oh, how I hate that man!'" He paused, and added solemnly, "I was shocked." Then he went on. "When I was sent up the river to Chinkiang there was Dr. Woodbridge and Dr. Woods. They spent much time playing chess, and were alternately friends and enemies. When I first arrived it was during a period of enmity. They were not speaking. Each poured out upon me the story of the other's total unfitness for the Work. I felt it my duty to listen to each impartially and to endeavor to reconcile them."

He smiled a wry smile.

"Did you succeed?" we asked.

"I succeeded to this extent—they united in turning on me!" He gave his dry silent laugh.

What Andrew never knew, and what I did not know until I grew up and saw for myself, was that, with all his seeming tranquility, he was a warrior with the best of them, a son of God continually going forth to battle, a fighting angel. One of my earliest memories in that square mission bungalow was of Monday afternoons devoted to what was called "station meeting," a gathering of the resident missionaries. On Sunday everyone had been religiously whetted by three church services—not only religiously whetted but physically exhausted and emotionally strained. Monday was the day after. I have sat, hundreds of Mondays, a small bewildered child, looking from one stubborn face to the other of my elders, listening to one stubborn voice and then another. What the quarrel was about I never in those days quite knew because it so continually changed. A great deal of it was about money— whether Mr. Wang, the evangelist at the West Gate chapel, should get ten dollars a month instead of eight, for instance. I hoped for ten because I rather liked round-faced merry little Mr. Wang who brought me packages of sweet rice cakes on New Year's Day. Hours went into the discussion of two dollars. But it seemed the two dollars would give Mr. Wang notions—he might want twelve some day —there would be luxuries, perhaps— mission money was sacred—a trust. Mr. Wang must have only eight dollars. Carie got up and went out, her face very red. I followed timidly.

"What's the matter, Mother?" I wanted to know.

"Nothing," she said, pressing her lips together. "Nothing—nothing at all!"

But I saw everything in her face. I went back, crushed, only to find Mr. Wang was quite forgotten now and they were arguing over repainting the church door or about an appropriation for tracts or over opening a new station. Andrew was always wanting to expand the Work, to open more stations, and the others did not want him to do it. Listening to them, my heart swelled with helpless tears. It seemed to me they were always against Andrew and Carie, those men and women with their leathery skins and hard mouths and bitter determined eyes. Andrew sat there, never looking at them, but always out of the window, across the valley to the hills, that brow of his white and serene, his voice quiet and final. Over and over again he was saying, "I feel it my duty to push further into the interior. I regret if it is against your will, but I must do my duty."

Thus Andrew did his share of quarreling, but in his own fashion. He never obeyed any rules at all, because they always seemed to conflict with what was his duty, and he always knew his duty. The others might vote and decide, for the Work was supposed to be carried on by a sort of democratic decision of all the missionaries, subject to their financial boards in America. But Andrew listened only to God. Lack of money never stopped him. If he had no money, and he never had it, he wrote to anybody he knew who had any, asking for it shamelessly. If he got it, and he often did, he was supposed by mission rule to report it and put it into the common budget. But though he would report it if he thought of it, he never gave it up and he used it as he liked—always to push on into the interior, to open up new little centers for his preaching. I have seen other lesser and more bureaucratic missionaries grow almost demented trying to control Andrew. They shouted bitter words at him, they threatened him with expulsion if he did not cease disobeying rules, over and over they called him a heretic, once even called him insane because he seemed to hear nothing they said. He was a rock in the midst of all the frothing—unmoved, unresentful, serene, but so determined, so

stubborn in his own way, that I know there have been those who, seeing that high, obstinate, angelic tranquility, have felt like going out and groaning and beating their heads against a wall in sheer excess of helpless rage. But Andrew did not know even that they were angry with him. Had he not told them God's will? He must obey God's will.

Well, God's will led him along the line of battle all his life. He waged continual war—battle and skirmish, but no retreat. One of his wars, which time and his own determination won him at last, was on the subject of an educated Chinese clergy. When he went to China he found the Chinese clergy for the most part very nearly illiterate. They had been coolies, servants, gatemen in mission compounds, humble men who were easily converted and who more easily stepped into the slight supremacy of standing in a pulpit and haranguing a passing crowd. Andrew was shocked to the soul. He was a scholar and a lover of learning, and he perceived the intellectual quality of the Chinese and how little Chinese of worth and standing could respect these ignorant men. It was, he felt, to bring the Church into contempt.

It seems absurd now, more than a half a century later, to realize what a tremendous uproar Andrew made by such a belief. He was called a heretic, he was denounced for liberalism and modernism, for not believing in the power of the Holy Ghost, for trusting to men's brains rather than to God's power—all the hue and cry familiar through centuries to those who have dared to differ from orthodox religion. For, cried the orthodox—do they not always so cry?—God could do anything. He could make a gateman into a great preacher. Human knowledge was nothing but deception, "filthy rags," St. Paul had taught them to call all human righteousness.

Andrew, his head high above the

surge, began to gather about him a little group of young intellectuals, five or six, whom he taught in a class in his own study. They were already learned in their own language. He taught them history, religious philosophy, Hebrew, Greek, homiletics—all the things he himself had been taught in seminary. He continued that class over years, its members changing. He never used an uneducated man in any of his churches. Fifty years after he began that war he saw a thriving theological seminary established and he closed his class. His world had caught up to him.

Then there was that question of religious denominations. One of the astounding imperialisms of the West has been the domination over the Chinese of Methodists, Presbyterians, Baptists, and what not, to the number of well over a hundred different types of the Protestant Christian religion alone. This has been, in China, more than a spiritual imperialism—it has been physical as well. There has been much talk of political spheres of influence, of Japan and Germany and England and France, dividing China into areas for trade and power. But the missionaries divided China, too. Certain provinces, certain areas, were allotted to certain denominations for propaganda and there was supposed to be no overstepping.

Andrew was, of course, a born overstepper, because he always did as he pleased. He went where he pleased to preach. If some irate Methodist missionary pointed out that in a certain town there was already a Methodist chapel and that therefore Andrew had no right there, he pshawed and preached on briskly. Accused, he said calmly, "The Methodists aren't accomplishing anything there. The man at their chapel is a stick. I can't let all the people in that town go without the Gospel." Yes, I know he was maddening.

For, illogically, he could be merciless on any who stepped into his preserves. A bogey of our childhood was a certain one-eyed Baptist missionary who, I know now, was a harmless good man, not more obstinate in his ways than others, but who throughout my childhood I felt was a spirit of darkness. I gathered that impression from Andrew because the man believed in and taught immersion as the one true baptism while Andrew, being Presbyterian, only sprinkled the heads of his converts. But the one-eyed Baptist went about in Andrew's territory telling everybody sprinkling was wrong.

It was a nice situation, humorous only to the impartial observer. For the ignorant people, believing that if a little water was a good thing for the soul, more was better, too often followed the one-eyed man, to Andrew's intense fury. Moreover, it seemed there were certain passages in the New Testament which disconcertingly supported the one-eyed missionary's theory that Jesus walked people entirely under the water. The only thing that really helped Andrew was that a good many of the Chinese were disinclined to get themselves wet all over, especially in the winter, so that immersion was unpopular except in the hot season.

The war went on year after year, and it was the more difficult because Carie maintained a friendship with the pleasant wife of the Baptist. We sat silent through many a meal while Andrew with unwonted fluency said what he felt about other denominations, especially about the folly of immersion, and most especially about the lunacy of telling ignorant people they must be immersed. In his defense it must be said that it was of course extremely trying for him to labor to secure a good Presbyterian convert in one season only to discover upon the next visit that he had been immersed into a Baptist. It was like harboring a cuckoo in the nest. One taught and labored and suffered all the trouble of instilling the fundamentals of Christianity into a heathen and at least one should be able to put down a new member in the statistics. It was nothing short of religious thievery when the member was added to the Baptist glory.

After thirty years of strenuous warfare, the situation was settled one morning by the one-eyed missionary being found dead in his bed of heart failure. Andrew felt he was completely vindicated. He was at the breakfast table when the sad news was brought in by the compound gateman. He poured tinned cream into his coffee and put in a little extra sugar before he answered. He secretly loved sugar and was very stern with himself about it. But this morning he stirred it up. Then he looked around at us all and said in a voice of calm and righteous triumph, "I knew the Lord would not allow that sort of thing to go on forever!"

Afterwards he was a complete and untiring advocate of denominational union. But that is the story of another war and he died before it was finished.

The truth is that the early missionaries were born warriors and very great men, for in those days religion was still a banner under which to fight. No weak or timid soul could sail the seas to foreign lands and defy danger and death unless he did carry his religion as a banner under which even death would be a glorious end. The early missionaries believed in their cause as men these days do not know how to believe in anything. Heaven was actual, a space filled with solid goods. Hell did burn, not only for the evil unbelieving, but far more horrible, for those who died in ignorance. To go forth, to cry out, to warn, to save others —these were frightful urgencies upon the soul already saved. There was a very madness of necessity, an agony of salvation. Those early missionaries were fight-

ing in a desperate cause—to save those who were being born more quickly, dying more swiftly than they could possibly be saved. They laid vast plans, they drew up campaigns over hundreds of thousands of miles, they sped swiftly from soul to soul. They even estimated two minutes to a soul to tell them the way of salvation. "Believe on the Lord Jesus Christ—you believe? Saved, saved!"

It is not a thing to smile at, not even in these days of casual disbelief. It was a terrible thing, a crushing horror, not upon the blessed ignorant who died peacefully and went to hell all unknowing, but upon those frantic desperate men and women who felt upon themselves the responsibility of saving souls. None but the strong could have borne the burden —none but the strong, none but the blindly hopeful, could have eaten, could have slept, could have begotten children and lived out their days under such oppression.

But they were strong. I have not seen anywhere the like of Andrew and his generation. They were no mild stay-at-homes, no soft-living landsmen. If they had not gone as daring missionaries, they would have gone to gold fields or explored the poles or sailed on pirate ships. They would have ruled the natives of foreign lands in other ways of power if God had not caught their souls so young. They were proud and quarrelsome and brave and intolerant and passionate. There was not a meek man among them. They strode along the Chinese streets secure in their right to go about their business. No question ever assailed them, no doubt ever weakened them. They were right in all they did and they waged the wars of God, sure of victory.

Ah well, they are all gone now! There are no more left like them. Those who take their place in our modern times are shot through with doubt and distrust of themselves and their message. They talk of tolerance and mutual esteem, of liberalizing education and of friendly relations and all such gentle feeble things. They see good in all religions and they no longer wage any more wars and they serve their lives out for a small security. There is no taste in them. I can hear Andrew reading sternly from the Book of Revelation, "So then because thou art lukewarm, and neither cold nor hot, I will spue thee out of my mouth!" The giants are gone.

My memory of that circle of half a dozen soberly dressed people is grim. Now, of course, after years away from them, after knowing what people are like in ordinary places, I realize the impossibility to which their human souls were stretched. The real story of life in a mission station has never yet been told. When it is told it must be told, if it is to be told truthfully, with such vast understanding and tenderness and ruthlessness that perhaps it never can be done justly. The drama in it is terrifying. Imagine two, four, five, six—rarely more—white men and women, some married to each other, the others starved without the compensation of being consecrated to celibacy, imagine them thrown together, hit or miss, without regard to natural congeniality of any sort, in a town or city in the interior of China, living together for years on end, without relief, in the enforced intimacy of a mission compound, compelled to work together, and unable, from the narrowness of their mental and spiritual outlook, to find escape and release in the civilization around them. Within those compound walls is their whole real world. Their real companionships are with each other, or else they live utterly alone. They seldom become proficient enough in the language to enjoy Chinese society or literature even if their prejudice did not forbid it. There they are, struggling to maintain standards of Christian brotherhood,

struggling against their own natural antipathies and desires, wasting their spirits in an attempt to be reconciled to that which is irreconcilable among them.

And what incredible stories, what pathetic, human, inevitable stories! They are hushed, guarded against, kept secret, for the sake of the Work, for the sake of the "home church," for shame's sake, for God's sake—but what stories!

There was that old white-haired gentle man who worked for so many faithful years, only to go at last so strangely mad, so quietly mad, shielded by his agonized loyal wife. The story crept out, as it always comes out, through servants. He had a concubine—a fresh-faced Chinese country girl. Yes, his wife knew. Yes, they had prayed over it in such distress, so long—there was that insatiable thirst in him for—for such things. It was hard to understand—he was so good, really. And then his wife had thought of old Abraham, longing for the young Hagar, and it seemed to her she was like Sarah, and Sarah gave Hagar to Abraham. And God was not angry—God understood. But the story came creeping out, and the old white-haired pair were hastily retired.

And there was the strange little gray-eyed, brown-haired, pallid Chinese child, running about with a native pastor's flock of children. And there was the tall lonely missionary whose wife was years away, educating her own children at home. No one ever knew how that story came creeping out of a little village. An enemy did it, perhaps. No one is without enemies in China. But when the Chinese pastor was asked why among his dark brood there should be the one pale child with foreign eyes, he answered candidly enough, "The white man who is my head lives a very lonely life. And did not David take another man's wife, yet he was the Lord's beloved?"

And there were the two old missionaries, man and wife for forty years, living

[185]

dangerous, brave, sacrificing lives, and suddenly their life fell into pieces when they were old, and the man, sensitive and worn to his bones, cried out that he had hated his wife for years, that his flesh had revolted at hers, and he had lived in desperate unhappiness. He cried over and over only one thing, shuddering, "I don't want ever to hear her voice again. I don't want to feel the touch of her hand!"

And there is the story of the pleasant-looking missionary, subject for years to moods of mania, when he imagined his kind dark-eyed wife was unfaithful to him, and he would seize a knife from the table or a chair or anything at hand, and try to kill her. Their four little children grew up with the horrible secret and not one of them spoke, because their mother, after the mood was over and after he had made her do penance by crawling around him on her hands and knees, laid it upon them with passion that they were never to tell. So they never told. They grew up with a strange quiet tensity of look, but no one knew. Then the faithful wife died and the missionary married again, a gentle spinster, and she would not tell, and so it went until at last he revealed the truth himself in a fit, and all the years of torture came to life again in the shuddering words of the children, released at last to speak.

And no one has told the story of the spinsters for Christ's sake, the women who in the sweet idealism of their youth go out to lonely mission stations. Year by year they grow paler and more silent, more withered and more wistful, growing sometimes severe and cruel with their fellowmen, and sometimes, too, growing into miracles of pure and gentle selflessness. Most of them never marry, because no man ever asks them—there is none to ask them. Sometimes they marry a man inferior, an older widower, a rough river captain—even, sometimes, though this is never to be told, their Chinese associates.

But that is so rare I think it truly need not be told.

And those missionary widowers, marrying so quickly when their wives die that even the polygamous Chinese wonder! The missionary cemeteries are full of wives. I think of one black shaft of a tombstone in a certain walled spot beside the Yangtze River where an old son of God lies buried with three wives and seven of his children about him. But the shaft is raised only to him. Yes, the blood of such white men runs hotter than the blood of the heathen, even though they are men of God.

Yet to understand the impossible narrowness of that mission life is to forgive every bond that is sometimes burst. In that hot foreign climate, in the storms of wind and dust, in the floods and wars and risings of mobs against them, in such uneasiness of life, in such impossibility of achieving what they have set themselves, in bitter isolation from their kind, in the inward oppression of their own souls, that oppression which looks out of their somber eyes and sounds in their voices, apathetic if they are not angry, the wonder is not that men of God quarrel with each other so often, but that they do not kill each other or themselves more often than they do.

They do sometimes kill themselves. There was that missionary wife who rose from her husband's bed after she had borne him eight children and ran in her white gown through the night on a Chinese street and leaped from a cliff into the Yangtze River. And there was that gay and pretty Southern girl who rose in another night and crept downstairs into her own kitchen and with a common chopping knife tried to cut her throat and could not die, and she went up into the attic, her husband and her four little children sleeping, and found a rope and hung herself, and she leaped from the window and the rope broke and still she could not die, and she staggered, dripping blood, upstairs again into the bathroom and found poison and so died at last. There are such stories, but nobody wants them told, for the Work must go on. I say the wonder is not that there are these stories and scores like them, but that there are not many more than there are. Conversion does not really change the needy human heart.

But of course I only came to know all this afterwards. In those days of my childhood I may as well confess I was afraid of Andrew and all of them. My own private real life was lived entirely elsewhere in a place where there was no God at all.

There were mornings, bright sunny spring mornings, when one woke up to imagination. Usually it was a day when Andrew was going away on a journey. I may as well tell still more of the truth. A certain relief came over us all when he was going away on one of his preaching tours. The servants ran briskly to fetch and pack. There was always a bedding roll to get ready, a long bag of brown homespun cotton cloth into which was put a thin mattress, a blanket, and a pillow. Andrew was fastidious about lice in inn beds. If he were traveling by land this bedding was thrown across the back of his white donkey. Then he, wearing a sun helmet and a light gray cotton suit, or earlier his Chinese robes, and carrying a cane under his arm to beat off dogs, would straddle the donkey and the bedding roll, his long legs dangling until his feet were not two inches from the ground. He always said drily that if the donkey tried to kick up he simply held his feet on the ground. But it was a sturdy beast and trotted off with dogged gaiety, its ears cocked wickedly, tail swishing. We watched that gaunt indomitable figure disappear down the cobbled, willow-shaded lane, and then a sense of

peace fell over us all. The servants dawdled. Carie went to the organ and sang a long time or she read a book, and I—I went out into the garden and played all day there was no God. And Carie often helped unconsciously by saying at twilight, "We'll skip prayers tonight and take a walk instead—just for once God won't mind." God! There hadn't been any God all day.

On one such evening I carried imagination to a dangerous pitch. I decided not to say my prayers at all. I could not sleep for a long time, dreading the darkness. For in the darkness I knew of course there really was a God—there was that Eye that saw everything. But I stuck to my wickedness and fell asleep to wake, to my astonishment, perfectly safe, the peaceful summer sunshine streaming in my window. I never feared Andrew quite so much again. God had not done anything to me.

Now that I am no longer young, I know that Andrew never meant to frighten a little child or dreamed that he did. There were times, I remember now, when he came back from his long tours spent and weary but in a sort of glory of content, his work well done, God well served. He seldom saw beauty, and yet there were times when he said at supper, "The mountains were pretty today, covered with red and yellow azaleas everywhere." Sometimes he even brought back an armful of the flowers, if it so happened that his heart was content with what had happened to him. Sometimes he told us what he had seen—a small hill panther had crouched at the side of the road, and he had not known whether to go on or turn back, but he had promised to be at a certain village at noon and there would be those who waited for him. So he went on without seeming to notice, and the beast had not sprung. Wolves he saw often in winter, sometimes running down into the fields where the farmers chased them. But I was disappointed when I first saw a wolf because it looked like a big village dog and little more, except it was an odd dull gray in color.

In the spring Andrew was always gone. He grew restless as winter closed and as soon as the spring floods began to well into the canals from the river, swollen with melting snows in the upper gorges, he began to plan his long preaching tours by junk or upon his white ass. When Carie lay dying she said to me, knowing well enough that some woman would have to look after Andrew, "Look out for spring! About the first of April he gets hard to manage. It won't matter if he's eighty, he'll want to get away over the country and behind the hills preaching." Well, it was a good thing he always had the Gospel to preach so that he could go into all the world and be happy, feeling it was his duty. Not everyone is so lucky. But then I always said Andrew had a happy life. God always seemed to have told him to do what he would have wanted to do anyway.

In all my life I heard Andrew speak of only two men with unmeasured praise, and though I never saw them myself, for I was born too late for that, I have always thought of them as giants. For all I know they may have been men of ordinary size, but I see them tall like gods. They take their place with Goliath and David, and for goodness they stand among the elder prophets. Otherwise Andrew would not have praised them. For he might give away silver and gold carelessly, but he never so gave his praise. I waited years to hear a word of approbation from his lips, and when it came I knew I deserved it or he would not have given it to me then.

It seemed that Andrew was utterly dissatisfied with the plans of expansion in the narrow mission group in which he worked. "Creeping from village to vil-

lage!" he exclaimed. "Satisfied with a street chapel or two in a town! Why, we have to think in terms of a continent and of millions of people!" He began to plan a scheme of rapid northward expansion which seemed nothing short of insanity to his fellow missionaries. But opposition was energy to Andrew.

It happened that this was the time when Carie came down with tuberculosis and they went to a northern seacoast where she could recover. While she was busy about this, Andrew investigated, as he set forth on his preaching tours, the methods of missionaries in that province of Shantung, a region which belonged to another religious denomination. So he found the two giants, whose names were Corbett and Nevius. They did not work together. In fact, I believe they were mortal enemies. But both were so statesmanlike, both so large in their plans, that Andrew admired them completely. He went with them, listening, observing, learning. For years he discussed the relative merits of their opposing systems of spreading the Gospel. One worked extensively, over wide areas, taking advantage of every chance, content with less than satisfactory results sometimes in order to see constant expansion. The other worked intensively, perfecting and completing each center before he opened another, making a continuous chain of churches rather than scattering them widely. Both were men of shining intellect, imperious will, and volcanic physical energy. But one was a rough crude son of an American farmer and the other a polished and cultivated gentleman. Out of such extremes do sons of God come.

Andrew, in the illimitable extravagance of his ambition, planned to adopt the best in both their methods. He would expand and develop, too. "Those months were the most useful of my life," he wrote. "Those two great missionaries set the plan of my own missionary career."

When Carie was well again and they returned to Central China, he was in a frenzy to begin his real work. He had already been nearly five years in China, but he felt that only now had he really begun. He left his family in a rented house in Chinkiang and set sail eagerly up the Grand Canal, alone.

5

I keep forgetting, as I tell this story, to say anything about the birth of Andrew's children. I am possessed by Andrew. I see him, as I so often saw him, eagerly, eternally setting out on a new journey. I hear him in his old age telling me, in his fragmentary fashion, his own story, and he never said anything about the children. I was not born yet, so I cannot tell my own story of him then. But when he sailed up the Grand Canal to begin his work of opening up new territories he had a son living and a daughter dead and another child soon to be born. Carie told me that.

He never told me anything of the birth and death of his children. He did tell me, chuckling, that in a city up the canal where he decided to make his first center, he rented what he called "a splendid house" for almost nothing at all. No Chinese would live in it because it was haunted by a fox. "It was nothing but a weasel," he said with a dry laugh, seeing no likeness between their fears and his own secret twinges at ghost stories. He had the place whitewashed and made clean and then went and fetched his family and left Carie to settle things while he traveled northward. But he always spoke a little fondly of that house. He was rather proud of himself for having found it, and he thought of its simple comfort warmly when he was on his prodigious journeys. I have no picture of

it from him for he could not tell such things. But they brought one of the stoves from Shanghai and it was warm in winter and he had a study of his own where he could put his books, and he had a good student lamp on a big Chinese table and an easy chair. Those were things to remember when he lay on a brick bed in an inn or jogged over the intolerably rough roads on his donkey.

That he might travel more quickly he planned and made with a Chinese carpenter's help a sort of wagon with springs of a crude kind. He stood by the ironsmith's forge while they were being beaten out upon the anvil, and around him gathered a great crowd, staring at his strangeness, dubious of those great iron pieces. Were they not parts of some sort of foreign sword? Then he bought a mule and hitched it to the wagon and clattered up and down the countryside in great content, to the excitement of all beholders.

So great was the envy of his wagon, however, that at last some robbers heard of it and came and took it and all he had, except his tracts and Bibles which they threw into a ditch. And Andrew walked thirty miles barefoot and in his underwear, and upon his back were three great open cuts which they had given him when he resisted. For he had put up a stout fight, Carie discovered upon close questioning. She got the story out of him by bits. Yes, of course he had said he wouldn't give up his cart. Why should he? What did he do? Why, he hit them with his whip until they pushed him off the seat, and then he jumped up and cracked a lot of their heads together! He was so much taller that he could do it, but there had been too many of them— he could not crack enough of them quickly enough. Carie washed his wounds and bound them and he complained bitterly of having to sleep on his stomach for weeks, and more out of his irritation than anything else he went to the local magistrate and demanded his cart and mule again. The magistrate was a peace-loving, opium-smoking old scholar and he said mournfully it was impossible—he would give Andrew money. But Andrew insisted on the cart and the mule. He threatened international complications if they were not forthcoming. Andrew always made use of international treaties and extraterritoriality. Had he not a perfect right to preach the Gospel? The magistrate sighed and promised. The mule never came back—the magistrate apologized profusely and said unfortunately he had been eaten. But the cart came back quite ruined, and Andrew looked at it a little grimly but satisfied. At least no one else was getting the good out of it. He went back to donkey riding again, as being safer and more suitable after all to a man of God.

This was Andrew's method of procedure in his days of militant expansion. He would ride into a large village or into a town he had chosen as his next center and search out the largest tea shop and tether his donkey to one of the bamboo poles that held up its blue cotton awning and go in and sit down at a table near the street. His great height, his big nose, his bright blue eyes, his whole most foreign-looking figure would within a quarter of an hour draw a great crowd. Within an hour, or as long as it took for the telegraphic speed of the mouth-to-mouth message, "A foreign devil is in the tea house on the Big Bridge," everybody in the town would be there, unless they were bedridden. The tea shop keeper never knew whether to be pleased or terrified at such a mob. Certainly he never had such a customer before as this giant.

But Andrew smiled amiably and drank bowls of tea, and asked questions about the town—how many families lived here, and what was the chief business, and

who was the magistrate? The few of the more bold among the crowd pressing against him answered, a little fearfully—for why should a foreign devil want to know these things about them?

The boldest would ask a question of him: "What honored country is yours, Foreign Devil?"

"My unworthy country? America!"

The crowd breathed more freely. Ah, America—America was good. There was an unblinking pause while they stared at him. So this was how Americans looked! They examined him minutely, and made the next question. "What is your business, Foreign Sir?"

"I am a Jesus church man."

Again the crowd stared, nodding to each other. Jesus church—they had heard that word. Well, it was a good thing—all religions were good—all gods were good. They felt easier, having placed him.

But Andrew shook his head. Not all gods were good, he said firmly. There were false gods—gods of clay and stone —but his was the one true god. They listened, humoring him. After all, he was a foreigner—he could scarcely be expected to know manners.

He handed out tracts and now they shook their heads. "None of us can read," they said apologetically. It was better to take nothing from him, not strange papers with pictures. "I have some books, too," he said. "I sell them for a penny apiece." Well, selling was different. That was to be understood. A few in curiosity, two or three, fumbled in their belts for pennies and took the small paper-bound books. He sat there for an hour or two, and then he went away. Behind him the crowd made their judgment—a harmless good man doing a religious penance, doubtless. He must have made a vow to a god to do a good deed, else why leave home to wander over the earth? He was laying up merit for himself in heaven, it must be. Perhaps he had committed a crime in his own land. Well, he was an ugly fellow with such big hands and feet and a nose like a plow, and eyes like a demon's —but a good man, doubtless, selling his little books to buy his rice on his journey. Well, it was time to go home.

In a few days, Andrew would be back. There would be a crowd again, not so large, but friendly and familiar. "Back again, Foreigner! You like our village!"

"Yes, it is a good village. I should like to preach here."

"Preach—preach what you will—we will listen!" they said, laughing.

So Andrew stood up in the tea shop to preach. "For God so loved the world, that he gave his only begotten Son, that whosoever believeth in him should not perish, but have everlasting life." Out of these words, solemnly repeated, Andrew had worked a brief compact exposition of the whole scheme of salvation. God— His son—believe—not perish—everlasting life. His whole creed was there. "I devised a short sermon," he wrote gravely, in after years, "which comprehended all the essentials of Salvation, so that the unsaved soul, hearing perhaps but once, could understand and so take upon itself its own responsibility."

Again and again Andrew would return to that place until his figure became familiar to them, and then he would look about for a room to rent, a room that opened upon the street. When it was found it was whitewashed clean, some cheap wooden benches bought, a rough table for a pulpit, a text painted on the wall behind it. Behind the table Andrew stood regularly to preach, twice a week, three times perhaps, as often as he could, and the crowd came and went. Weary farmers set down their baskets on their way back from market and listened as they rested. Curious citizens came in and sat a while to hear a new thing. Mothers came in out of the sun to sit on the benches and nurse their babies.

But the women were always an aggravation to Andrew. "They never really listen," he complained. "They call across the room to each other, asking silly questions about cooking and children. They never understand anything, so it is no use wasting time on them."

"Well, I suppose they have souls, Andrew," Carie always said with spirit.

But Andrew would never answer. It was evident that he doubted it. Anyway, a woman's soul could scarcely count as a full soul. In his records of converts he always noted them. "Seventy-three received this year (fifteen women)." A really successful year was when the percentage of women was low. When they came up for examination into church membership he never treated them quite as he did the men. "They haven't much real idea of what they are doing," he said. "It's beyond them."

As soon as there was a little group— two, three, four converts—he pushed on to fresh villages, leaving in his place an older convert from an earlier center, whom he had trained to be a preacher of sorts. Twice a year, on his long spring and autumn tours, he would visit every village, examine new converts, baptize those who seemed to him sincere, hear complaints and troubles, and sprinkle the heads of infants whose parents were converts. One of the proofs which he insisted showed the stupidity of women was that these mothers whose babies were sprinkled could never understand that it did not make the infants members of the church. Time and again at a communion service I have seen his face grow stiff with horror as he saw an innocent Chinese mother cram the holy bread into a tiny baby's mouth and pour in a gulp of wine. There was always a roar of protest from the baby—not one of them seemed willingly a Christian! Andrew always "spoke" to the mothers. They looked at him, frightened at his serious, shocked face.

"Will he die of it?" one sometimes whispered.

"No—no—it isn't that," he would explain. "Don't you see . . ." he went on to explain. They listened, trying to understand. They all listened, men and women, as he preached, trying to understand.

There was something about those little handfuls of converts that wrings my heart even at the distance of these years. They were infinitely pathetic somehow. Why had they come out from among their people to listen to this stranger? Why did they come out from the safety of their people to believe him? They were so alike in every village—one looked and saw the same ones, the old woman whose patient face was shaped and sculptured by disappointment, deep and long. Life was nearly over, and then what was there? Her eyes were always too intelligent, too profound. She had been born with more wisdom than her fellows. It had not been quite enough for her, the common life of marriage and bearing children. She had enough for all this and something more. Ask her why she was there and she would answer a little painfully, "I have tried all the other ways to find peace, but I have not found peace."

"What ways, lady?"

"I have prayed to many gods. I have listened to many priests, but I have this aching in me." She puts an exquisite old hand delicately upon her breast.

"What is it that aches there?"

"I do not know."

"You have sons?"

"Yes, I have sons—three sons—it is not that."

"You have everything?"

"Everything—but no peace."

"How do you know you have no peace?"

"I wonder so much—night and day I am restless with wonder."

"What wonder?"

"I ask myself, why am I alive? Why are all these about me alive? What does birth matter and marriage and birth again, since at last there is only death? What does this mean?"

"And you hope to find peace here?"

"I do not know—only here is a god I have not known, and here is a strange priest I have not heard."

"You believe what he says?"

"I do not know, but I feel at least he is to be believed because he so believes himself. It is something when a priest believes himself. So I will try."

There is another old woman who sits near her, a common old soul with a pocked face who sits sleeping while Andrew preaches, her jaw hanging.

"Good mother, why are you here?"

She grunts, opens her eyes and laughs and rubs her head to wake herself.

"Why, you see, it is like this. I have no son, accursed that I am, and only two daughters, now married. I am old, so my man, who is only a clod at best, has not fed me for these ten years, and I do as little work as I can. I mend socks for the soldiers or I wash vegetables for an innkeeper or I scrub out night pots for the slaves of the rich who are too dainty to do such things for their mistresses—anything I can I do, because I cannot be always going to my daughters' doors with my bowl empty, or their husbands make it hard for them. So I must shift for myself. I came here to see if this foreigner would give me a little work."

"But you said you believed in his talk! You let him put water on your head!"

"Eh, yes—a little water—well, I let him have his way, because I thought he would be pleased and help me a little. Do you know him? Will you speak for me? Tell him . . ."

On the other side of the aisle where

the men sit, there is that slight pale lad who sits with his knees crossed and one restless foot tapping the brick floor as he listens and does not listen to Andrew. For sometimes he opens a hymn book restlessly and sometimes he stares out of the little dirty-paned window.

"Why have you come, young sir?"

"I want to learn English."

"Why?"

"I want to get away from this miserable village. I want to get a job in a big city—Shanghai. If I could speak English I could get a job in a big foreign office."

"Who told you?"

"I have heard it said."

"You do not believe what he says?"

"This tall foreigner? I do not believe in any religion. I do not want religion. I want money. I want to see the world."

There is an old man—there is always an old man.

"Oh sir, why have you taken the bread and wine?"

"Religion is good—all religion is good —it brings peace."

"Do you believe in other gods as well as this man's god?"

He smiles gaily and delightfully, his face as calm as Buddha's. "I believe in all gods—all gods are good."

There is a tall Mohammedan. There is Arab in him; it is in the lean line of his cheek and in the curve of his nostril and in the thin arch of his lips.

"You have left Allah?"

"I see that Allah for whom I have sought is this man's God. He has compelled me to belief."

"How has he compelled you?"

"There is fire in him. There is fire in me. The flame in his soul leaned over and caught at the flame in me, and I was compelled."

"Have you not been disowned by your friends, your family?"

"Yes, I am disowned. I have no friends, no family. My name is gone from the family names. They struck it away on the day when I told them I was a Christian."

"What will you do now?"

"I follow after this man."

"And then?"

"I will follow him."

This man indeed followed Andrew all his life, and Andrew made him into a great preacher. He might have been Andrew's brother, they were so alike; both of them tall and lean, their faces spare, their noses bold. Andrew was fair, and the wind and sun had burned his face dark red, and the same wind and sun had burned the Mohammedan's face a dark copper brown. But they were soul brothers.

Thus they came, some for one thing, some for another. Those who came only to see and hear a new thing fell away. But there was always the handful who stayed to listen, to learn, to eat at last the bread and drink the wine. Then, having eaten and drunk they clung to Andrew. For after that they were lost. They had separated themselves from their fellows and they could never be again as they had been. Christians! The color of their souls was changed. They had taken foreign substance into themselves. They could never go back to the old close, quarreling, merry-making life of streets and tea shops and market-places. Nor could they ever again go before the old gods. Their brothers, their fellows, never trusted them wholly again. They had eaten the flesh and drunk the blood of a new god.

Somewhere in this time Comfort was born, but it was entirely insignificant because it made no difference to Andrew, especially since she was a girl. Yet he should have been a little grateful because she helped him, merely by being born. It happened this way. Carie had lost two children in swift succession, and suddenly she broke, she whom Andrew had always thought was so headstrong, so invincible. She broke and begged to be taken home.

Nor was Andrew himself unmoved. Carie told me once she had never seen tears in Andrew's eyes, but the nearest she had seen to a dimness in their clear bright blue was when his son Arthur died. That night when his little fair body lay waiting for burial, Andrew and Carie read together their usual scripture before they went to bed. Andrew turned to the story of King David mourning over his dying son. "O my son Absalom, my son, my son Absalom!"

"He choked a little," Carie said. "Then he went on and read the rest in his usual firm way. 'Would God I had died for thee, O Absalom, my son, my son!' He shut the Bible and was himself again."

For Andrew so believed in God and in Divine Providence that it was not in him to grieve. "The Lord giveth and the Lord taketh away. Blessed be the name of the Lord!" For him this vast serenity covered the universe.

But when the second child, a girl, died, Carie became nearly demented with grief. Years after he said in a shocked voice, "I never saw so hard a heart, so unreasoning a mind, as were hers in those days. Nothing I could say would move her. The doctor in Shanghai said she must be diverted or she would lose her reason. So I engaged passage for Europe. I would have preferred the Holy Land, but she would not go there because somebody had told her the village dogs were mangy like those in China and the people were poor. So we went ashore at Brindisi. I remember at Lucerne there was very nice honey for breakfast. In Rome there was a great number of naked statues. It seemed strange when one considers that Rome is the center of the Christian religion. For I suppose, though Popish, Catholicism is

nevertheless a form of Christianity. I grew tired of Europe."

The truth was, of course, that Andrew grew quickly tired of anything except his work. For he had made huge plans for which any life was too short. The continent of China lay before him. Only by unceasing steady marching on could he succeed in completing, before he died, the campaign he had so plainly in his mind. Carie used to say she believed Andrew's brain was a map of China. He knew every province, every city, every river and town. He marked as his own those where he had planted his little chapels. Once one was established, and added to his chain of centers, he went on to new territory.

To this unending zealous preaching, this desperate salvation, he brought a deep inward emotional tensity that ate him up, body and soul. It flamed in him like fever under his serene exterior. When he was visiting cathedrals in Rome and Florence, he was still really in China, planning, planning, thinking, worrying lest the apostle Chang was too weak to be left alone, lest Li would be too domineering over the souls left in his charge.

But he was more afraid of his fellow missionaries than of anyone, lest they change his plans, dismiss or move his ministers, disturb with meddling his intricate campaign. When he came back to the hotel room he would take a sheet of paper and begin printing in square, clear Chinese letters his warnings and admonitions and instructions. "Do not listen," he wrote over and over to his comrade, Ma, once the Mohammedan, now Ma the Christian, "do not listen to any of the others, but to me who am your spiritual brother. Remember the plan we made together—follow it until I come." He stared out into the Roman street and saw the sunlight fall upon a marble church.

"Rome is full of images," he said, "infinitely worse in their nakedness than the gods of the heathen." He would put his hand to his forehead in a gesture of agitation. "I ought to be about my Father's business," he muttered. "I must be about my Father's business!"

He went about Europe like a chained and quarrelsome lion, intolerant of all local customs. He was particularly furious at the incessant tipping. What—give a fellow he had never seen a sum of money large enough to hire a week's preaching of the Gospel, enough to buy an Old and New Testament, for carrying his bags? He lugged them himself, striding into hotel lobbies, brushing aside lackeys like flies. Only once was he beaten. He put Carie and Edwin into a train for France, and then, since there were ten minutes to wait, he went into the station to the lavatory. There he glared down the station attendant who held out his hand and strode on. But Andrew was worsted for once. The attendant locked him in and listened unmoved to Andrew's poundings and all but profanity. No one knows what Andrew said, since the attendant spoke no English and Andrew would say nothing himself beyond the bare facts. He came loping toward the train at the last minute, to the intense relief of Carie and Edwin. "Got locked in," he muttered, panting.

Carie instantly saw what had happened. "You have to pay them a little," she said.

"I wouldn't have if the train hadn't been going," Andrew said, firmly, finding his breath.

"After all, it's their country," Carie said gently. "We're foreigners here."

"That doesn't excuse robbery," said Andrew. Obviously there had been a tussle of wills, and as Andrew said, the train was going. The sole effect on him

was to make him more obdurate than ever. He was particularly triumphant over the French and came more nearly than any other American ever did toward no tipping in France. Yet Andrew cared nothing for money—he could give it away with mad generosity when it was to buy Testaments and tracts and books of biblical research, or if it was to help a struggling divinity student toward graduation from seminary. But merely to give it—that was as foolish as it was to waste time away from the Work. He felt it equal to sin, and he was always intolerant of sin. Years later his too sensitive children suffered and shrank from the contempt upon lackey faces as his tall lean figure marched by, laden with bags and bundles.

"People don't," they murmured in the misery of adolescence.

But Andrew set his big jaw firmly. People! He listened only to God.

After Europe, he looked with impatience toward his own country. There at last was a Christian nation, where men were honest and not looking always and only for money. He was droll with suppressed gaiety on the day the ship docked at last at New York. He carried the bags ashore and deposited them abruptly in the nearest horse cab.

"Take me to a decent and reasonable hotel," he commanded the driver.

Carie, with the memory of the fray in Europe, said with unusual caution, "Hadn't you better ask the fare?"

But Andrew, with unusual recklessness, said, "We are in a Christian country now, thank God!"

They drove rattling through streets they did not know. "It's a long way," Carie said.

"Pshaw, Carie, the man knows what he is doing," Andrew replied. The horse stopped at a jerk of the bridle before a modest hotel.

"How much?" asked Andrew.

"Five dollars," the cabman said.

Andrew was dashed. Five dollars! It was a lot of money. But it had been a long drive. He paid, still in high humor. "We're home," he said, climbing the stairs with Carie and Edwin. They entered the room which they had taken. Carie walked directly to the window, as she always did in a strange place. She gasped.

"Why—why—Andrew, come here!" she cried, and burst into laughter.

"What is it?" he said in alarm. He came to her side and his gaze followed her pointing finger. There, not two blocks away, was the ship they had left nearly an hour before.

"What are you laughing for?" said Andrew, with a certain grimness. Five dollars!

"Because," she gasped, "—because it's such a—a Christian country!"

They went home by train, down through the states, through wooded hills that looked strange and furred after the shorn Chinese hills, over rivers that looked like creeks after the flooding Yangtze and the Yellow River, through towns whose houses looked unreal, they were so orderly and clean after the heaped mud and the confusion of Chinese villages. For ten years in China Andrew had not even seen a train, and he took an innocent pleasure in speed and ease, although still not too much ease. To have ridden in a Pullman he would have thought unbecoming in a missionary. What, take the money the church had gathered that the Gospel might be spread in heathen lands and spend it upon a softer bed for his body and for the bodies of his wife and children! He would have been made miserable. They traveled tourist or in day coaches, and even so he doubted the luxury. As for dining cars, he looked on them as sinful extravagance. To pay so much for mere food! He bought sandwiches and enjoyed them doubly as food and sacrifice.

The return home was a strange division. When ten years earlier he and Carie had gone away, they had felt they were leaving home indeed, forsaking father and mother to be worthy of their cause. The great old sprawling farmhouse had stood as certainly for home on this earth as heaven above was home for the soul. His parents had seemed endless in life, secure upon their land. But now he came back to find that the house, the home, was like a shell outgrown. His eyes had seen strange things. His feet had traveled many miles over other soil. He had begotten children under another roof and three of them lay buried in foreign earth. This old farmhouse was shrunken and old—and gone into decay. What had seemed so spacious and sound in his youth was grown into an old frame structure that needed paint and patching. The wooden pillars of the porches sagged, the roof leaked and the fence was so broken that the pigs could come in easily now. Within the house the hot old man still lived, but his heat had passed into smoldering. The quarrel between him and the woman had never mended. Every night he lay on the floor before the fire as he always had, staring into the coals, and she berated him in the same way for not sitting decently in the armchair opposite her own.

"Foolishness—you're getting old—you'll catch your death . . ."

It was true that of the two of them she was the stronger, the quicker, the neater. But then she did not fret herself as he did. She did nothing except sit on the porch or by the window and enjoy herself. Every now and again, upright and chipper, she would dart into the kitchen and find something to eat, a wedge of pie, a slice of salt-rising bread and apple butter, a cold fried chicken leg, a piece of ham, and with this she went back to enjoy herself.

"Snacking!" the old man would grunt. "Everlasting snacking!"

But she stayed as lean and strong as a hickory tree and lived far beyond him.

Every son had long gone out of the house except the youngest, and now he was grown and chafing to go. Son after son, they had gone out to preach and he wanted to go, because he too had the call. But the old man would not let him. One of the boys had to stay on the land. So the youngest son, tall and with the ice-blue eyes they all had, pushed the plow rebelliously and planned how as soon as the old man was dead he would be as good as his brothers. He would go to school and to the seminary and stand in a pulpit and direct the people and tell them what was God's will. Meantime he married a buxom Irish girl with snapping black eyes, a famous cook and house-keeper. It was she who scrubbed and cleaned, baked and mended in the house, and added her word to the old man's or to the old woman's. She had a tongue of her own and an Irish temper, the kind the black-haired, black-eyed Irish have, and her cheeks were red, and her mouth sullen. Yet her heart was kind enough and her table was laden with food and anybody was welcome to sit down to it.

But the brothers and their wives were scattered over the states. David the learned had long been minister in the small village which had been Carie's home, Hiram the handsome had married a young beauty and bluestocking and knew what a rare thing he had done. He was preaching in the South. Isaac was in Missouri, frail still from the years in prison, Christopher the Methodist was doing what the others grimly called "rampagin'" around in the Methodist church." John the prudent, married to his rich widow, was managing her fortune, living in her huge comfortable brick house in the midst of broad and fertile acres and being elected to the legislature. The house was empty of them all.

Andrew could not stay there, either. When he came home the old necessities fell upon him—cows to be milked, hay to be cut, horses to be fed. He fell into the old destroying labor and it was horrible to him. Every moment he was mindful that there were millions in China dying without the knowledge of God which he was able to give them to save their souls, and here he was milking cows and making hay! The old dreadful impatience came upon him.

And he was still Andrew the younger. The moment he came into this house he ceased to feel himself God's chosen. He became the younger son, less favored than any of the others. His mother, staring at him, remarked that he was yellow. His father snorted, "Heathen climate and eatin' heathen stuff!"

His hands grew hard and broken again at the nails. He had for years been secretly fastidious about his hands, ever since one of his brothers—Hiram, perhaps—had teased him about their size and boniness. "They look like an old man's hands," he always said. And his mother, hearing, always remarked placidly, "Andy ever did have hands like an old man, even when he was a baby." When he was really an old man his hands were extremely beautiful, large and skeleton thin, but delicate and full of grace. But then Andrew hated manual labor, although he did it conscientiously, as he did everything, to his best ability, hating it.

In after years the one great grievance

he kept remembering of this first visit home was that no one asked him anything about his life or his work.

"I couldn't understand it," he said earnestly. His blue eyes were full of pain and clear wonder. "They never asked me anything about China."

It was an old hurt, carried in his heart over all the years. For he had come home a man, full in stature and wisdom, ripe with experience beyond any of theirs. He had been far beyond the horizon of hills and fields, beyond even the West that seemed so far, beyond the seas. He had eaten strange foods, had walked the streets of other countries and had learned to speak a foreign tongue. But here he was only Andrew come home again. No one cared that he spoke, read, and wrote Chinese excellently; no one asked him, "What do they eat over there and what do they wear?" They examined briefly a few gifts Carie brought. The old man was far more pleased when she took his old coat and ripped it apart and turned it and made it look new again.

Andrew, dwelling upon it when he was an old man, said, the painful dry red creeping into his cheeks, "They said I was very quiet and that I didn't talk. But they didn't ask me anything. Why should I tell them what they did not care to know?"

They were an undemonstrative clan. Carie said once, laughing, with a catch of sadness in her voice, "Poor old Grandfather Stone! I suppose no one had kissed him for years. I remember the first night we were there Edwin kissed us goodnight as he always did and then in the fullness of his warm little boy heart he went and kissed his grandfather on the cheek, and the old man looked so astonished I was afraid he would frighten the child. He never moved or said a word and his face did not change, and Edwin drew back, dashed. I was so sorry—sorry for them both."

So to be at home was not comfort for Andrew. It was only to return to the old inferiorities. Nevertheless, it was Andrew out of all the sons who, on his furlough, helped his father to collect his rents from lazy tenant farmers upon the place and put his accounts in order. Andrew who re-roofed the enormous old barn and painted the house and mended the stairs. Duty drove him as ambition or love or pleasure might drive another man. He never shirked what he hated, if he once saw it his duty. For God had said, "Honor thy father and thy mother." Sternly and with grim patience he honored them.

But there were times when Andrew could find the satisfaction for which his soul thirsted. He was sent to preach in churches for missions. He did not preach often in city churches to proud people, smartly dressed, who wanted a condensation of China's needs into half an hour. Andrew went to country churches, where people were not hurried, and where they expected something long enough to be worth putting on their Sunday clothes for, and driving a long distance over rough dirt roads. Farmers and their wives listened peacefully to the stories Andrew had to tell of sin and misery, comfortably aware that they themselves had no sin and very little misery. After he had finished they did not look at the clock, and they put a little into the collection, and somebody always asked him home to dinner.

Those dinners! Remembering them in after years Andrew would exclaim with a sort of accusing pleasure, "Such waste! Fried chicken and cold ham, beaten biscuit, four or five kinds of vegetables and potatoes, salads and preserves and pickles, and pounds of cake and pudding and like as not ice cream! It would have served the Lord better to have put more in the collection plate and less in their stomachs!"

But then Andrew kept his horror of self-indulgence. He loved good food as well as any man, but he would not eat more than he thought necessary for strength to do God's work. The rarer the dainty, the more stern he was to refuse all or more than a morsel. Plain food, eaten slowly and sparingly, was his rule. And yet his innocent pleasure in a cup of tea on a cold afternoon, in a bowl of hot soup at supper when the day's work was over, was as keen as any gourmet's at the sight of terrapin or caviar or any useless and delicious food. The result of doing his duty was of course that he lived to eighty as strong and spare as an oak, and when his flesh was washed for burial it was as smooth and fresh upon his body, below the strong dark sunburn of face and neck, as any child's could be.

He recorded little of those two years in his own country. They stayed the two years sorely against his will, because Carie was with child and she had refused to go back until the child was born. He would have persisted and won except that Carie's father, that man whose stature was the stature of a little man, but whose soul was the soul of Hercules, and more bold, reminded him of his three dead children.

"This child shall be born under my roof," he decreed. So Andrew waited with Carie in her old home, impatient to save other souls already born, until this small soul appeared. It was a girl, not quite worth waiting for. Andrew never made any bones about that. Years later when the child was grown and began writing books, Andrew was not impressed. Novels—they were worthless, a waste of God's time even to read, much less write. He picked up one of hers once, a thick volume, and glanced at it, and turned a leaf or two, and closed it. "I think I won't undertake that," he remarked with his habitual vague gentleness, and not in the least meaning to be

unkind. Once he said, in duty, "I hope you never write anything not true, daughter," but he did not wait for her answer. It did not matter what the answer was. If he had spoken, his duty was quite finished.

Andrew never pretended he liked daughters as well as sons. His daughters existed, as his wife did, to take care of him. This, if he had been aware of his selfishness, they might have found difficult to bear. But he was not in the least aware of it. He was as touchingly, as confidingly, selfish as a little child. He looked to wife and daughters naïvely for all material things, taking for granted the comforts of food and proper clothing, warmth and light and all that he wanted for home. Once when he was an old man, or nearly old, and Carie was gone and he was dependent for these things upon a daughter who was herself a mother, a wife and bread-winner to boot, he fell very ill, and after a few days of incessant nursing when he would have no one but his daughter near him, the doctor compelled him to go to a hospital. He was very sad and miserable, having no confidence in strange women. "I want to go home," he said the third day. "I have a daughter at home who has nothing to do but take care of me." It was what daughters were for.

But when he was young he did not need them, and he was in haste to be about God's business. Once again he bade his home and parents good-by. But this time it was not in doubt and ignorance of what was ahead. He was in the full strength of his maturity and confidence. He knew to what he was going, and he was sure of himself now, as well as of his mission.

He was never to see home or parents again. When, years later, he returned once more, they were dead, the obstinate, placid old woman and the domineering high-spirited old man, who declared before he died, "God's cheated me! I begat seven sons and I haven't one left to live on the land," and so went grumbling into eternity. As for house and lands, they were sold at a bargain, and when the price was divided between seven sons and two daughters, there was only a pittance for each. They had chosen one brother to do the selling for all, and when he had done it, they railed at him for being a bad business man—all except Andrew who, ten thousand miles away, cared nothing. He took his pittance and put it into his New Testament. But then Andrew, like all his brother sons of God, was a very bad business man, too.

6

When Andrew's feet touched Chinese soil, he changed. Anyone seeing him in his own country would never have recognized him in China. In his own country he appeared a little ridiculous—a tall thin figure in ill-fitting garments made by a Chinese tailor, his prophetic head stooping on his gaunt shoulders, his eyes doubting and bewildered. On shipboard he appeared to smarter looking passengers as the missionary of story books, absorbed in his mission, mingling with no one. Not that he cared what they thought of him! He came and went among them, oblivious of them. It did not occur to him, I think, that ship's passengers had souls. Certainly women had not. He saw their frivolities with strong disfavor. But then he was one man whom no woman could blandish. Once on board ship he sat on deck reading a Chinese book, seeing nothing that was going on. It happened that a collection was being taken at the time among the passengers to buy prizes for some sports, and a committee of pretty women had been chosen to do the soliciting. Evi-

dently they considered Andrew difficult. I saw them arguing among themselves, throwing glances in his direction, to which he was completely impervious. Suddenly the prettiest and gayest said, boasting, "I'll do it! I've never had a man say no to me yet!" She sallied forth and putting on her very bewitching smile, she sat herself down on the arm of Andrew's chair, and began, coaxingly.

What she said no one ever knew. For Andrew gave her a look like the wrath of God and rose in mighty dignity and strode down the deck, his coat tails flying. But then he never looked at any woman. I used to complain to him that he never recognized my friends, and indeed that he passed his daughters on the street without speaking to them. To which he replied gently and firmly, "I never look a lady in the face. I consider it rude to do so."

By ridicule and contempt he was totally unmoved, for the simple reason that it did not occur to him to consider what people thought of him. Had their laughter been pointed out to him, he would not have cared. "What can man do to me?" he used to say. The world was divided into those who would be saved and those who would not. Those who would not were already lost and not to be heeded as alive any more.

It must be confessed that into this latter category he put most white men and all white women. "They have the means of salvation," he used to say, "and they do not take it." He was thinking of the churches in every town and village in his country. But I think he felt about souls very much as some people feel about eggs—he wanted them brown, and a brown one was worth any number of white ones. So far as I know he never endeavored to save the soul of a white man or woman, not even his own children. Certainly he never said a word to us on the subject of religion. Night and morning he held a simple form of prayers in his home for us, at which he did no preaching. He read a chapter from the Bible, heard us, when we were small, recite a verse apiece, and then he prayed.

When he prayed he became transfigured by his own belief. I have heard many men pray carelessly or fulsomely or for the ears of men rather than to God. I have seen them reading prayers aloud, openly or secretly, prepared prayers. But Andrew, when he prayed, did so with utter intense sincerity. He never opened his mouth and began to talk. He began always with silence, a moment, two moments, as many as he needed, to realize himself in the presence of God. Over his face would come a deep and solemn tranquility. We felt him no longer among us. Then, his very voice changed, deepened, full of reverence, he addressed God and with him drew us, too. He never, in all the thousands of times I heard him pray, asked for any material benefit, except, in case of illness, for the sick one's recovery if it were in accordance with God's will. His prayers were always for the soul, for further understanding of God and duty, and the strength to do God's will. Even grace before meat was, after thanks, "Bless this food to our use and us to thy service, forever, amen."

So Andrew did not hear laughter or see ridicule. He was safe in the sanctuary of his own soul. But when he stepped upon the Chinese shore, he no longer had the air of a foreigner that he had in his own country. He was home again, not home in a physical sense so much as home in his place, in his work, in the fulfillment of life. Happiness was in his look, in the unwonted eagerness of his step and voice, in his impatience to be out of Shanghai and back in the interior among the common people whom he had come to save. All the paternal instincts of his heart went out to those who were his

flock. His children never felt that warmth, but it was there—any Chinese soul in search of God could feel that priestly fatherliness in Andrew. He could be as gentle, as persuasive, as brooding over a soul as any father over an earthly child. He went back to them gladly, and they gave him the honor he never found in his own country.

There was therefore no strangeness in that return. He took passage upon a Yangtze River steamer and upon its deck piled the box of books he had brought back, the boxes of fresh tracts he had bought in Shanghai, and boxes of cheap writing paper, for he had already in mind a new task which was to occupy the rest of his life. Among the boxes was the round-backed trunk in which his wife Carie had packed her trousseau ten years before, and his own smaller round-backed trunk. But Carie's trunk held children's clothes now, too, and a little stock of needles and pins and thread, bits of lace and wool, all the small things which women need to make small garments, and which were not to be bought in the streets of a Chinese city. They all walked across the narrow gangplank, Andrew and his son Edwin and Carie carrying her baby daughter, then four months old. And once again they marched upon the heart of China.

Some of the most redoubtable battles that Andrew ever fought were upon those Yangtze River steamers. They were small, stockily built vessels, for the most part built in England, and their polyglot crews were headed by blasphemous, roaring, red-faced old English captains who had rampaged along the Chinese coasts for years and had retired into the comparative safety of the river trade. Not one of those captains but was full of tales of the pirates of Bias Bay and of bandits along the shores of the river, and they all had one love and one hate. They loved

Scotch whiskey and hated all missionaries. Andrew was unmistakably and proudly a missionary, intrepid in independence, afraid of no man, and meat for any self-respecting captain. The fray usually began with some insult tossed out by the captain, for Andrew was always quiet and apparently gentle in demeanor. The favorite insult had to do with the obscenity in the Bible. The captain would proclaim in a loud hearty voice to his mate, "Fact is, it beats me how these missionaries can hand around a book like the Bible. It's got more dirty stories in it than you can find in any other book. Corruptin' the heathen, that's what it is!"

A dark red would begin to creep up out of Andrew's collar.

"You seem to know certain parts of the Bible very well, Captain," he would remark.

"You can't deny it, can you?" the captain retorted.

Andrew, lifting his piercing blue eyes to the captain's face, replied with the immense tranquility that we all feared when we heard it. "The Bible, it is true, has certain accounts of sinful men and how God dealt with them. They were punished for their sins. He who reads aright, reads to the salvation of his soul. But there are those who read to their own damnation." And he would help himself serenely to the inevitable rice pudding and stewed prunes of the ship's fare.

Sometimes the fight went no further than a snort from the captain. But if it went on, Andrew fought it to the end with great pleasure and without animosity. It was only in the very lean years a little later, when the printing of his New Testament was eating up all we had, that he escaped the duels with the river captains, and then because we could not afford to travel upstairs with other white people. We put on Chinese clothes and traveled below decks with the Chinese. Andrew took advantage of the enforced congregation then, and went among them with his tracts, preaching and talking. They listened to him willingly enough, those who were not smoking opium or gambling, because there was nothing to do. They listened, yawning aloud with boredom, as he told them fervently how Christ died for their sins. They did not know what he meant by sins, or who this man was who wanted to save them, or why he did. They stared, half-listening, dropping to sleep in grotesque attitudes upon the deck, where they sat leaning against their bundles.

As for me, beginning then to see and feel, to perceive without knowing, I can never forget the smells of those ships. For we were come into the lean years as early as my memory goes, and I remember the darkness of the square low-ceiled saloons. They were always the same. At one side was the huge opium couch of wood and rattan with a long low table to divide it. There were always two drowsy figures outstretched, their lamps smoldering upon the table, and the thick foul sweetish fumes rising and creeping into every cranny. From the half-opened doors of the tiny cabins came the same smell, so that the close air seemed swimming with it.

Almost as large as the couch was a big round table upon which meals were served twice a day, but every moment otherwise it was used for gambling. Early in the morning the click and clatter of bamboo dominoes began, and it went on at night until dawn. The table was always crowded with players, their tense faces fierce with eagerness over the game. In the middle of the table was a pile of silver dollars which everyone watched covetously, closely, with terrible longing. The pile dwindled and grew, but occasionally it was swept away by a single lean dark hand. Then a strange growl went over the crowd of gamesters and over the crowd of onlookers always pushing one another around the table. They would not have stopped even to eat except that the dirty stewards swept the dominoes ruthlessly to the floor and set wooden buckets of rice upon the table and clapped down four or five bowls of cabbage and fish and meat, and bowls and bamboo chopsticks. In the same grim silence in which they had played they ate, bowl after bowl, searching in silence for the best bits of meat and vegetables. When the passengers were satisfied the stewards and cabin boys, all dirty and all insolent, gobbled up the remains.

But Andrew was imperturbable. He took his bowl and filled it sparely with rice and cabbage and went to the deck and stood eating, looking away from the grimy multitude, out to the smooth green banks of the river. He had a way of maintaining himself intact wherever he was, and people gave way to him in a sort of astonishment because he was continually in places where one did not expect to see such a figure as his, moving with dignity among the mean.

But he was always quite at home anywhere. No magnificence could awe him nor any poverty daunt him. He slept peacefully in the dirty upper berths of the vile little cabins. In the lower berth with Carie I remember seeing his large bare feet protruding far beyond the end of the berth above. They were always too short for him, those berths, and he used to take turns resting his feet or his head, for as he remarked, he couldn't sleep both ends at once. But he never complained, having chosen what he wanted to do.

As for Carie, she spent her time keeping the children as antiseptic as possible with carbolic lotion and watching that their possessions were not taken from them. For the river ships were full of

professional thieves. When they became so great a pest that business was lessened because of them, the owners of the vessels paid the thieves' guild a certain sum of money to stay off the ships for a while. But there were always some and they were skillful at abstracting whatever they wanted. Once Andrew came back into the little cabin and Carie's sharp eyes spied an emptiness about his vest.

"Your watch is gone!" she exclaimed.

It was indeed, and a few minutes later when Andrew had need of his fountain pen, that was gone, too, and he felt for his purse and it was gone. While he had been out in the crowded saloon preaching, some clever-fingered thief, pressing close in apparent zeal to hear, had taken everything. Andrew looked stricken for a moment, especially over the pen, which was a gift and dearly prized and much used.

"Oh, pshaw!" he exclaimed.

It was as near as he ever came to "damn" and it meant the same thing and he always felt better after he had said it. But nothing cast him down for long. He was an invincible optimist, being always sure he was doing God's will, and therefore that everything would be all right in the end.

Back in the interior city where they had lived before, Andrew found no great welcome from his fellow missionaries. He found that his furniture had been cast carelessly out of the house which Carie had made into a home. Everything had been put into an outhouse, and the white ants had reduced his goods to nothing. "I took up my bookcase," he said solemnly, "and it fell into dust." Worst of all, his few precious books were ruined with mildew. He never quite forgave or forgot that. "I had a good commentary of the Bible," he used to say, remembering, pain in the memory. "I tried to paste the good bits onto separate sheets of paper."

There was some discussion over the house, now occupied by others. "We thought you weren't coming back" the other missionary said, excusing himself.

"Not coming back!" Andrew exclaimed. "I don't believe it!"

Then the story came out, bit by bit. He was, he was told, heretical in his views. He believed to much in human knowledge—else why did he spend time in educating his pastors? Why did he not, as the other missionaries did, trust to the inspiration of the Holy Ghost? Christ took ignorant men and made them his chief apostles. Indeed, they felt so strongly about it that they had written to the home board and to the supporting churches urging that he not be retained because of his unsound views. Andrew listened grimly until they had had their say. Then he told them what he thought of them.

"What did you say?" we asked in after years.

"I told them they were lazy," he said. "I told them they wanted to live in comfortable houses and to care for their own families and pamper their own bodies. I told them they were not worthy of their high calling. In short," he said with energy, "I told them they were hypocrites."

"Father!" we breathed.

"Oh, I said it all very kindly," he said peaceably.

But the upshot of it was that they told Andrew he might go where he liked and they would vote that he be allowed to do so. He always ended the story by saying triumphantly, "They cast a vote of confidence in me and gave me the money to open a new station wherever I liked."

He was too guileless of soul to see what they had really done. They wanted to be rid of him at all costs—rid of his indefatigable energy, to be rid of his undying determination to be worthy of the calling which to him was holy, to be rid of his singleness of heart in his duty. Most of all they wanted to be rid of his sympathy for those whom he had come to save. He grew to love greatly the Chinese. It was a complaint against him that if the choice were given him to believe a Chinese or a white man, he always believed the Chinese. "I've learned bitterly that I can trust them more," he used to retort, grimly. He was rewarded by their devotion to him, and this did not make him better-loved by his fellows. The truth was that Andrew was completely intolerant of the policies of missions. It was the policy of the missionaries to stand together at all costs against the "natives." If any individual missionary had a clash with a convert or a Chinese preacher, all the missionaries upheld the white man, regardless of right or wrong. "It wouldn't do," it was often said, "to allow the natives to undermine the authority of the missionary." For then what would become of the authority of the church?

But Andrew would sweep such talk aside with a gesture of his great hand. "Oh, pshaw!" he would say. He had no reverence for any human authority whatever. "There's the right of a thing," he used to say. And many a humble Chinese pastor, struggling in a little village church at ten dollars a month, had Andrew to thank that he had even so small a place of security. That miserable wage! Andrew battled for wages all his life—though never for his own. And when he could get nothing he squeezed out a dollar or two himself for the man who had been refused.

Yes, they wanted to be rid of Andrew's intolerance of race superiority and priestly authorities. "A prince of the church!" he used to say. "Oh, pshaw—there's no such thing possible!"

So he packed his few remaining books

and Carie packed everything else and they went northward again into a new city.

There was no home to be rented in this city. No one would rent to the foreign devils. The best that Andrew could do was to find three small rooms in an inn so poor that the opium-smoking landlord was willing, being hard-pressed by his hunger for the drug, to let him have them at a high rent, since he had no guests anyway. The rooms were earthen floored, and the windows were very small, mere holes in the mud walls. But once a roof of any sort was over his family's heads, Andrew let it go at that and hurried to his own business.

And now it seemed to him he had never had a greater opportunity. For hundreds of miles he was the only missionary, the only white man. There were no other denominations with their interfering teachings. He had to himself an area as large as the state of Texas, full of souls who had never heard the Gospel. He was intoxicated with the magnificence of his opportunity.

But he had not come away alone. By now wherever he went there were some who followed him, Chinese preachers who chose him and his ways. Chief among them always was the tall Mohammedan, Ma, whose Arab blood was so clear in his thin haughty face and in his proud bearing. With this man and the few others Andrew planned his new campaign. The field—he always called the area for which he felt himself responsible his field—was drawn out upon a map, and a certain part apportioned to each for surveying. For Andrew must always know the material aspects of his fields—how many walled cities there were, and how many souls lived within the walls, and how many temples there were and what religion they belonged to,

and what the chief business of each city was, and whether people lived well or poorly. These walled cities were to be the centers. Then he must know how many walled villages there were, and how many market towns, and where the chief tea houses were where farmers from the lesser villages gathered after they had sold their produce and had time to linger and listen. His goal was a church in every walled city and a chapel in every market town. But there was never any force about this. He always used to say proudly, "I never established a church or a chapel in a place where people did not want it."

"How did you know whether they wanted it or not?" we asked him when we were old enough to be wicked.

"They always did want it after I talked to them and told them what it meant to refuse God," he said.

What Andrew never knew was that one religion more or less meant nothing to the people. There was always the possibility that there might be an extra god somewhere of whom they had not heard, and whom they should propitiate for benefit. To add a white man's god could do no harm. Buddha himself had been a foreigner, though black. It was only when Andrew preached boldly that his god was the one true god that hostility arose. It was when Andrew told men that they must leave the worship of ancestors in their family halls because to bow before a man was to give what belonged to this god only, that many went away and ceased to follow him. But Andrew was never daunted. He had the faith that those whom God had called would remain, and those not predestined to remain would go away, and he let them go, unmoved.

Nevertheless, Andrew at this time of his life certainly set himself to the winning of souls. For one thing he put on

Chinese garments and let his hair grow long and braided it into a queue. This was because his tall body and his foreign looks were terrifying to country people. Sometimes when he went into a village the whole population fled across the fields, leaving only the yellow dogs to bark at him. But he was never at home in Chinese robes. His long legs would get entangled and he grew impatient at once. "Oh, pshaw!" he would mutter and tuck the robes into his girdle as a coolie does. The long hair was especially intolerable and after much groaning and endurance he cut it off and bought a false queue which Carie sewed firmly inside his round black satin Chinese cap. It was not a bad imitation and freed him from the outrageous business of combing tangles out of his hair—it was not a bad imitation until he took his cap off, as he did everywhere, and hung it up on the wall. Then the effect of the queue was odd, to say the least.

But the Chinese costume did not last long. The loose sleeves and flying skirts soon became intolerable. Andrew liked his clothes buttoned tightly about him, and above all, he liked them plain. The silks of a Chinese gentleman he would not wear because they were too fine, and the cotton clothes of a poor man were limp and hung so grotesquely upon his huge frame that Carie refused to let him wear them. So he went back to his own garments after a while.

Andrew hated anything pretentious or strange in apparel. He scorned mightily the robes of the professional priests; nothing infuriated him more than a bishop's costume and he particularly scorned a clerical collar. "Nobody knows where they button," he used to say. "They slip on like a halter, maybe." Then he would add, with a touch of characteristic grimness, "A man oughtn't to need a uniform to show he serves the Lord God.

It ought to be apparent in all he says and does."

He stoutly refused to wear anything but a plain business suit. He did own a Prince Albert, unwillingly bought for his own wedding, and some of the rousing scenes between him and Carie were over the wearing of this coat. Carie sometimes won by coaxing and a touch of flattery.

"You're tall enough to wear a long coat, Andy. Tall men look so nice in them."

Andrew was more susceptible even than most men to a little flattery from Carie—he had never been quite able to forget Mrs. Pettibrew—and he more often than not capitulated only to come home bitterly complaining of the discomfort of sitting on his tails.

"You shouldn't sit on them," said Carie. "Divide them, and sit between them."

But Andrew pshawed.

"I can't have my mind on such things in the presence of Almighty God," he retorted.

So the Prince Albert turned green with age and he would never buy another. Instead he went about obviously in the cheap suits the Chinese tailors made for him. Yet he had his own curious formalities. He would never take off his coat in the presence of a lady, or on the hottest day sit down coatless to a meal. Nor would he ever wear any but white shirts and stiff winged collars, always very clean. He never looked himself without those collars. If one caught him, collarless, wrapped in his dressing gown on his way down the hall to or from his bath, his neck rose a little too thin for the large and nobly shaped head. It gave him a curious childlike and helpless look. One was glad to have him put the collar on again, because without it that childlikeness in him was exposed and he was somehow betrayed.

And he had that quality of childlikeness. He was always easily deceived. There was not a shred of shrewdness in him. He believed happily, for instance, everyone who came to him saying that he wanted to turn Christian. Andrew was incapable of distrusting any convert, or of questioning anyone who said he believed on the Lord Jesus Christ. It would have been to distrust Christ himself, for he thought one who believed was predestined to be saved, and he received each professing soul with a deep and touching confidence.

At a baptismal service Andrew was an amazing experience for anyone who saw him. Four times a year he received converts. They gathered in the chosen center, coming in from all over the field, a small crowd of simple country folk for the most part, but with a scattering of townspeople and, rarely, one who looked learned or a man of place. Andrew did not receive them lightly or baptize them at once. They stayed for as long as a week sometimes, while he taught them and examined them in their knowledge of the new religion. For weeks and even months before, his assistants had been teaching them, those who could not read to read the simple tracts Andrew had prepared for them, the others the Scriptures themselves. When they came up for baptism Andrew questioned each one carefully, both as to knowledge of the principles of Christianity and spiritual experience. Sometimes when ignorance was too blatant, he regretfully bade them to go home and prepare further and come up again. But when there was earnest profession of belief he received them. In the church, before the congregation, they came up, one by one, and he called their names, and dipped his fingers in the plain pottery bowl he held, and sprinkling their heads, he prayed, thanking God for every soul thus given to him.

The expression upon the faces of the baptized varied from terror to hopefulness. Often there was the look of those who searched sincerely after God. But as often there was the look of a smug and pious rogue. Nevertheless Andrew received them all as precious, and after they were baptized, he gave them communion. What they thought of the whole proceeding varied according to the sincerity of their purpose. There were those who declared publicly, as soon as the water touched their heads, that they felt as if a stone had been taken away from the door of their hearts, and there were those who said privately that they felt nothing at all, and could notice no change in life whatever, and it was a hoax.

But none of them mattered. What mattered was that on those days Andrew's soul touched ecstasy. He was literally transfigured with a joy not of this earth. He came home to Sunday dinner looking as though a lamp were burning brightly within him. He was not gay—his joy was too deep for that. He sat quietly, eating in his sparing way, not hearing anything that was said around the table, but there was a luminescence about him. I used to look at him and be sure I saw a pure pale light standing around him as though it came from his body. His eyes were particularly pellucid and blue. After dinner he invariably shut himself in his study for many hours, to emerge at last in a happy exhaustion.

Because of such hours, which none of us shared, indeed which no one could share with him, that study was like no room in the house to us. We never thought of playing there or indeed even going into it for any reason except to take him a necessary message. Later on I used to have to go there for him to hear my Latin lessons, and I never stood up to recite to him—and not to stand was un-

[207]

thinkable—without feeling that more than man was listening.

Out of that new field the converts came in like homing birds. It was a poverty-stricken region, plagued by famine, for the Yellow River wound its willful way through those plains, shifting its bed, drying up one course to flood another. The people were angry with their own gods and weary with suffering, and one heard it often said, "No god can be worse than ours! Let us try the foreign god and see if any good comes of it!"

Some good came to a few, for Andrew and Carie got together food, begging money from home and the home churches, and relieving what distress they could. The people, eagerly hoping for far more than was in Andrew's power to give, crowded into the chapels, clamoring to be saved. When they found there could not be enough for all, many went out again, and yet some stayed, so that Andrew was greatly encouraged.

He was away from home continually, preaching and teaching. With him went his band of followers, whom he was training into a Chinese clergy. In each center as it was established he put a trained man to preach and to conduct a school. For Andrew loved learning, and wherever he put a church he put a school, too, where for a small sum the children of church members or any others could come and learn to read and write and be taught the principles of the Christian religion. If for reading they read the classics of Confucius, it did not disturb him. There was a magic in the Scriptures which could not be overcome by heathen literature. Thus he believed.

In the midst of all this success and growth he was struck a blow. It came from a point at which he could least have expected it. He came home one day from a long preaching tour. It was early spring and he had been away many weeks. Now he felt he had earned a week at home. It

had been a wonderfully good tour. Everywhere he had been heard eagerly, and many had wanted baptism. Now, happy to his heart's core, filled with the knowledge of success in the work and of the consciousness of God's blessing, he let himself think of the pleasure of a hot bath and a clean bed, of good food, of the pleasure of speaking his own tongue —it had been long since he had heard or spoken English—and of seeing his family. He deserved a holiday—he could enjoy himself for a little while without a sense of guilt in enjoyment.

But when he entered the courtyard of the inn and got down from his donkey there was Carie, waiting for him—not only Carie but the three children—a son had been born not many months before —and the children's nurse. They were dressed for travel, and all the household goods were packed into loads ready to be carried by waiting men.

"Why—why—" Andrew gasped, stammering, "what does this mean, Carie?"

"It means," she replied, "that I and the children are going to find a place where we can live. You can preach from Peking to Canton, but I and these little children will never go with you any more."

I know that speech of hers by heart, because she said it to me so many times in telling it. And she knew it by heart because she had said it so many times in the weeks that Andrew had been away. She said it over and over when she was nursing the baby through pneumonia, with the water flooding into the rooms so that the furniture had to be put up on bricks and they walked about on planks laid like gangways from room to room. Hers had not been the joy of saving souls and preaching to the crowding multitudes. Bit by bit she had saved one life, the small life of her baby son—if indeed she had saved it, because he was still so frail.

I do not know exactly what took place

there in that courtyard. Andrew always looked grim when he came to that point. "She was utterly beyond reason," he would say. For neither of them was it a struggle between a man and a woman. It was a woman defying God. She fought against God, against Andrew's call, against the success of his work, against the promise of the future.

"She did not care a whit for all the souls yet to be saved," Andrew said once in the bitterness of remembering. "She was like a wild wind—nothing could stop her."

In the end she won, as she had determined and planned to do. The rooms were empty, the landlord paid, the carts engaged and waiting to take them to the junk already hired. She had closed every door behind her. Andrew need not come, she told him—she could go alone. But he went with her, bewildered, angry, protesting. He turned for a moment to his comrade, Ma, and hastily promised to come back the instant he could settle his family somewhere. But he was greatly shaken. From within his own home a blow had been struck at him. He never quite forgave Carie for it, and from that day he went more solitary than he had before.

But then Andrew was born a solitary. He never had an intimate friend. When he was young he needed none. He had his dreams of escape from the labor he hated, and his plans for learning and his mission. Even when he was married he had no thought of companionship, for he had not seen a woman companion to a man. Among men he heard a crude scorn of women as creatures full of notions and whimsies, necessary to man and to be respected only in the simple functions of mating and housekeeping, and this scorn was slacked only by the brief aberration of courtship, to be resumed once it was over. It did not occur to him to look

for or desire intellectual companionship or spiritual understanding in a woman. Occasionally, it is true, a woman was misled by a certain benignity in Andrew's look and by the quiet certainty of his manner and was drawn to him, and she made a sign to him of her interest. Nothing distressed Andrew more deeply or embarrassed him more profoundly. There was once at the breakfast table when, examining his mail, a look of shock spread over his face as he read a letter he had just opened. He handed it at once to Carie. She read it in a twinkling, her dark eyes firing with anger.

"The woman's a fool!" she said in her downright fashion. "You leave her to me—I'll answer that letter, Andrew." She folded it and put it in her pocket. Then she glanced at him sharply. "You didn't go talking to her alone or anything like that to put ideas in her head?"

A clear sweat stood out on Andrew's high beautiful brow. He shook his head, too agitated to speak. Then he cleared his throat. "Wait a minute," he said hoarsely. "She asked me to talk with her a few minutes one night—I remember Mr. Jones was called out. She did not grasp fully the significance of St. Paul's conception of salvation by grace, and I explained it to her."

"And then she thanked you and said she had never understood it so well before!"

"How did you know?" he asked amazed.

Carie gave her short musical laugh. "I know how women get around men—they always begin by wanting advice on something or wanting something explained! Don't bother any more about it. I'll attend to her."

Andrew finished his breakfast in silence and went away, at once relieved and slightly sheepish. Immediately after breakfast Carie sat down at her desk, and wrote swiftly for a few moments. "There!"

she exclaimed, addressing an envelope. "Poor silly soul!" She laughed, restored to good humor. Then she added, "Of course I knew Andrew was as innocent as a lamb! But that's always the kind that gets taken in."

I don't believe she ever fully trusted Andrew about women because he was so guileless. When she lay on her deathbed, in her anguish and anger because she loved life, she said something bitter about his marrying again soon. And he came away, hurt. "She seems to think I'm—I'm—an old Abraham!" I heard him mutter down the hall. But it was not that. I think she knew she had never penetrated to that fastness of his heart where he lived alone, and so she was doubtful and wondered half sadly and half bitterly if perhaps another woman might enter where she had not.

What she never realized was that no one could enter there. Andrew did not know how to open the door to anyone. There were times as he grew older when he longed to have someone come in, when he hungered to feel someone close to him, but no one could come close, because he did not know how to let anyone. He kept his soul guarded and his heart closed. A caress, even from one of his children, abashed him, and he could not respond to it and so they ceased to give it. They were grown before they realized that he was secretly pleased by such a sign of affection, and that a word of praise or approbation made the very tears start to his eyes sometimes. But people did not praise him easily because he was too shy to praise others, too afraid of seeming fulsome. In that childhood home of his there was much rude fun made among all of them, and only he was so sensitive as to brood over the thrusts and suffer. And then no one thought of praising anyone. It would result in sinful conceit. So he grew up with a tongue that could criticize but

could not, whatever the impulse of his heart, shape itself to the softness of praise. When his children were little they did not love him for this, but when they grew up and he was an old man, with the transparencies of old age, they saw that under a different and a kinder creed this soul would have flowered into a mellower humor and a freer kindness. There was the love of kindness there, and the craving that a child has, kept through all the scores of years, for affection and understanding. But none of this could he express.

So he felt that Carie never understood him—it did not occur to him to wonder whether he understood her—and he said nothing to her. He took her and the children down the canal to the river and then he found an empty house upon a hill, and he left them there and went on his solitary way again.

But God comforted him.

7

Those eight years before the Boxer Rebellion were the years of greatest danger in Andrew's mission. Since he never stayed in established places, but was always pushing out into new and unknown places, he often found himself among hostile people. The Chinese have always been distrustful of foreigners, not only foreigners from other countries but even people of their own nation from other provinces or regions. This is perhaps because each village and town has maintained itself for centuries as a separate locality. There has been almost no government from above or outside, and the clan feeling is very strong. In some places it was the usual custom to kill any stranger who came unexplained by burying him alive. It was the very common thing in a village, as it is today, to set the savage half-wild dogs upon any new-comer. Andrew went on, doing no more than carry a stout stick with which to beat off the dogs. And the dogs, soon discovering him to be unafraid and wary of their tricks at his heels, learned to leave him alone until he pushed on into stranger places. They are cowards, those dogs!

No one will ever know exactly what dangers he endured, because he never talked about them without a great deal of questioning and drawing out. Then in a few sentences he might tell a story that another would have made into a day's tale.

There was the time when he lay asleep upon the brick bed of an inn and awoke, conscious of a light, to find the innkeeper standing beside him, a bean-oil lamp flaming in his left hand and in his right a meat-chopper from the inn's kitchen. Andrew, opening his eyes, fixed them full upon the man's face and cried aloud to God.

"Deliver me, God!"

He spoke in English and the man grew afraid.

"What are you saying?" he asked.

"I am calling to my God," Andrew replied, never moving his steady blue eyes from the man's face.

The man lifted the meat-chopper firmly and brandished it. "Are you not afraid?" he shouted.

"No," said Andrew quietly. "Why should I be afraid? You can do no more than kill my body, and my God will punish you."

"How?" asked the man, pausing again.

"You will live in torment," said Andrew with such calm certainty that the man stared at him a while and went muttering away at last.

"What did you do then?" we asked Andrew, breathless.

"I turned over and went to sleep," he replied.

"He might have come back!" we breathed.

"There was a guard over me," he said simply.

Once he was pushed from a crowded ferry boat into a river by a rough fellow who first cursed him, and finding him unmoved, jostled him and tripped him over. But Andrew came up out of the muddy water and caught hold of the junk's rudder and held on. The crowd stared down at him, but not one offered him a hand. But he did not ask for a hand. He clung on until the river bank came under his feet and then he walked out, dripping wet, but imperturbable, to hunt for his box on the ferry boat. It was gone; the fellow had taken it.

The crowd laughed. "It was full of silver dollars," they cried. "All foreigners travel with boxes of silver dollars!"

Andrew smiled and went on his way content. His few silver dollars were safely in his pocket and the box had been full of tracts and Gospel sheets. "God has ways for men," he said in telling of it, and was convinced that the man's soul would be saved.

More than once he was laid upon and beaten when he appeared unexpectedly in some strange town. They beat him, apparently, for no reason except that they had never seen anyone like him before, as dogs will set upon a strange dog they have not seen.

But the things he really minded the most were not these. He was a fastidious saint physically, and he came home often quite ill with sickness at what he had had to endure of filth. Once he came in green with horror.

"What is it?" Carie cried.

"I have eaten serpent today," he said in a ghastly voice. "I ate it at an inn and did not know it until afterwards." And immediately he was sick with the thought.

The common custom of hawking and spitting he could not endure. He who was so infinitely patient with men's souls had no patience at all with their bodies. When the trains first began to run he rejoiced in the signs put up against spitting elsewhere than in the numerous spittoons provided. But no one paid any attention to the signs. The Chinese were accustomed to spit where they pleased. Most of them could not read, and those that could paid no heed. Physical convenience is the law of life in China. Andrew came home one summer evening looking very content.

"There was a great fat fellow on the train today," he said abruptly at the supper table.

We all looked at him, waiting.

"He had off his shirt and sat in his drawers and his belly was like a great frog's," he went on, disgust in his eyes. He wiped his mouth carefully. "He spat everywhere except in the spittoon. I could not bear it, and pointed to the sign."

"I hope it did some good," said Carie, skeptically.

"It did not and I told him what I thought of him," said Andrew.

"What did you tell him?" we asked.

"I told him he was filthier than a beast," Andrew said gently.

"Father!" we cried.

"Oh, I told him very kindly and pleasantly," he replied, in the same mild voice, and could not understand why we laughed.

He had, of course, enemies. Most of them, it is true, were among his fellow missionaries, but these he considered his natural enemies. Missionaries and magistrates he put in the same class as his enemies, that is, persons designed by the devil to thwart the will of God, or what he, Andrew, wanted to do. Magistrates he was ruthless toward, and he quite openly used every treaty right he had to force them to allow him to rent property for chapels. For though he never opened

chapels unless there were those who wanted it, still there were always opposing groups who did not want the foreigner's religion in their town. These Andrew disregarded completely. If there were one soul who wanted to hear of God, it was that one's right to hear, though there might be a hundred who did not want to hear. So he went boldly to magistrates' courts, presenting himself again and again, waiting hours upon their whims. Sometimes a magistrate, not really meaning to see him at all, put him off from day to day with one excuse and another. Day after day Andrew presented himself at dawn to wait until night, only to come again, until everyone was weary with him. Nor would he use the slightest touch of silver upon the palms of the underlings. He knew very well that money would have opened doors, but he had no money of his own and he would not so use the church's money which he held to be for the preaching of the Gospel alone. At last, if the magistrate proved obdurate, Andrew would use force—that is, the force of the treaties made after the Opium Wars by which Chinese citizens were to have the right to be Christian if they liked and missionaries the right to preach. If the magistrate were himself a doughty soul and would not be awed by treaties even with the threat of gunboats behind them, Andrew appealed to his own consul who, however he might curse missionaries— and how many of them do curse missionaries and groan, I suppose, very truly, that life would be simple without them!—would nevertheless be compelled to send an official letter to the magistrate. This letter, written upon official paper bearing the large strange seal of the unknown United States, always did what Andrew wanted. Grudgingly, in terms of carefully worded contempt, the permission would be given. But Andrew cared nothing for man's contempt. He went away to preach in triumph, being the stubbornest of the stubborn sons of God.

Well, all those years we at home scarcely saw Andrew, and to his children he was a stranger, coming home very seldom, and when he did, not as one who came home but as one who came only for a night's rest before he went on again. Their lives were built without him, their days filled with other presences than his. They were fatherless, because his life was dedicated to others, but they did not even know him well enough to miss him. He felt this vaguely, sometimes, when he came home and saw his son growing tall, and his daughter ceasing to be a little child, and the baby who had been born at the inn. But that one died when he was five, just before the last child, a girl, was born.

Sometimes he tried to enter into their lives. There were two times in the year when they remember him a little differently, not as a journeying angel who tarried with them a night, but as a man who shared the things they had to do. Of these two times one was Christmas and the other was when the boxes came from Montgomery Ward, and Christmas was really the less exciting.

For Christmas, of which Carie made so much for the children, was a somewhat doubtful occasion to Andrew. There had been no celebration of Christmas in his childhood home except going to church and having a dinner. There was no giving of gifts, no Santa Claus. His idea of gifts was strange, too. He could never think of things to give the children, except things he had wanted as a boy, and which they did not want. But if he did not know how to give gifts to his children, he knew less what to give Carie. Even the children felt the pain of an inadequate gift to her, and they knew enough to feel an ache in their hearts for her on Christmas morning when she opened a brown paper parcel and put it

quietly aside without comment. But her eyes were shadowy. Yet we knew he meant nothing—only he never knew her, he did not know what she liked or what she wore or what she needed. The children, passionately adoring her, worked to give her what they could, spending weeks before Christmas to make "something pretty for Mother." They knew the secret craving of her heart for pretty things.

But of course Andrew, underneath all, could not bear the spending of money for anything that did not further the cause of his life. Money was the power to save souls—money to rent chapels, to open schools, to buy Bibles. He did not want anything for himself. So there was always a little ache about Christmas. And then he would murmur doubtfully, "No one knows the authentic date of Christ's birth. Besides, there is evidence that the festival is mixed with heathen traditions. We do not really know what we are celebrating—perhaps even the birthday of an ancient heathen god!"

"Fiddlesticks, Andrew," Carie exclaimed. "The point of it is to give the children a good time!"

But no one had ever troubled to give the child Andrew a good time, and he was more doubtful than ever. The truth is he was never free from the weight of his task. His happiness was measured by his success in that, and that alone. God had him.

But the Montgomery Ward boxes were another matter. They were necessities, ordered months before, paid for, and safely arrived. The children anticipated for weeks that morning when Andrew, looking up from the letters before him on the breakfast table, would say solemnly, "The boxes have come!" If he were not at home they could scarcely bear it, for Carie would not open them until he came. But he was nearly always there in the early winter. There was a regular routine to be followed, always exciting. Andrew must go down to the Customs office on the Bund and present the bill of lading and get the boxes through Customs. The children at home were waiting at the gate of the compound, if it were fair, climbing high so that they might catch the first glimpse of Andrew around the corner of the old Buddhist temple in the valley. If it were raining, they waited at the front door, their noses pressed white against the glass pane. Meanwhile Carie was preparing a place in the back hall for the boxes.

There was no greater ecstasy than the moment when Andrew appeared from behind the temple, followed by four or five coolies with boxes slung on ropes upon their carrying poles. The sound of their rhythmic step-keeping call floated up the hill and came nearer and nearer—"Heigh-ho—heigh-ho—" Soon, soon the boxes would be dropped in the hall, and the men clamoring about them in the dear confusion of the hour. Andrew would be waging a war over the tips the coolies were shouting for, slapping their sweaty breasts, pointing out the welts upon their horny shoulders.

"These foreign boxes are full of lead!" they would shout. "They are fit to kill us—and we came up the hill—and what is this mite upon my hand!" They would throw their coins down and spit upon them, and Carie would implore Andrew, "Give them a little more, Andrew—just this once!" And then very unwillingly he would give them a little more, and they would subside into grins and go away. And there were the boxes!

Some child always had the hammer and the big nail puller that Andrew had bought for such days, and breathless they watched while the strong iron teeth sank into the wood as Andrew pounded and clutched the nail head and the nail came up, screeching with reluctance.

Every board was saved as it came off, because the boxes were good American

pine, dry as no wood in China was ever dry. All our bookcases and bureaus and the chests in the attic were made of the Montgomery Ward boxes. Under the lid was strong brown paper. Carie pulled it away, and there were the things from America! It was our most real, most tangible touch with our own country.

Now, looking back, the things seem very simple, such things as the Americans order every day from their grocers and think nothing but necessities. But to us they were the dearest luxuries, things that could be bought nowhere around us, foods to be tasted and savored and enjoyed as precious, tools that seemed magic in complexity, garments made and ready to wear, marvels of fashion.

But really there were tins of coffee and bags of sugar, cakes of yeast and soap, a round keg of molasses for Carie's famous gingerbreads, and spices which perhaps had grown in the Orient and now were back again ready to be used. There were needles and pins, hairpins and threads, all the small things not to be found in Chinese stores—some ribbon in gay colors to be used to tie back little girls' curls on Sundays (dyed tape on other days) and there were other little luxuries —sassafras tea, which Andrew loved on a cold winter's night at supper, and a few pounds of hard peppermint candy, some packages of gelatin, jars for fruits that Carie put up against the winter. For clothing there were the necessities of long underwear for the damp Chinese winters in badly heated houses—Carie knitted our stockings and sweaters and little cuffs she called wristlets. And last there was always a little special thing that each child had chosen out of the fabulous catalogue. Oh, the lovely hours we all spent poring over the catalogue, searching for the one thing, costing not more than the dollar we were allowed, the heart-burning decisions as to whether it were better to have several small things costing less or the one beloved thing costing a full dollar! And the agony when the one beloved cost a dollar and nineteen cents! There was no use in going to Andrew—no child thought of it—but Carie, always too tender-hearted, could be persuaded, and when the bill was presented to Andrew's stern eyes, Carie could be trusted to speak up and say, "I told her she could, Andrew—I'll make it up out of something else, or take it out of the housekeeping!" So Andrew let it pass—although to do him full justice he sometimes let it pass anyway, if the work were going well and he was in a high humor.

Each child, then, had his little package, precious to receive, precious to unwrap and to look at and fondle and play with and put under the pillow at night. Yet the catalogue was a book of heart-burning, too. So many things cost much more than a dollar! There was one of Andrew's little girls, for instance, who yearned deeply over years for a certain large baby doll. To this day she has not forgotten that doll. The legend underneath read "life-size." That meant as big as a real baby. She remembers its round bisque face in a frilly lace bonnet, its chubby hands, its long dress and little knit jacket. But it cost three dollars and ninety-eight cents and was of course hopelessly out of possibility. She bought a little doll or two, but they were never the same. She prayed resolutely for years that some Christmas—but there never was such a Christmas. She had little cheap dolls, dressed exquisitely and completely by Carie's hands. But they were not life-size. Every Christmas Eve that child, having prayed hundreds of prayers, went to bed with her heart beating with hope. But the first glance at the stocking and at the tiny heap of packages swept the hope away again for another year. If Carie had realized, she would have somehow seen to it, by some prodigious slash-ing sacrifice, that the small heart had its desire. But she never knew, for the child never spoke, not dreaming that the fabulous sum was within her parents' possibility to give. Santa Claus—or God—might give it, but not Andrew who needed all the money. And Carie had no money of her own. So the doll remained upon the pages of the catalogue to dream over and at last to relinquish, except to this day that child, now long grown, cannot pass the doll counter in a toy shop—cannot have her fill, for that matter, of real babies.

But there were many little white children living in the heart of China to whom Montgomery Ward took place with Santa Claus and God. One child came home one day to say solemnly to her mother, "I feel sure Miss Nan and Mr. Rob are going to be married."

"How do you know?" the mother inquired.

"Because I saw them looking at a Montgomery Ward catalogue together," the child replied, astutely.

All this time a slow storm was rising out of the deeps of China. None of us realized it, certainly not I as a small child living in Andrew's house. Yet I remember being afraid in the night because of things I heard Andrew and Carie talk about. People were not as willing to hear Andrew preach as they had been, it seemed. He came home more often than he used to come, and very often he was dejected and downcast so that before he came Carie used to coax us to be especially good, to be affectionate with him and remember how tired he was.

"You children can't understand all the hard things he has to bear while you live safely here—" She paused, as though listening, wondering, perhaps, how safe the children were.

But they were warm-hearted little things and ran about doing things for

Andrew's coming—picking flowers he never noticed, and putting his old leather slippers at the door for him to slip on when he came in—a thing he did notice and enjoy. There was a sort of symbolism in those large worn leather slippers, shaped to the angles of Andrew's feet. To a small child, carrying one in each hand, they seemed as enormous as a giant's shoes, and they had a sort of magic, too, because when Andrew put them on a different look came over his face. It was his home look—a desperate weariness of the body, a lightening of the heart, and a certain famishment in the eyes. But perhaps it was only eagerness for home and his own about him, an eagerness he was not able to put into words.

As the years went on which led to the Boxer Rebellion, he was more and more dejected when he came home. He spent hours sitting in his study, doing nothing, apparently. We used to see him sitting there in his old imitation leather armchair that he had picked up in a second-hand shop in Shanghai. It had, as long as I can remember, pieces of excelsior stuffing coming out of it, and spots where his body pressed upon it most hardly, especially in two spots where his elbows leaned when he prayed.

There was talk, too, because Andrew and Carie never hid the realities of their lives from their children. Andrew would say suddenly at the table, "I've had to close up three more chapels this last month. The landlords wouldn't let me keep them. I can't find another place—nobody will rent me a place to preach in now. Something's wrong."

Or he would say, "We're having meetings at the houses of different church members. We have to have them as the Christians did of old—at midnight, secretly, as we are able."

Many and many a night the children woke to hear the clang of the compound gate and to see the flicker of Andrew's big old kerosene oil lantern which he carried at night and kept spotlessly clean himself. It was one of his small fastidiousnesses—a clean lantern, or at home, the lamp clean and trimmed. For in those days we used oil lamps and American kerosene oil. When we saw the flicker of light upon the whitewashed wall, we knew that was Andrew coming home from a secret meeting of Christians.

The whole house came somehow to be filled not with fear but with a sort of solemn waiting. One by one the servants, on some pretext or another, left, until there were only the nurse and her son. And Andrew was at home more and more, his face growing daily more grim. He went several times to see the American consul and came back to say to Carie, "He can't do anything—they're all waiting."

And one night he never came home at all! It was nearly noon of the next day before he came in, and his wrists were bleeding where thongs had held him. When Carie, frantic with anxiety, cried out, he answered soberly, "Be glad I am alive. I was at Lin Meng's administering communion to his old mother when soldiers came in. They took Lin away and tortured him until he died. But he remained true. They took his ten-year-old son, but let him go today, and he came back and told me and loosed me. I was left bound, and the woman died as I stood there, bound to a post." His face worked, and he sat down and groaned. Then he looked at us all strangely, his ice-colored eyes shining, his voice solemn and triumphant. "Lin Meng has entered into the presence of our Lord, a martyr, to stand among that glorified host!"

He got up quickly and went away into his study, to be alone a while.

So it was everywhere. For soon there began to come rumors of death. In one town in Shantung the small missionary community were all killed, including the children. Several times missionaries we had never seen before were brought to us by secret friends among the Chinese, ragged and starved and ill, and Carie cared for them and sent them on to Shanghai and safety. There were sometimes children of eight or ten with them, a very few, but never any little ones or any babies. These had died of dysentery, of fever, of hardships too dreadful to be told. The children of Carie never heard the rumors, but they saw Carie rock herself in weeping and anguish and fear for her own. So the storm mounted and mounted, until that day when the American flag raised at a point long agreed upon warned us to leave instantly, and Carie took the children and went. But Andrew stayed, alone.

It is not possible fully to know what was in Andrew's mind when he went back, the solitary white man in that whole countryside. Never, not then or after, did he leave his post when danger came. He went back quietly. On the way he was spat upon many times, and curses were shouted after him. But curses were common and he paid no heed to them. He entered the empty house, bathed and changed his clothing, and sat down to his supper. One young lad, the son of the children's faithful nurse, remained to serve him.

The story of the Boxer Rebellion has been many times told and there is no use in telling it again. It remains, like the tale of the Black Hole of Calcutta, one of the festering spots of history. If the number of people actually dead was small, as such numbers go in these days of wholesale death by accidents and wars, it was the manner of death, the innocence of little children and babies, that makes the heart shudder and condemn even while the mind can reason and weigh. The mind can acknowledge the force of the

Chinese right to refuse foreigners upon their soil, it can acknowledge the unwarranted imperialism of such men as Andrew, righteous though they were, and honorable in intent and of good meaning. The mind says people have a right to refuse imperialism. But the heart shudders. For those who were martyred were the good and the innocent, none the less good and innocent because they were blind. For the glory of God had made them blind. They were drunk with love of God, so that they saw nothing but His glory, could only see the one necessity, that all others should become like themselves. And so forsaking all else they went out as blind men do, trustful, not able to see danger, or if seeing, not believing.

There is no reconciling these two, the mind and the heart. The mind may say a thousand times, and rightly, "They had no right to be there. They provoked what they received." But the heart answers, "They were innocent, for they believed that what they did was of God."

So there is no answer and there can be no just decision. Certainly Andrew belonged to the blind. It was his strength that he believed so deeply in what his soul said that the eyes of his flesh were never opened from birth until death. He never saw men except "as trees, walking." He would have been amazed if anyone had told him that the Chinese had the right to protest the presence of foreign missionaries upon their soil. It was as though they protested the actuality of the true God, his God. No man had any right against God.

He stayed stubbornly on in the square mission house with the one Chinese lad all through the hot brilliant summer. The lad, hanging about the streets at night, brought him rumors each day of new massacres of white people in other places. Andrew was the sole white man in the region. He came and went quietly, preaching openly in the streets until the fury of passersby and their shouts grew too threatening for him to be heard. Then with that high serene stubbornness of his he handed out his tracts, saw them dropped or torn, and went away to try in another street. His quietness, the extreme dignity of his tall figure, his lack of any fear seem to have preserved him. I know that from Ma, the Christian, who stayed by him still. Once he said to me of Andrew, "I thought many times that he would be killed. Many times I stood near, thinking I must, like Stephen, be witness to the death of a martyr. There were stones flung at him—once a stone cut him on the cheek, but he did not even put up his hand to wipe away the blood. He did not seem to feel it."

"Were you afraid?" we asked Andrew when he was an old man, remembering.

He considered. "There have been times in my life when I have been afraid. But it was always over small matters." He meant thieves, noises in the night, those stirs in the darkness which moved some childhood fear hidden in him so deeply that he did not recognize it. "But I never was afraid when I was on God's business," he said.

"Yet some were killed," we murmured.

"It is not death one fears," he said. It was one of his simplicities to which there was no answer.

But he was sustained in all those days so that afterwards he remembered with clarity, not dangers or fears, not stories of disease and death, but a sort of ecstasy. He lived, it seemed, outside himself.

"I seemed," he wrote, "without the body. For I was conscious of the presence of God with me like a strong light shining, day and night. All human beings were far away from me. I had almost no human intercourse except with Ma, once a Mohammedan, but now the Christian. He remained faithful. And every day I taught him exegesis of the scriptures, and

together we planned for more effective spreading of the Gospel when the storm was abated."

For Andrew never doubted that the storm would abate, that evil must break down and good be triumphant. He prayed aloud in every prayer he ever made, "Keep us faithful until that sure day when evil is gone from the world and God is victorious." That sure day! Upon such surety he built his life, and being without doubt or shadow of turning, he lived happily in any circumstances. What more, indeed, does anyone need than the surety of his heart's wish?

Months went on. The summer ended, and the rebellion ended, as all the world knows, by a punitive expedition of the Powers from whom the slaughtered missionaries came. The foreign armies marched into Peking, the Empress Dowager fled with her court; apologies, indemnities, fresh concessions followed in the usual order. But the people remained sullen. They maintained a menacing refusal to hear anything about a foreign God. Andrew grew impatient. The cool weather came on, the sort of weather when he ought to be out over the country, preaching in sunny market-places, stopping in villages, talking to peasants gathered about the threshing floors. But they would not hear him. They threatened him, they set their fierce dogs upon him, they refused him room to rent or space even to stand. Twice a chapel was burned.

"God has not yet had time to work," Andrew wrote Carie.

It occurred to him that it had been nine years since he had seen his own country and that a furlough was due him. Carie, too, living in close rented rooms in Shanghai, was ready for a change. Well, he would give God a little more time, then. A year of furlough, and then he would come back, and he and the Christian Ma would begin their campaign again. He shut up the square mission house and went to Shanghai. His children had almost forgotten him, although every night they had prayed, "God, please keep our father from the Boxers."

He appeared taller than ever to them, thinner, and his eyes were hoary blue in the burned red-brown of his face. And he was shy with them and did not know how to talk to them.

8

Of that second return of Andrew's to America I can write with some authority because by then I can remember him on my own account. It is true I cannot yet give a consecutive story because my memory is not long enough for that. I see him not as a day-to-day figure, like Carie. The days came and went, and into them he broke irregularly and with violence. He must always have created a stir of some sort when he came, because those impressions of his presence are much more vivid than anything else, although a great deal was happening to me which had never happened before—all of America, in fact. I remember, for instance, my first glimpse of Cornelius, Carie's beloved brother, who had stood next to God all my life. He came out of the big white house in which Carie had told me I was born, his white hair glittering in the sun. He looked the oldest man in the world, and I thought he must be Hermanus, and I cried out, "Grandfather!" But Cornelius laughed, and behind him I saw still another older, more silver-haired figure, and that was Hermanus. Yet in all this excitement, in the excitement of cousins to play with, of an orchard heard of but never before seen, of cows and horses, of unwalled mead-

ows—how strange and naked I felt at first with no wall to shield the house and garden, and then when I became convinced bandits would not attack us or anyone come in and steal our things, how glorious and free!

Yet upon all these memories Andrew's figure breaks in, in its own startling fashion. We stayed at Carie's home all summer and I was in a long ecstasy of happiness, day after day. Andrew was away visiting his own brothers and sisters —Carie, I think, felt them difficult to visit with two small, amah-bred children. And he preached at churches whenever he was invited. I remember my anxiety, when he was asked to preach in Carie's home church, that he would not be able to preach in English, and my amazement when he not only preached but preached very long indeed. He had, I felt, more than enough to say. That was the church where Andrew's brother David was minister, David who looked so much like Andrew that I was quite bewildered by it. But he was quieter than Andrew, paler and more gentle. He was a silvery pale old gentleman then, his very skin as pale as silver, so that he looked ghostly. Even the blue of his eyes was beginning to be dimmed by a silver film of rheum.

Andrew threw the family into consternation because he was so late in arriving the Saturday before the Sunday he was to preach. I felt quite miserable and somehow responsible for it. Hermanus kept watching and snorting about the delay and Carie kept apologizing, and I felt, since Andrew was my father, I ought to be able to do something about it. It was a hot August day and most of the afternoon I sat on the stile under the huge old maple, watching the dusty road. Around the supper table the aunts and uncles looked severely at Carie. "Is he usually late like this?" they inquired of her.

"No—no, indeed," she replied hastily, "I can't think what's keeping him. He wrote me he was riding horseback from Lewisburg today over Droop Mountain."

"He'll be worn out if he does get here now," Hermanus said gloomily and added, "He's not such a good preacher that he can get up and do us credit offhand."

Carie did not answer, though I saw a kindling in her eyes. I felt at once an odd aching—it was strange that she, my mother, should be scolded like a little girl, and I wanted to defend her.

Then suddenly Andrew walked in, his suitcase in his hand, his shoes very dusty.

"Well, sir!" cried Hermanus.

"My horse went lame when she'd gone less than two miles," said Andrew, "so I walked."

They all stared at him.

"Walked!" cried Cornelius. "Over Droop Mountain—and a bag!"

"There wasn't any other way to get here," said Andrew. "I'll just go and wash myself." He disappeared and I can still remember the clamoring and the astonishment. He had walked fifteen miles over a great mountain, carrying his suitcase.

I was suddenly very proud of him and piped, "There're always books in his suitcase, too!"

But Hermanus said grimly, "He'll be no good at all tomorrow." And when Andrew came in presently, very washed and speckless, he shouted to my Aunt Dorothy, "Go and fetch some hot meat! The man's famished!" and sat there, snorting a little from time to time while Andrew ate.

Whether or not Andrew was any good I do not remember, because the next morning after breakfast I suddenly announced my decision to join the church. It had not occurred to me until I saw my favorite cousin, just older than I, trying on a new white frock before breakfast. "I'm going to join the church today," she said complacently, turning around and around before the mirror. I stared at her, pondering. I also had a new white frock, ready for some occasion not yet arrived. Indeed, it had been a sore point between Carie and me that as yet there had been no occasion good enough. The idea struck me. I flew to Carie.

"I want to join the church, too!"

She was in her room, twisting up her heap of bright chestnut hair. She twined the coil in her hand, and looked at me in the mirror, her face very solemn.

"You can't just join the church like that," she exclaimed, outraged. "It's a very important step—you must think about it a long time."

"I have," I said quickly. "I've thought of it lots of times!"

"Then why didn't you say so before?" asked Carie shrewdly.

I twisted a bit of my frock. "I've always been afraid to go up alone," I said. "But today I could go up with Hilda."

Carie looked at me, thinking. "I don't know," she said finally. "You'll have to ask your father."

Andrew came in at that instant, his eyes tranquil from morning prayer.

"This child wants to join the church!" Carie cried.

I felt his eyes rest on me with more interest than I had ever felt in them. Indeed, except when I was in fault, I did not remember that they had ever turned full upon me before. But to one in fault they were piercing, terrifying. Now they were different. There was an eagerness of interest in them—they were almost, if not quite, kind.

"What makes you think you want to profess Christ?" he asked gravely.

I pleated my frock and said nothing, not knowing what to say. They stared at me. I could feel the two qualities of their stares. Carie's was shrewd and a little skeptical. A few more moments and she would be ready to forbid the whole business. But Andrew's gaze was softening, expanding, becoming exalted.

"You love the Lord Jesus Christ?" he inquired.

Suddenly there was nothing of father and daughter between us. He was the priest inquiring of a soul. Even I was awed and paused for a moment's searching. Did I not love Jesus? I had never thought about it, taking it for granted He was, I had been told, kind to children.

"Yes, sir," I faltered.

He turned solemnly to Carie. "We have no right to forbid a soul's profession," he said.

"But the child's too young to know what she's doing!" Carie exclaimed.

I would not look at her, knowing the penetrating power of her dark and searching eyes. Besides, did I not love the Lord Jesus Christ?

"Of such is the Kingdom," said Andrew simply.

That settled it. Without a word, but her eyes still skeptical, Carie produced the white frock and I put it on and she tied the sash and adjusted my big leghorn hat, and we went to church. The family had been told of the situation, and my cousin and I walked side by side, behind Hermanus, feeling very special.

"You have to answer questions," Hilda whispered.

"I don't care," I whispered back. Had I not been nurtured on the Child's Catechism and the Westminster Shorter Catechism and hundreds of psalms and hymns? It is true that at least a million times I had been pettish and complained to Carie, "I don't see what good all these catechisms and verses will do me!" To which she invariably replied, "The time will come when you will be glad of them." Perhaps, I pondered, this was the time—although I had never believed her.

That was why Andrew's sermon seemed so long. I did not listen to it, because I never listened to his sermons,

feeling I could hear him talk any time at home. But being a shy child I began to wish I had not said I wanted to join the church. Now that it was inevitable, for Uncle David had been told, and it would never do to back down before all the family, my heart was throbbing in my throat like a dry and rasping machine. Only the thought of my frock upheld me. It was much prettier than Hilda's, and everybody would see it.

Of the rest I remember little. Before the benediction Uncle David rose and announced the receiving of two members, and invited all who would to remain after the benediction. Everyone remained. Carie slipped the hat from my head, and Hilda and I walked up the aisle together, an unending aisle, it seemed to me, although afterwards Hilda said I went so fast she had almost to run. I know I could feel my curls bobbing up and down against my back. There was a moment of complete silence, and then Uncle David's silvery blue eyes looked into mine and he asked a question or two, to which I answered faintly, "Yes," and again, "Yes, I think so." He handed me an old silver plate covered with lace, upon which were morsels of white bread, and I took a bit. Then he gave me a chalice of wine and bade me drink. I ate and drank. But the bread was dry and tasteless in my mouth, and the wine burned my tongue and I hated it. And I had to take off the white frock just as soon as we reached home. When it was all over it was rather disappointing.

Andrew, it seemed, could not live in entire peace even in America where there were no missionaries and, presumably, no heathen. The next memory I have of him is in an old rented house in a small college town in Virginia, we having gone there to be with my brother Edwin who was in the university. Andrew had no idea of settling down. He felt, since America was full of money, that he had better get what he could to carry on his work. So he deposited his family, or tried to do so. But there was some sort of difficulty about the house. It was rented from a stately old Virginia lady who lived in a huge columned affair on the hill above, and who, although she went regularly to church and dropped two coins into the plate on foreign mission Sundays, profoundly distrusted all missionaries when it came to personal dealings. Whether she had previous unfortunate experiences, I do not know. But Andrew could brook arrogance from no one, having plenty of his own, and especially he could not endure it from females, who he considered should be meek and yielding. It was a case of flint against flint, and a good many insults were given and taken.

It was not possible for a child fully to comprehend what was going on. One thing was clear. Andrew would not give her as much monthly rent as she wanted, and when she asked what guarantee she had for the year's rent, he replied with that furiously tranquil look of his, "The same guarantee, Madam, which I have—that the Lord provides for His own!" Evidently she was not fully reassured, in spite of being a Christian, for Andrew paused in the middle of a very favorite potato soup that night at supper to remark—as Carie put it, "out of a clear blue sky"—"That woman is a she-devil, that's what she is!"

"Why, Andrew!" Carie exclaimed.

We all waited for more, but Andrew had fallen placidly to his soup again, and there was no more. But whenever I saw Mrs. Estie riding by in her carriage, under a lace parasol, her ink-black coachman driving a pair of gray horses slowly down the tree-arched street, I looked at her hard. A she-devil! She sat very proud and erect, her white hair waved, her fine old profile conscious and haughty. She had once been a Southern

belle and she had never got over it. But that disease is a curiously inverted one. It sickens almost to death any number of persons about her, but it remains robust and incurable in the woman who possesses it.

I have only one more memory of Andrew during that strange American year. He was almost always away, collecting money, but once he was at home and we were all going somewhere together to make a family call. I had, I remember, been dressed first, in a new frock of blue sprigged muslin. The skirt was smocked with blue silk upon a yoke, and the sleeves were short and puffed, and there was lace at the collarless neck. My long curls had been freshly spun about Carie's forefinger, and a blue bow sat on top of my head, and I swung my big hat. Thus arrayed, and feeling perfectly satisfied with myself, I stood at the steps into the street, waiting and spotless, when two small boys paused to stare. I pretended to pay no heed to them, of course, although I was acutely conscious of them. Indeed, I was a little sore from a recent experience with a detestable boy, the dunce of my third grade class, who had chosen to subject me to his adoration in spite of my furious and loud protestations of my hatred.

These two unknown and personable little boys, staring, were therefore in the nature of balm, although outwardly I appeared oblivious of them. At last one of them heaved a sigh and said to the other, "Ain't she pretty?"

But before he could answer I heard Andrew on the porch.

"Oh, pshaw!" he exclaimed. He had come out ready to go, and caught the little boy's remark.

"You go and find your mother!" he commanded me. And as I turned reluctantly, for I would not have dreamed of disobeying him, I saw the two little boys hastening up the street, pursued by his blue and baleful glare.

"Hm!" I heard him say loudly after them. And he stood there with a look of distaste upon his face, as though he smelled sin afar off.

Searching memory, we seem to be suddenly back in the square mission house again. After the crowded American year it was very still, very lonely. For us who were the children in Andrew's house, there were no white children to play with, and the days were long and filled with whatever we could find to put into them.

Certainly Andrew was not in them. For now began the most prosperous part of his missionary career. He came back with a good part of the money he had wanted and he found a strangely peaceful, an almost ominously peaceful, China. During the year something had happened. Instead of hostility he met everywhere a mask of courtesy and compliance. He could rent rooms anywhere he liked for chapels and schools, and people crowded into them. It is true that they seemed people of a new class, people with axes to grind, with difficulties to adjust, lawsuits, grievances, ambitions. Andrew found himself, as all white men did at that period, possessing a power of which he had been unconscious.

The explanation, of course, was the summary punishment given by the white men to the Chinese for the Boxer uprising. Word had gone all over the Chinese empire, that word flying like wind from mouth to mouth, more quick than written page or telegram today. White men, being strong and swift and fearful in retribution, came to be feared and hated and envied and admired and used. Every white man was a little king.

Andrew took it as God's triumph. He proceeded in great strides over that part of China which he considered his spiritual kingdom. With Ma the Christian to help and to advise and save him mistakes where he could be saved, he opened church after church, trained preachers to put in them who were responsible not only for their congregations but also for a certain amount of territory around them, and beside every church was a school. At one time Andrew had over two hundred churches and schools in his diocese. Twice a year he had a general assembly of all workers, and it was a sight to see the crowd who gathered to make reports, to receive instructions and teaching. For Andrew never ceased to train and to develop and to teach those whom he had chosen to teach others. And Ma the Christian was always at his elbow, dark and silent except for a whisper to which Andrew gave instant heed.

There was something curiously imperial about the whole thing, and none the less because it was an empire of the spirit, although Andrew was guileless to the core and had no such dreams. But dark Christians had such dreams, and that kingdom was not wholly of God. There were those in it who used the power of the name of the white man and the white man's religion to further their own ends. For in that time it was enough for a man to boast before a magistrate, "I belong to the white man's church, and I have his protection," for the magistrate to fall silent and give him his way without regard for justice.

But Andrew did not believe such things could be, and would not believe, though he were told. Andrew's children, looking back, remember that Carie told him a good many times and warned him often. She was nearer the common people than he could ever be. Women were not afraid of her and they gossiped and told tales, and she heard that the preacher Li was charging three silver dollars for every admission to the church and if anyone paid five, admission was sure, but if you tried to get in on the old confession of faith it was impossible. Or she heard that the older T'ing had three concubines secretly, and that the preacher Rao was an opium smoker. She repeated everything to Andrew, and he refused to believe anything. It was a curious aspect of his nature that he was able to disbelieve anything he did not like to believe.

"If you would only try to see for yourself, Andrew," Carie would exclaim. "Don't let yourself be taken in!"

But Andrew would only answer, "It is the Lord's business, and his is the responsibility for these souls—not mine. I merely sow the good seed—he will separate the tares from the wheat."

It did not disturb him at all when a flagrant hypocrisy among them became open.

"Christ, too, had his Judas," he said, and was not troubled.

Carie was not the only one who battled with Andrew on this point. The other missionaries attacked him again and again and there were some who tried to discredit his whole work, feeling it was better to have only two converts and have them real, than Andrew's hundreds. But Andrew only laughed at them in his silent and dry fashion. He had a strange laugh, a wrinkling of his leathery face, a sudden shining in his eyes that did not in the least soften them, and one "Haw!" of sound. And with a touch of unaccustomed shrewdness he would say, "Polson and his precious pair of converts! Just as likely as not one's a hypocrite and that's fifty percent of his membership false! It's safer to have five hundred."

The missionaries made all sorts of checks and rules designed to curb Andrew's ways, but he was bound no more than Gulliver by the threats of the Lilliputians. He went his own way serenely, and they foamed and scolded and Andrew's children early were imbued with the feeling that the hands of their own

kind were forever against their parents and therefore against them. Later, when they grew up, they were surprised to discover that these same people were good enough in their way, simple honest folk who were trying to do their duty as much as Andrew was. But between them and God were the mission officers and mission rules, while Andrew dealt only with God.

It fits here, perhaps, to tell Andrew's side of the war of the New Testament, which was the major entanglement and achievement of his life. Early in his career Andrew decided that the Chinese translation of the Bible was balderdash. There were all sorts of absurdities in it because, he said, the translators had not sufficiently understood Chinese idioms. Elijah's chariot, for instance, was translated "fire-wagon," a word later used for railway train, so that the passage led innocent heathen to believe that Elijah went to heaven on a railroad, and a good deal of geographical confusion resulted from this idea. Andrew decided, therefore, that as soon as he had time he would make a new translation straight from the Hebrew and Greek into Chinese. It was about this time that the missionaries themselves became convinced that they should have a new translation and chose a committee to make it, and Andrew's scholarly proficiency in the language being one thing at least which they appreciated, he was asked to be a member of the committee.

The scheme was simple. The New Testament was to be the first portion translated, and its chapters were divided among the committee in equal shares. Each man was supposed to work on his share at home with an approved Chinese scholar to help him, and in the summer they were to meet at a chosen spot to compare, criticize and confer upon each other's work.

It was to Andrew a work of the most

sacred sort. With Ma as his aide, he pored at night over his assignment, all through one winter and spring. Early in July he and Ma went north to the meeting place. There was a certain solemnity about the departure. Carie had been at great pains to furbish up his clothes and by dint of much talk and some flattery she had persuaded him to get a new white suit. Her saint should be as personable as any of them.

He was to be away eight weeks. We settled down to the long hot summer with a certain sense of freedom. With Andrew gone leisure descended upon the house like coolness over heat. We all had things we wanted to do. Carie was going to teach me how to sing alto that summer, and she had saved up a little secret hoard out of the housekeeping money and had bought from Shanghai four new books that we were going to read aloud—two of them novels for a treat. And we were going to make new curtains for the living room. And Carie was going to have the umbrella tree cut out of the garden. Trees were a continual argument between Andrew and Carie. Carie loved sunshine, but in the warm heat of the Yangtze Valley the trees grew huge and weedy and shaded the house and made the mildew grow overnight like frost upon shoes and garments and the straw matting. But Andrew never wanted any tree cut down at all. The umbrella tree had been a particular bone between them. He would not hear of its being cut, although its huge fanlike leaves flapped all over one corner of the porch, and the garden snakes loved to creep around its wet branches. Carie abhorred the tree and her too quick imagination imbued it with a sinister influence. She had said months before to us, "The minute Andrew is out of the house this summer I'm going to have that tree cut down. He makes a fuss for it, but I don't believe he'll notice it if it's gone."

And Andrew was scarcely out of the compound gate before she had the gardener chopping at it. She stood triumphantly to see it fall. It fell with a groan and instantly a great beam of sunlight shot into the shadows of the porch.

"There!" Carie said. "I can breathe again!"

It was well she did not delay, for in less than two weeks Andrew was back. He had told us nothing, for his letters were always noncommittal. "The flies in Chefoo are fearful," he had written. "It is an Egyptian plague and the mosquitoes are worse." He made a few complaints about his fellow workers. "Barton is lazy. He does not begin work before eight o'clock of mornings. It's his English morning tea habits and too big a breakfast, I tell him." But later there had been other more severe complaints of the English missionary. Andrew wrote in every letter, "Barton wants everything his own way." Carie, reading that, laughed and said, "There isn't another like him there, is there?" She wrote him, counseling patience, forbearance, the possibility that eight might be more right than one, and the majority should decide. But when did majority mean anything to Andrew, who was so used to being the minority of one? "Barton is insufferable," he wrote.

"I'm afraid Andrew isn't going to make it," said Carie regretfully.

It was the day after that he appeared, Mr. Ma darkly silent behind him. Andrew had on his new white suit, which he had forgotten to wear before, but had remembered when he thought of seeing Carie. He looked splendid and triumphant and very happy to be home. He was unusually jovial all evening, although we could not make out much of what the trouble had been, except that Andrew had wholly approved of no one's translation except his own. In fairness to him it must be said that this seemed to be a fairly unanimous state of mind among the committee. But Barton had been the worst.

"The fellow isn't even educated," Andrew said, eating his supper with a vast relish. "He quit school at sixteen and went into a draper's shop in London—he doesn't know a word of Hebrew and Greek."

"Maybe he knows Chinese," Carie said. She was always somewhat inclined to take the other side against Andrew.

"Pshaw!" said Andrew. "I have no confidence in him."

"What are you going to do now?" we asked.

"Make the translation myself," he replied.

"So you will know it's right?" asked Carie, laughing.

But Andrew looked at her with surprise and gravity.

"Exactly," he replied.

As for the umbrella tree, Carie was right. He never noticed it was gone, although two years later, when Carie in a mischievous mood told him of it, he instantly declared he had missed something all along, and had not known what it was. And he was so positive that we did not dare to laugh until he had left the room.

So in that manner began the work which to Andrew's children took on, as the years passed, the aspect of a giant inexorable force which swallowed their toys, their few pleasures, their small desires, into its being and left them very little for their own. But that does not matter in this tale. For to Andrew it was excitement, creation, fulfillment. And he had the need to create, unrealized until now. More and more he put the work of superintending the churches and schools into the hands of the Christian Ma, and more and more he immersed himself in Greek roots, in Pauline theology, in Chinese idioms. He withdrew yet further from the world, spending days and nights in his inviolable study. We could hear the strange music of Greek as he read aloud the text, and the chanting intonations of the Chinese. Slowly, very slowly, the heap of pages in Greek, interlined with Chinese written in his large script, grew upon the table under the paperweight which was a Buddha that one of his converts had once worshiped, renounced, and given to him, and which now stood there ironically holding together the Christian scriptures.

His fellow missionaries objected vigorously to this use of Andrew's time. Nobody, they said, had given him permission to translate the New Testament alone.

"Nobody except God!" said Andrew, and he looked as high and as cold as an alp.

Most of these wars and skirmishes between Andrew and his fellow missionaries took place, not from day to day, but at an annual gathering known as "mission-meeting," where all the missionaries and their wives came together to give reports and to discuss rules and make laws and policies. Not that the wives had anything, presumably, to do with it. The mission of the church in which Andrew had been bred and now worked was and still is made up of a group of Americans from the South, who present a mixture of human qualities of the most curious and fascinating sort. To this day they maintain an incredible narrowness of creed which accepts in entirety the miracles of virgin birth, water changed into wine, the dead raised to life, and the second appearance, hourly expected, of Christ. Their judgment upon those who do not or cannot so believe is inhumanly cruel —such persons simply do not exist for them—no friendship is possible, no acquaintance desired. But within their own group of sympathizers they are friendly and kind enough, endlessly helpful in illness or need. Religion in their case, as in so many another, has hardened their hearts and made it impossible for them to see, except through the dark glass of their own creed, what life is or ought to be.

One of the more amusing aspects of their creed was the wholehearted adoption of St. Paul's contempt of women. In that little band of missionaries no woman ever raised her voice before men, either to pray or to speak in meeting. In their meetings the women knelt mutely before the men, who knelt before God and alone could speak to him. And Andrew was one of them. Once at a prayer meeting an English woman of another faith in all innocence prayed aloud when, according to the custom, the meeting was thrown open for prayer. Three out of the five men present rose and stalked out. I opened my eyes to see how Andrew was bearing it. He was restive upon his knees, but Carie was kneeling beside him, her eyes wide open, fixed upon him, daring him to move. Andrew would not look at Carie and he did not go out, but he was doing what no one had ever seen him do before—his eyes were wide open and he was staring out of the window. As far as he was concerned, there was no praying going on.

The annual mission meeting was, therefore, as good as a circus. For the wives of these early missionaries were no weaklings. They were pioneers as much as their men were, and if they could not speak in public they made up for it by a great deal of private speaking. There was Mrs. Houston, for instance, from Georgia. Everybody knew the story about her. When Mr. Houston came to marry her on their way to China, he grew nervous as the train approached the town where she lived and he went straight on to the coast and took sail, without stopping for the wedding at all, although the bride was dressed and waiting and all the guests were in the church. But Jenny

Houston was not in the least daunted. She packed up her wedding finery and came straight after him to Shanghai and married him and made him a strong, able, domineering wife, who, in a voice full of Southern softness and drawl, commanded him altogether for his own good.

And there was Sallie Gant, so much better a preacher than gentle little Lem Gant, her husband—Sallie who proclaimed loudly her complete obedience to the Pauline creed and bowed her handsome blonde head to that yoke. And yet no one needed to do more than see the two together to know that Sallie had Lem's gentle soul between her thumb and forefinger and that she pinched it cruelly.

For of course the inevitable result of this religious subjection of women was to breed in them an irrepressible independence and desire for self-expression, born of their innate and unconscious sense of injury and injustice. All subject people so suffer. If men were wise they would give women complete freedom and their rebellions would dissipate into mildness and uncertainty.

But in those repressed, strong, vigorous missionary women the blood ran high. Their very faces were stormy and hewn into lines of determination and grimness, with more often than not a touch of humor. There was a good deal of pathos about them, too, particularly among those not yet quite old, who still longed for a little pleasure or were interested in a new dress or what "the styles" were at home. If one were to choose between the men and the women, the women would have won for the look of strong patience in their eyes and for the stubbornness upon their lips. And in mission meeting, though only the men could rise and speak before the assembly, beside every man sat his woman, her hand ready to grasp his coat tails. How many times I have seen a man leap to his feet, his grizzled beard working, his eyes flashing, and open his mouth to speak, only to sit abruptly, subdued by a strong downward pull upon his coat tails! There would be a vigorous whispered conference between man and woman. Sometimes he was as stubborn as she, and if he could not say what he wanted, he would say nothing. But more often he stood up again after a few moments, the fire gone from his eyes, and clearing his throat, he would begin to speak, and his voice came out as mild as a summer wind. They all knitted, those women, while their men gave reports and passed laws of the church and made prayers. Their strong hard fingers flew while they had to remain mute. Into those stitches went what curbed desires and stubborn wills and plans! They would have burst, I think, without that vent.

But there were some women who were not married and had no men to speak for them. These did full work in the mission and then they wrote out the report each year of what they had done and asked some man to read it for them, and sat silent while men voted what money they should be given and what they should do with it. There was little Dr. Greene, for instance, who ran a big hospital for women and children and had a school for nurses besides, and was one of the most extraordinary women who ever lived. Florence Nightingale's life was a mild story compared to Dr. Greene's lonely hourly struggle in that far interior city of China. She was very beloved and the sick came to her from far and near, for they trusted her. Yet every year she gave the written report of her thousands of cases, her incredible, terrific operations, her huge numbers of lives saved, to some man who read it aloud to other men and then they voted what she could and could not do. It is true she sat peacefully smiling, not knitting, just resting for

once, and when they had decided for her, she went back again and did exactly as she pleased. But I remember her best thus: I as a child was once in the courtyard of her hospital and a poor slave girl was brought in dying of opium which she had swallowed. Dr. Greene, hearing of her extremity, rushed into the courtyard, but it was too late—the poor thing died at that instant.

I had seen plenty of dead people, even at that age, but this was my first sight of a soul passing out of a body. And the girl was so pretty—so pretty! I could not keep from crying and I begged Dr. Greene, "She won't go to hell, will she? God wouldn't send her to hell, would he?"

Dr. Greene's gentle pale face moved a little, and she sighed, "I don't know, my child—I don't know. It doesn't bear thinking about." And she stroked the girl's fading, cooling hand.

It was a heresy, of course. It would never have done to say such a thing in the presence of the saints. Not to know! It was a sin not to know.

And yet these stormy, human Christian saints, as full of their original sin as any people could be, with none of the tempered grace of the civilized heathen whom they were trying to convert, could at the appointed hour lay aside their differences and their furies, and together break the bread and drink the wine of communion, and then a strange strong peace filled the house in which they sat. It was the peace of complete belief in that which they lived, the absolute certainty of their minds, the total surrender of their souls to that to which they had committed themselves. It made no difference whether, absolutely speaking, they were right or wrong. They came, believing they brought salvation and happiness to all who accepted their creed. And in a sense they were right. All who could be-

lieve as they believed were saved from the doubt and distrust and the unhappiness bred of a mind uncertain of its own being. But none were as happy as they were themselves, for none were so blind in their sureness. Their hearts were empty and swept, the light in their minds extinguished. No question was allowed to enter them. One of them once roared at me, discovering in my trembling hands Darwin's *Origin of Species,* "I would no more think of reading a book against my belief or talking with an unbeliever except to preach to him, than I would of taking poison into my body." Yes, they built their own citadel, and the walls were high as heaven, and there was only one small gate by which to enter. But if there was war within, there was also peace.

Andrew always came out of the mission meetings greatly whetted and refreshed by the conflict and by communion. He was one of perhaps three men in the group of two score or more who paid no attention to any pull on his coat tails. Sometimes Carie, driven to speak by intense disagreement, would make her whispering at his ear, but I never knew him to be in the least affected by it—that is, not in the way she hoped. "Oh, pshaw!" he would say aloud, and get up in his seemingly mild fashion and say exactly what he had been going to say anyway. The knowledge of impotence was bitter in Carie. "Your father is stubborn as a mule," she once said passionately, and then added furiously, "and he's right a good deal of the time, which doesn't make things any easier!" However Carie might complain privately about Andrew, publicly she always upheld him.

Once, in a romantic adolescent moment, dreaming over Tennyson's *Princess,* I looked up to ask her, "Mother, were you and Father ever in love?"

She was sewing at some everyday garment, and for a moment I could not fathom her sudden look at me. It was—was it pain, shock—what was it? But it was not surprised enough for pain or shock. It was as though I had opened a secret, unconsciously. Then the look closed.

"Your father and I have both been very busy people," she said, her voice practical and a little brisk. "We have thought of our duty rather than how we felt." She turned a hem quickly and went on sewing.

But Andrew was not to be moved by wifely counsel or by love. It was about this time he developed a new war. There was, of course, always the war of the New Testament. Each year in mission meeting he reported how many more chapters were done, and listened benignly while the others voted he was not to go on with it and that no money was to be given him for it. But the new war had to do with the establishment of a center for training Chinese clergy, a theological seminary, in short.

It was an enterprise far too large for any one group to begin and maintain, but several denominations had decided to subscribe to it, and Andrew's denomination was contemplating the matter. From the first Andrew was eager for it. To found a stable seat of training for the leaders of the Chinese church—his mind leaped ahead, planning. And he had risen to his feet at once to speak for it.

So was begun that long war which was continued year after year. For Andrew and a few others had overpersuaded, by their fiery tongues, the more conservative majority. It soon appeared that the union would never work. There were the Methodists and their bishops concerning whom Andrew remarked drily, "They are perfectly willing to unite with everybody provided everybody joins the Methodists." And the Baptists who insisted that the budding Chinese clergy must be taught the essential doctrine of immersion, and the Episcopalians—but then, no one expected the Episcopalians to join anything. And most dreadful of all were the sects which were tinged with modernism. It soon became evident that union with other denominations was impossible, and the war was on. But year after year at mission meetings, Andrew, son of generations of grim Presbyterian fathers, Calvinist, predestinarian, believer in the second coming of Christ, fought the battle for union.

"Not for modernism," he would proclaim when he was accused. "Never! But the only way to change a thing is to stay in it and change it from within. You can never accomplish anything by pulling out and going off by yourself!"

It was a long losing war, continued over twenty years. I say losing, because his denomination pulled away at last from the union—they came, every man and woman of them, from seceding Southern blood. But Andrew never gave up. He flouted them all by giving the last years of his life to the union from which the majority had long since voted to withdraw. But then, as I said, a majority vote meant nothing to Andrew. He spent all his life being a ruling minority of one.

In these eight triumphant years after the Boxer Rebellion Andrew saw his work established over a wide territory. His lists of converts were well up into hundreds each year. His New Testament translation he was publishing book by book as he finished it, and the four Gospels he put into one early volume. Again he was heaped with criticism—it was, they said, too "common" in its style.

For again Andrew was too forward for his times. He had already realized that one strong reason for ignorance and il-

literacy in China was that the language of books and the language of the people were entirely different. It was a situation paralleled in ancient England, where almost all literature was in Latin, of which the common man knew nothing. Andrew, therefore, in deciding to use a simple vernacular style in his translation of the Greek New Testament, was revolutionary in the extreme, antedating by a score of years those later Chinese revolutionaries who brought about what was called the Chinese Renaissance, on exactly the same principle that Andrew had seen so clearly. But they were too patriotic ever to recognize as forerunner a white man and a Christian.

Andrew had chosen, then, to use not the classical Chinese beloved of old scholars but the strong vernacular Mandarin of the people. He could not, it is true, make it too vernacular, because of his own purist instincts, but he chose a clear, somewhat compressed, plain style, without allusion or furbishing, corresponding somewhat to the Moffatt edition of the English Bible. The few old Chinese scholars who were converts complained that the vernacular had no literary value, and that Andrew had made a book fit only for the common people. Andrew, himself a scholar, smiled his wry independent smile.

"Exactly!" he said. "Now when a common man learns to read a little he can make something out of Christ's teaching."

And he went on translating and polishing each book as he finished it, paying for it all by incredible pinchings and scrapings and even begging. He was not in the least proud about begging for money to carry on his work. He scattered his little books everywhere he went. But he would never give them away, having observed that any bits of valueless paper procurable were at once made into shoe soles by the indefatigable Chinese wives. So he made everybody pay a penny or two for salvation. But he paid more than any of them.

All these years Andrew's children were growing up in his house. In after years, after he had been old and was dead, they looked at each other trying to remember him, but they could not. They remembered him in certain moments of vivid action, but there was no continuity to their memories. The days went on without him in the peaceful busy round of the house. He came home at certain times and nothing seemed quite natural until he was gone again. They tiptoed about, because he was tired, they fetched his slippers and books, they gave up Carie to him, and wandered a little desolately on the fringe of rather stormy talk about "the Work," or about the newly come missionary. "A good man, but not overly bright," Andrew summed him up at the dinner table.

These visits of Andrew's to his home were not perhaps entirely fair to him, for Carie was too soft-hearted to whip any of her children, and yet she had been reared in the belief that to spare the rod was to spoil the child. So major punishments were reserved for Andrew's coming. He did not waste much time over causes. After all, there were only two or three things a child could do which in Carie's opinion merited whipping and chief of them was a lie. And he always took Carie's word.

Andrew, in his study, would look up from his book at a small liar, standing trembling before him. "Go out and cut me a switch," he would say with ominous mildness. When it was brought in, he examined it for size and pliability. It need not be large, but it must not be small.

"Down with your things!" he said, if

he were satisfied. He turned in his swivel chair. "Stand still!" he commanded.

We never thought of disobeying him, or even of roaring unduly, although with Carie and her wavering punishments we bellowed shamelessly in the full knowledge of her soft heart. But once the most naughty of Andrew's children bent the switch secretly in a dozen places and presented it thus, apparently whole but really shorn of its strength. Andrew laid it upon the small thigh where it fell harmlessly. He saw instantly that he had been deceived. "Oh, pshaw!" he exclaimed. A glint of steely humor came into his eyes, but he rose and went out and cut a beautiful switch from a willow tree and snipped off the twigs and smoothed it down to extremest efficiency.

But wait! There were a few times—was it perhaps Christmas Eve or a birthday?—when Andrew played crokinole with us. We do not remember any other games with him. Carie played checkers and taught us chess, which she loved, and advised authors for our education. But one year the Montgomery Ward boxes held a crokinole board, and there were evenings when Andrew played. He enjoyed it immensely, taking an unexpected pleasure in it, and forgetting everything else for the moment. He had an extraordinarily long strong forefinger and great accuracy of aim, and he knocked the little round wooden pieces with terrific force into the net bags where they were supposed to go. We all crouched a little and held our breaths, because if they hit a small peg in the middle of the board they bounced and struck like a shot. One small daughter of his went with a sore spot on her little breast bone for days.

And wait again! There were certain other evenings when prayers with the servants being over, he read aloud to us all and to Carie while she sewed. It was always the *Century Magazine,* to which he subscribed regularly for many years, and each year sent to Shanghai to be bound. There were years of them in a row on the bottom shelf in his study, and one after the other of his children in their time stole in and surreptitiously slipped out a volume and spread out the others to cover the space. For they wanted the books for the stories in them and Andrew did not approve of "story books." Only once did he read aloud a novel and he was inveigled into it by seeing the first few pages inadvertently. He had picked the book up to forbid it, and glancing at it had broken into his "haw" of laughter at a sentence he saw. The book was *The Casting Away of Mrs. Lecks and Mrs. Aleshine.* He kept on turning over the leaves and we held our breaths again. He put it down and said nothing. But after supper he took it up.

"I suppose you'd like this," he said to Carie and began to read it aloud. We all sat and listened and laughed, and none of us laughed as much as Andrew. His eyes would run ahead and begin to shine and his voice choked and his face turned red. He tried to go on, but it was too funny for him. He laid the book down to laugh and to gasp over and over, "Oh, pshaw— oh, pshaw!"

It was a sad day when it was over. We had never had such a good time before. I have never seen the book again, but it remains to me the funniest book in the world. Not even Mark Twain was quite so funny. Carie thought Mark Twain a little coarse and Andrew found his humor marred by certain irreligious tendencies. But Mrs. Lecks and Mrs. Aleshine! They were two absurd and delightful old women, and Andrew could laugh at them with no sense of sin. Remembering, one day, it made us wonder what manner of man Andrew might have been with that strong wry sense of humor—what manner of man he might

have been, that is, if God had not caught his soul and Calvin had not held fast his heart!

9

That those successful years were happy ones I know from Andrew's own record. "It seemed that before I knew it eight years were gone and it was again time for furlough." The early term of service had been ten years; now it was shortened to eight—an unnecessarily short time, Andrew felt. For why should a man need a rest from work which his soul delighted to do? He would have taken no furlough except that a daughter was ready to be sent back to college, and Carie wanted to go with her. America was strange and different now, and the child was used to nothing but these quiet Chinese villages and hills. Besides, there were the kinfolk. So grudgingly Andrew gave up the year, consoling himself with the hope of getting money for his work and of working on his translation.

To those children of his who accompanied him that was a memorable journey. For Carie suddenly decided that she could not again cross the Pacific which made her desperately ill, that the children ought to see Europe, that she wanted to see Russia, and that they would therefore all go up the Yangtze River to Hankow and take a train for the north and thence to Russia and Siberia by train to Germany. It was a stupendous plan, for we always remembered that Andrew was no executive when it came to the matter of tickets. He could direct the efforts of hundreds of churches and schools and thousands of souls, but the intricacies of ticket buying confused him. The whole journey was a series of major and minor catastrophes. His children remember less of Russia than they do of Andrew,

cooped up in a small railway compart-
ment with nowhere to put his long legs
all day. He who needed space and privacy was reduced to nothing of either.

There was not even a lavatory, and we
were compelled to do all our washing in
turn out of a small enameled basin we
had brought along, and water was very
scarce and to be had only at stations and
then by rushing out with a can and
buying it.

There was one dreadful morning when
the smallest child forgot to empty the
basin after she had used it, and Andrew,
always absent-minded and now in deepest gloom over his situation, sat down in it
and ruined his only pair of trousers. He
had not recovered from this when he
found a cup half full of water, and wanting to use the cup, he threw the contents
out of the window. He was too nearsighted to see that the glass was up, and
the water flew back at him, wetting his
front very thoroughly. Carie laughed. It
was too much. He sat down. "There is
nothing to laugh at," he said severely,
and for the rest of the day he stared
gloomily at the flat Russian landscape
and muttered over and over, "I don't see
anything to this country—there's nothing
to make a fuss over, here!" The hearty
Russian fashion of kissing appalled him.
He watched the bearded dirty peasants
greet each other with loud kisses and
shuddered. This was worse than a
heathen country, he said.

Later, he was to grow more appalled.
When we stopped at various places for a
few days he wandered inevitably to the
churches, and stood there by the hour,
watching the hordes of people come in,
poor and ragged and miserable, most of
them, but a few of them rich too, and poor
and rich all bending to kiss the relics of
cloth or bone or skin left from some dead
saint. Strangely, he felt no pity or responsibility for these souls. "They have
the Bible," he said. "They could get at

the truth if they would. But it's an easy
way—to live in sin and go and gabble to
a priest and kiss a bone and call it
salvation!"

So we were all glad when we got
Andrew into Germany, and yet the very
first day in Berlin we saw a sight we had
never yet seen—Andrew so incensed that
he offered to fight a cabman! The fellow
was a huge, burly, heavy German and he
shook his fist under Andrew's nose in the
railway station in the presence of innumerable people because he considered
his tip inadequate, whereupon Andrew,
who felt tips were of the devil anyhow,
doubled up his fists and pushed them into
the fellow's fat jaw. We were so amazed
we could not believe this was our Andrew. Carie screamed and held his arm
and fumbled in her own bag for coins to
placate the Teuton, and at last roaring
throaty oaths, he went his way, and we
led Andrew hastily to a hotel, taking care
to hire the meekest looking porter in
sight to transport our bags. Andrew went
with us, looking more ungodly than we
would have believed possible, giving as
he went his opinion of the white race,
which for the moment was even lower
than usual. Indeed, I believe this incident
more than anything else was responsible
for Andrew's strong stand against the
Germans in the World War, and his
complete readiness to believe all atrocity
stories.

"That fellow!" he would mutter for
years after, "The Germans are capable of
anything!"—this in spite of his own early
German ancestry and an innocent pride
he always took in his proficiency in the
German language.

How Andrew looked in America a certain daughter of his will always remember. She sat, a timid freshman among
other freshman in a college chapel, waiting in some anxiety. For Andrew had
been asked to lead vespers, and among
the few friends she had eagerly made, the

first friends of her own race she had ever had, she was anxious that all impressions be of the best. She looked at Andrew with some misgiving as he came in, tranquil as ever, behind the president. No man could move with greater dignity than he before a service he was to give. Everybody looked at him and his daughter saw him with new detachment, a very tall, slightly stooped figure, the noble head carried with native pride, his big profile pointed straight ahead. But then she only saw that his frock coat was the same old coat, rusty and given a little at the seams and of an obsolete cut, and well she knew the scene there had been before he put it on.

Carie said, "Andrew, you're not going to preach at the college in that old gray suit!"

"Old! It's not old—it's a good suit—good enough for a preacher."

"Andrew!" Carie's dark eyes went on speaking, fixed upon him. He looked away from her doggedly.

"A preacher oughtn't to be all dressed up," he muttered.

Her eyes, pinning him, went on speaking.

He went on, restlessly, "I tell you I hate that old long-tailed coat! The armholes are tight."

"I've been wanting you to get a new one for years." Carie's voice was dangerously mild.

"What for?" Andrew demanded. "It's perfectly good!"

"Then why won't you wear it?"

"Oh, pshaw!" he said, and got up, beaten.

There was a whisper beside his daughter in the chapel. A girlish voice said in a soft, innocent, Southern drawl, "He looks as though he'd be right long-winded!"

There was a bitter moment and then Andrew's daughter said, her lips dry, "He's my father."

There was a shock of silence, "Oh, I *am* sorry!" the pretty voice said.

"It doesn't matter," said Andrew's daughter sternly. "He *is* long-winded!" and sat there suffering, while Andrew preached on and on.

For she never knew what to do with him. He fitted into no niche as a father. Great missionary he was, intrepid soul, but there was no fatherhood in him. He had to be viewed, to be considered, not as a father but as a man. His children were merely accidents which had befallen him. Else how explain that amazing incident when having discovered to his horror the minimum cost of a college education, he decided he would not rob the New Testament and so wrote to a certain rich man of his acquaintance to ask if he did not want to educate an incipient missionary? Carie, opening in his absence the polite, amazed refusal, was quite out of her mind with outraged pride and could not keep it to herself. That daughter of hers, hearing, was struck to the heart. She felt somehow that she had been sold into slavery. The ugly college sitting-room where she and Carie sat is forever imprinted upon her mind. From outside came the voices of girls, American girls, born free of the bondage which all unconsciously Andrew had laid upon his children. Not one of them knew what it was to be always nothing in comparison to a cause, to a work, to a creed.

"He needn't bother about me," she said, strangling with pride and hurt. "I can look out for myself. I'll leave college this very day and go and get a job at the ten cent store. I can look after myself. He doesn't even need to feed me."

"Don't—don't take it so!" Carie begged her. Tears were in her eyes. "I oughtn't to have told you. He didn't mean anything—you've got to understand that he isn't like other men. He's—he's like somebody in a dream!"

Yes, that was it. Andrew was somebody in a dream, a soul possessed, to whom life and the human heart had no importance. He never lived on earth. She knew what Carie meant. She did not blame Andrew, not really—but she felt herself fatherless. In after years she grew closer to him, as close as any human could, and came to understand and value him, to know why he was as he was, both great and small. But all that later knowledge cannot quite wipe away the bereavement of that hour. For Andrew's children were bereaved in what they never had, in what he could not give them, because he had given everything in him to God.

Andrew came back to find again a new China. During all those years of too great peace, too easy triumph of God's will, something had been happening. It was a deep rebellion, a revolution brewing upward from the South, taking that easiest way of all revolutions, of antagonism to the foreigner and an outburst of nationalism. Andrew and Carie and their youngest child were scarcely back in the square mission bungalow when the false peace of eleven years exploded, and Sun Yat-sen and his followers overthrew the old empire.

It is another story, often told and belonging now to history, and other events have robbed it of much meaning. But Andrew at the time viewed it with enthusiasm. He was so weary of the corruption of Chinese officials with whom he had often to deal that he would have welcomed any force, even to an earthquake and their being swallowed up. So when old careless opium-smoking viceroys and mandarins and magistrates began to escape into hiding, he took open part with the revolutionists. Especially was he happy at the passing of the Empress Dowager. He could see no drama or

beauty in that splendid old figure. To him she was that most horrible and unnatural of all creations, a woman ruler. He did not even hold Queen Elizabeth in honor. Indeed, his estimation was low of any nation willing to set a woman to rule. "Jezebel," he called the Empress Dowager, and would recount with relish the end of that queen, when having been thrown from her high tower she was devoured by dogs. There was that in Andrew which could have stood by gladly and watched it as a just retribution. Born a generation earlier he would have burned witches. There was a deep unconscious sex antagonism in him, rooted in no one knows what childhood experiences and fostered, sad to say, by the presence of Carie, that flashing quick mind which he could never comprehend, but against which he struggled to maintain himself. For he could not bear better than another man a woman more clever than himself. Besides, St. Paul justified him.

He allied himself, therefore, with the young men's revolution. For it was a young men's revolution and Andrew was always drawn to young men. He gloried in every step they took—even in their ruthless new laws that cut off queues by force. Andrew liked ruthlessness. A thing was always either right or wrong, and if it was right, it was right to enforce it.

It was somewhat dismaying to discover that in spite of Sun Yat-sen's being a Christian, there was a strong anti-Christian feeling in the revolution. But Andrew had complete faith in the triumph of God. "Tares in the wheat," he said. "God will uproot them and cast them into the fire."

So he began again his long journeys by horseback and by boat. Ma the Christian had held the churches together wonderfully well, working with that dark burning eagerness which was so compelling that it made men uncomfortable, not sure whether it was good or evil. He had been so much with Andrew and he so loved him that he had unaware taken for his own many of Andrew's gestures and tricks of speaking and preaching. If one shut one's eyes and only listened, it would have been hard to tell which of them was preaching or praying.

But Ma was not a revolutionist. He had not Andrew's optimism and guileless faith in men who said their purpose was good. He kept silent publicly, but in many ways he restrained Andrew.

"Let us wait twenty years and see," he kept saying to him, "twenty years for a test." When the years had passed and most of the self-denying ardent revolutionists were long established in power and had reverted to all the old official corruption and to not a few tricks from the West besides, he was quietly complacent. "No governor is good," he said. "A good governor has never been heard of, in the past or now."

But Andrew could not believe ill of young men. And he welcomed every change—indeed, he had a childlike love of the new, always thinking it must be better than what was old. Not until he was set upon and stoned in a certain city by young revolutionists, and driven out because he preached a foreign religion and was a citizen of an imperialistic foreign power, did he even concede the presence of tares. Imperialism! It was the first time he had heard that word, but he was to hear it often in the years to come. He never had any idea what it meant. "It's one of those words people use," he used to say in his own imperial fashion, and there was an end of it.

But his work proceeded with increasing difficulty. He had long since so enlarged his territory that the white horse, which had replaced his donkey, was growing old, and was not enough. The newly running train to Shanghai reached a part of his field, but there was a large area which could be reached only by boat. For years Andrew had waged battles with junk men in the process of hiring a small junk to take him along the interior canals of the country.

The boatmen of China are undoubtedly and universally of the breed of pirates. There is not one who has not a pirate's heart born in him. Time and again Andrew would be delayed in setting forth on a tour because the boat captain was demanding more money than he had agreed upon. So the idea came to Andrew to buy his own boat, and he happened to have a sum of money for it. A man in America had given it to him to build a chapel in memory of his dead wife, but Andrew decided it would be more useful to God to buy a boat with the money. It did not occur to him that the donor might not want a boat in memory of his wife. And according to his custom, Andrew, having thought of a good thing, proceeded instantly to its completion. Only when the boat was built and finished did he write to the man and tell him that there was a boat instead of a chapel.

Andrew did not at all anticipate the outcome. The man was filled with fury. It seemed his wife was always seasick and particularly hated boats. He refused the boat and demanded the return of the money at once.

Andrew was amazed at such lack of reason. He folded the man's letter and remarked in a tone of complete and calm righteousness, "How can he ask for the money back when he knows it is spent? Besides, I told him very clearly that a boat would be more useful now to me than a chapel." With infinite dignity he added, "I shall pay no attention to him." It was perhaps his most frequently repeated phrase in a disagreement.

But the man was a rich man, accustomed to having his own way, and he considered Andrew as a little higher than a menial, but not much. Missionaries! What were they? Servants of the church, and he practically owned the church, because he gave it so much money. He complained furiously to Andrew's mission board, who wrote to Andrew sternly. This board, it happened, was the one organization Andrew heeded somewhat, because it could deprive him of all funds, salary as well as work funds, and he never distinguished clearly between the two. He used money as long as it was there, chiefly for his work. Even Carie could not touch it. He did not believe in women having checkbooks, and the idea of a joint bank account filled him with horror.

"Why, you might take out money, and I wouldn't know where I was!" he exclaimed once in consternation when she suggested a checkbook of her own.

"I never know where I am!" Carie retorted. "I have to feed and clothe you and the children and I never know what there is to count on."

It was a crisis in a long war between them, waged through their whole life. Andrew never thought food and clothes ought to cost anything. Anyway, the Work came first. Carie made miracles out of pennies, but he never knew it. She said once with a twinkle and a sigh, "Andrew ought to have married that widow in the Bible who had a bottomless cruse of oil and a flour bin that was never empty. Ever since he heard of her nothing I can do satisfies him!"

But he was harder on himself than on anyone else, and none ate more frugally or clothed himself more poorly than he, for God's sake. Nevertheless, there was that war between them, and it went on for forty years, when suddenly, for no apparent reason, Andrew gave up one day and handed her a checkbook to a joint account. Carie by that time was

past the need of it. The children were grown and her great desires were over. Nevertheless, for victory's sake she took it and under direction made out a check or two and then put the book away. But it was a comfort to her. She could draw a check if she wanted to, at last.

To be confronted, then, by his mission board with a demand that he account for a thousand dollars given for a chapel and spent on a boat was somewhat terrifying even to Andrew, and catastrophe to Carie. She reproached him, seeing her children with nothing, and in a foreign country where the people were increasingly unfriendly.

"If you wouldn't be so headstrong!" she said mournfully, and quite hopelessly. Andrew not headstrong would not be Andrew.

But any such reproach was always strength to Andrew's purpose. "I know what I'm doing," he said severely.

Unfortunately for its own authority, the board member who wrote the letter was foolish enough to add, thinking it would be a whip over Andrew, "Mr. Shipley is one of our wealthiest donors and it is most unwise to offend him in any way."

A glitter of ice shone in Andrew's eyes as he read this. So he was to obey a man merely because he was rich! A rich man could very hardly enter the Kingdom of Heaven, and yet he, Andrew, was to obey him before God! He sat down at once in the freshness of his scorn and wrath, and wrote what his children called one of his God-almighty letters, inquiring of the board in simple, brief phrases what they meant by bowing their heads to Mammon and how they thought themselves worthy of their positions as directors of God's work? As for him, he would not listen to any rich man or to them, but only to God. The boat was built and he would use it.

He never again heard anything on the

subject from either the rich man or the board, and he used the boat happily and in triumph for many years until he grew too old to make his journeys any more.

After the first success of the revolution was over it came to be apparent that the changes it had brought about were not fundamental. Sun Yat-sen, living so many years abroad as to have become a foreigner in his own country, made a profound mistake in the object of his revolution. Observing Western countries, he decided that a good central government could make all the changes he longed for in China, and that the first and most important step was to change the form of that government, and this he did, and it remains the chief thing he did do. For what he did not understand was that central government in China is not important as it is in many other countries, and never has been. The life of the people, their lives and rules of life, have proceeded not from central government but from themselves and out of their family and group life. To overthrow a central government and change its form was not of deep importance to the people. The Chinese people have not, as has England or the United States or France, created slowly, by one means and another step by step through centuries, their own form of central government. Such government in China has been primarily by conquerors, either native war lords or foreign ones, who established a sort of suzerainty. The people were not ruled by them in the sense that other governments rule by force or that laws were made and obeyed. The life of the people went on, therefore, in the same old ways fundamentally, because the real and local government was not changed.

And the foreign powers made haste to present claims and protect treaties and the lives of their citizens. The weak new revolutionary government, inexperienced and easily alarmed, did not dare to create enmity so soon. Within a very few years Andrew was able to proceed as boldly and safely as ever, preaching wherever he would, and because he was a foreigner he was free to do as he liked. Again his work prospered.

It never occurred to any of us that Andrew could ever grow old. His body had always been the same, lean as a pine, his skin weathered to a dark bronze red. He never added a pound to his weight, and his waist stayed as slim as it had ever been in his youth. There never was, in fact, a saint who had the flesh so subdued as he. Wherever he was, in whatever inconvenience of circumstance, his regimen remained immovably the same— a cold bath at rising, and he rose invariably at half-past five; from six to seven he spent in prayer and meditation; at seven he breakfasted, invariably the same breakfast, and it always included a dish of porridge made from native wheat washed and sun dried and ground in a little stone handmill. Work began immediately after breakfast and continued until noon, when he dined, to work again until five o'clock, when he walked for an hour before his supper. In the evening he preached at some chapel, or if he were free, he read and was in bed by ten. It was the simplest routine. Even his meals were absolutely regular in quantity. He enjoyed food, when he let himself. He was as rigid with himself as though he were his own physician. None of us remember a single lapse or any indulgence. And his magnificent body remained a miracle of vigor, his eyes clear and vivid, and his skin, where it was not burned, as white and smooth as a little child's. Nor was his face tortured by lines. He was never wrinkled, even when he grew really old. His high smooth brow was still tranquil, his lean cheeks unlined. Such it was to have a mind untroubled and sure of itself. He was a perfectly happy soul, living in a strong and subdued body.

So he went unscathed through sickness and disease everywhere about him and remained whole and untouched. If he had a little malaria, a dash of quinine instantly restored him, so quick to respond was his healthy body. And as time went on he seemed to build up his own immunity and never had malaria at all. Time after time he went into famine areas to do relief work and others came down with typhus, but never he. Smallpox he escaped, though even he wondered at that, because for years he did not think of being vaccinated. "It slipped my mind," he said calmly. Only once was he desperately ill in all the years of his youth and maturity and that was from a sunstroke, caught on a fiery July day in Shanghai. For six weeks he lay unconscious, fighting his battles in his dreams, arguing with his enemies, the missionaries and the mandarins, and planning for new fields of work. To enlarge, to expand, to reach more souls— that was his endless passion in his delirium as in his life.

But unconsciously he felt the shortening of his years, for in the decade after he was fifty he worked as he had never worked. His Testament was finished and he was revising edition after edition. He was on innumerable committees, for his energy and forthrightness were admired and trusted even by those who hated him. There have not been too many like him in that respect.

To be a missionary is an acute test of integrity. For a missionary has no supervision. He lives among a few equals, the other missionaries, and a great many whom he feels his inferiors, the natives. His governing board is thousands of miles away—there is no one to see how many hours he works or whether he is lazy and self-indulgent. And the climate, the small but absolute security of salary,

the plentiful number of cheaply paid servants, all make laziness easy, and a man's fellows are loath to tell of him even if they see, and the Chinese converts are helpless for they do not know to whom to complain. There is no one beyond the missionary for them. These stand next to God and are supreme in authority, having the right to give or withhold funds which mean life.

A missionary's integrity, therefore, must be beyond that of any other white man's, and sometimes, perhaps even more often than not, it is. For the Standard Oil or the British-American Tobacco Company can check sales lists and have the solid proof of money received, but even a list of church members means nothing at all—not in China, where the gift of tongues is universal, and where histrionic power is a common possession. The newest convert can, after a minimum amount of rehearsal, rise before the congregation and make a prayer so rich and fluent, so copious in spiritual experience that it would be the envy of any American bishop. Missionaries are human enough, God knows, and so do the Chinese. Doubtless most of them struggle against laziness as we all do, and some give up to it, but most of them struggle along. But Andrew was a flame of integrity. It was impossible to imagine him struggling. He was always in complete command of himself. His duty was done to the last ounce of its demand. Even his enemies never questioned that burning integrity. As for the Chinese, they trusted him like children. If he said a thing they knew it would come true. "He says it," was good collateral anywhere. Curiously—or was it curiously?— the fact that the Chinese loved him and trusted him increasingly did not make the missionaries love him better. But then it is quite true he always took sides with the Chinese. He believed, for instance, in a day too early for such belief, that the

Chinese and American workers should have equal power of decision regarding policies of the work. He took no stock in the idea that the white men ought to stand by each other and maintain a fiction of rightness and authority before the Chinese. Such notions in his day were heresies.

So the idea of age came as an absurdity. It is difficult to remember when it began. He was making his long journeys as he always had, examining applicants for church membership, examining school curriculums, holding conferences with preachers and teachers, going incredible distances on foot and horseback, by rail and by water. In these later years he met with little physical hazard because he was so known and loved.

Once in the hills of Kiangsu he was taken by bandits and they asked him who he was. When he told them they let him go and gave him back his purse they had taken.

"We have heard of you in many places," they said simply. "You do good deeds."

Andrew, seeing them in such a mood, stayed a while to preach to them and tell them the story of the robber who hung beside Christ on the cross and was received into heaven when he repented. He must have preached rather long, for some of the young ones grew restive, but the old bandit chieftain shouted at them— and Andrew told this himself with a grin—"Be still! Don't you see the man is trying to get to heaven by this task he has set himself to save our souls? We must help him by waiting until he is through."

So he compelled them to stay and Andrew gave them each copies of the Gospel tracts he had written and came home in much triumph, confident forever after that he would meet some of those bandits in heaven. For, he argued, he had been sent to save them.

"Weren't you afraid?" we inquired of him.

There was, he admitted, a nasty moment when one of the young bandits had a knife at his stomach and was making unpleasant screwing motions. "But it was certainly very nice afterwards," he said. "They sat so nicely and listened—they were really very nice men, in spite of their unfortunate calling."

There was something puzzling about Andrew. He seemed sometimes almost a fool for naïveté. One could not be sure that he really understood the situations in which he found himself. But he was God's fool.

When did it begin to occur to us that even his magnificent and unfailing body must break? I think it was when the Chinese began to say to us, "He must not rise so early and travel so far and work so hard. Persuade him to rest and take a little more food. He is no longer young."

Not young! We looked at Andrew. He seemed the same. He pshawed away any change in his routine. No, he wouldn't take any more vacation. Why should he go into the coolness of mountains and rest when his Chinese colleagues could not?

It was after a long and particularly hot summer, which he had spent alone, that we noticed a weariness about him that had not been, a slackening that could not be defined, because he worked as hard as ever. But he did not work so eagerly as he had always done and he was sometimes too tired to eat at all. There was one evening, for instance, when he came home very late, having taken a much later train than usual from an out-station. He made no explanation, however. Instead he went upstairs and bathed and shaved freshly and came down to supper looking unusually well in a white suit of Chinese linen.

Something disturbed him, though—we

could all see it—and when he was pressed he said shamefacedly and with a shade of bewilderment that was a little touching, "I don't know how I could have done it. But I went to sleep on the train and slept beyond my station. When I woke the train was at the end of the line and I was too late for the service, so I could only turn around and come home."

It was so unlike him to oversleep that we searched him for something wrong. But he seemed himself, after all. Then a week later he came back from a journey with a slight paralysis of the face—a drooping lid to his left eye, a twisted corner of the left side of his mouth. This was serious. He could not articulate quite clearly, but we understood that he had sat up all night in the coolie class to save money.

Carie was angry with anxiety. "Save money!" she cried. "And what of yourself? What's the good of a dollar if you're dead?"

He looked at her speechless, humble with his state. The doctor was called and he said a rest was necessary and at once. Andrew's furlough was years overdue. Indeed he had quite forgotten about furloughs, and Carie had made up her mind she would never cross the sea again anyway. But the youngest child was ready for college and she pressed upon Andrew the need of someone's taking her back to America, knowing that unless she could make it seem his duty to go he never would, especially when after a few days in bed his face straightened to normal again and he pshawed over the idea of more rest. But she prevailed, and exactly forty years after he had left his own country, Andrew went back again for what was to be his last visit. For he made up his mind to that, fearful lest he die away from China. His illness, slight as it was, had made him realize his mortal body. He would go to America but only for a few months—he did not want to be away from China where he had lived his life and where his friends were and, most dear of all, his work. He went off, very resolutely, standing quite still by the rail of the ship's deck, staring at the fading outlines of the Shanghai Bund.

"I'll be back in exactly four months from today," he said. He had already bought his return ticket and had it pinned with a safety pin inside his "cholera belt," a strip of flannel he wore about his waist night and day.

We were not able to comprehend from his letters all that he felt about America. There were hints that it was an entirely new country, not in the least the sort of place he and Carie had known and which they had for nearly half a century away from it called "home." Carie, reading his scanty short sentences aloud looked up to say, "Andrew can tell less than any man in creation, but I never knew him to tell as little about anything as he does now about home. It doesn't seem worth going at all."

When in four months to the day we met Andrew in Shanghai, looking very well, we all cried at him together, "What is America like now? You didn't tell us anything."

"I didn't dare begin," he answered a trifle grimly. Then he added, "There were things I didn't want to put down on paper."

"What things?" Carie demanded at once.

"All kinds of things," he answered.

Bit by bit we pried out of him the salient facts of an amazing postwar America. Everybody was drunk, he said over and over—well, practically everybody. Andrew was no teetotaller, not with St. Paul advising Timothy to take a little wine for his stomach's sake. And he used to say meditatively that it must mean something that every race of humanity on earth had some kind of liquor. Carie flew at him when he talked thus— she had her own reasons for hating liquor. Besides, nothing started her off like quoting St. Paul. We listened solemnly while Andrew told us of drinking and smoking—even the women.

"The women are the worst," he said guardedly, and after a pause he said diffidently, "I scarcely know how to tell you about the women in America."

"What do you mean?" Carie demanded with sternness.

He hesitated, being always the shyest of men where women were concerned.

"It's the way they dress now," he went on. We waited. "They wear hardly any skirts," he said quickly.

"Andrew!" cried Carie.

"It's true," he said. "Everywhere I went the women had dresses up to their knees. It was awful."

"Don't tell me my sisters did it!" Carie exclaimed.

"Well, theirs were better," he admitted, and then repeated with a sort of gloomy reminiscent pleasure, "Yes, everywhere I went they had all their dresses up to their knees."

We stared at him, shocked into silence.

"Their legs were awful," he said, remembering. "Big and fat, long and thin—"

Carie could not bear it. "It does seem you needn't have looked at them," she said with severity.

"I couldn't help it," he said simply. "They were lying around everywhere."

We sat in silence, overcome by the idea of a ruined America. It was Carie who brought us back. She rose briskly.

"Well, you're back safely anyhow," she said. But somehow she made us feel it had been a narrow escape.

Later from various relatives we heard bits about Andrew in America. He had expressed himself very freely, we gathered, on almost every part of life. "Andrew acted as though he didn't know he wasn't in a heathen country," Christopher the Methodist wrote.

"So I was," said Andrew grimly in parenthesis, reading the letter. He looked up. "Chris doesn't preach strong enough sermons," he went on. "I heard him— you can't save souls by a lot of soft talk."

"Andrew looked very well," his sister Rebecca wrote. "He's as stubborn as ever."

"What did you do at Becky's house?" Carie inquired.

"It was the hottest day of summer and she wanted me to wear my long coat when I preached," Andrew said guardedly.

Carie looked at him, speechless. There had been a sharp, short argument over the frock coat when he left for America, and she had put it into his bulging suitcase. But after he had gone, when she was putting away the winter things, she found it hanging in his closet hidden behind his overcoat. She had been exasperated, but helpless.

"He's in the middle of the Pacific or I'd go right after him with it in my hand," she declared, her eyes snapping.

Andrew looked away now. "I wouldn't have worn it if I'd had it," he said. "I wore a white suit as I do here when it's hot."

"But nobody wears white suits in America!" Carie cried.

"Then I was the only sensible man in the nation," he retorted.

Well, we never could do anything with him. And he came back from his four months' rest feeling as strong and eager as ever and plans were sparkling out of his eyes and in the eagerness of his step.

He was nearly seventy years old, but he looked fifty. His hair was graying, but it was thick on his head, and his mustache and bushy eyebrows were as red as ever and his eyes as icy blue. He was at home only one day and was off again with Ma the Christian, sailing joyously down the Grand Canal to tour his field and talk over everything that had happened since he left. Ma, twenty years younger, looked older than Andrew. He had in recent years developed a slow chronic tuberculosis of the lungs which kept him bone thin and made his eyes more burning and hollow than ever and his black hair look dead and dry. His hands were the hands of death, they were so shadowlike. Andrew plied him with condensed milk and raw eggs and a great deal of prayer, and the disease seemed stationary at least, although Andrew regularly remarked, "Ma will never pull through another winter." But he did, to live in the end years beyond Andrew, still with that cough of his. Something else than food and flesh kept him living.

Looking back over the span of Andrew's life it can be seen that this tour was the height of his life. It was the hour when all his life's work lay before him in full fruit, organized, operating, in large measure self-governing and self-supporting. He had always believed, in opposition to the policy of many missionaries, that the Chinese Christians should have full powers of self-government. They should, he said, be free of all rules and domination from the missionaries. He even went so far, heretic as he was, to say that if the forms of church government and creeds found in the various Western denominations did not suit them, the Chinese should make those which would fit their own souls, only bearing always in mind the Holy Trinity. Such ideas made him loved by the

Chinese and hated by many a missionary with an autocratic turn of mind, and most missionaries are autocrats. Andrew was himself, for that matter, for he knew he was right.

That autumn, then, was the height of his life. The work had gone well while he was away, and he spent the long shining autumn days, from morning until darkness, in surveying his field. I know that the beauty of the countryside struck him with unusual clarity, for more often than ever before he spoke of the splendor of the harvest fields of rice. It was a good year and there would be no famine that winter and such confidence alone brought exhilaration. He hated to preach to starving people, lest they were listening for the sake of a little food rather than for salvation.

And it was a glorious country. The wide golden Yangtze flowed through its midst and sprang aside into hundreds of canals and streams that fed the most fertile valleys in China. Beyond the valleys were rolling bamboo-covered hills where old temples had stood for hundreds of years, and where drowsy priests smiled amicably when Andrew told them their gods were false. He always felt he had to tell them, not rudely but with a twist of humor.

He would point his stick at a bowl of food set before a god and remark gently, "I suppose he will eat that when nobody is looking?" And the priest would grin and nod or he would say comfortably, "He sees it and takes the essence of it and he does not mind if we poor priests take the worthless matter that's left and eat it."

Then Andrew would go on and talk a little about the true God, and the priest would listen and murmur, "Every man has his own god, and to each his is the true one, and there are enough for us all."

[243]

But such tolerance did not suit Andrew. He was fond of quoting a Chinese proverb which says that around the mouth of hell the priests cluster thickly.

Through the valleys and beyond the hills ran the old cobbled roads, worn into ruts by squeaking wheelbarrows—it is bad luck for a wheelbarrow to have no squeak, so that every man encourages it in his own—and smooth with the short-stepped trotting feet of donkey caravans. Andrew had always a strong feeling for the little gray donkeys of China—indeed, there was a softness in him for all animals, but particularly for horses and donkeys, and at home for a cat. There was something about a cat by the hearth which he liked. When he was old he sat by the hour with the cat spread across his knees, stroking it gently. And when he was younger he would often delay his hurrying trips to blame a donkey driver because the beast's back was sore from overloading. He knew, he said, that God's plan provided no place for beasts in heaven, and man ought therefore to take especial care that they had at least a comfortable life upon earth, since there was no other for them.

Everywhere he went he was welcomed and loved. It was an experience to travel with him and see how for hundreds of miles he was known and loved. "The Old Teacher has come back!" people shouted to each other from doorway to doorway. "Old Teacher, Old Teacher!" people called to him, and little street children trotted behind him to his great pleasure and followed him into chapels and crowded the front benches, enduring his long sermons with fair patience until they were over and they could roar out a hymn, which they delighted to do, and clamor for a Bible picture. The picture of Christ they always examined with particular closeness. Once a small dirty urchin, looking at a picture in the middle of the sermon, interrupted Andrew.

"Why, this Jesus looks like a Chinese except his nose is too big. His nose is like your nose, but his skin is like mine!"

And Andrew, who would have tolerated nothing like this from one of his own children, smiled and explained that indeed Jesus Christ was not a white man, and went on with his sermon. He had infinite patience with the people to whom he felt himself sent.

Everywhere he went that autumn the churches seemed peculiarly prosperous. The members were not of the poorest class any more. They were rich silk and tea merchants, owners of restaurants and shops, and they gave money willingly for the upkeep of the church. So far as eye could see, everything was in order among them. The services of the church were performed regularly and the churches were crowded. The schools, too, were doing well. The old days when the missionary had to bribe people to send their children to Christian schools by giving them everything, even food and clothes, were over. There could be tuition fees nowadays, when Western learning was coming into fashion and even the government schools were being reorganized and the old classics were being set aside for science and mathematics and most especially English. Everybody wanted to learn English. If a boy knew English maybe he could get a job in the Standard Oil or the tobacco company, or maybe he could even get a scholarship from the Boxer Indemnity to go to America and study. Little village boys with a turn for letters began to dream of going to America as their fathers used to dream of passing the old imperial examinations and becoming mandarins.

Not that Andrew ever encouraged any boy to go to America. It would be the ruin of him, he used to declare. America wasn't what it was, what with the automobiles and nobody going to church. He saw somewhere the figures of the year's deaths by automobile accidents in the United States and he never forgot it. He used to quote it solemnly when people talked of progress and motor cars. "Thirty thousand people a year, and most of them in hell! That's the sort of people who drive like that, undoubtedly."

Once a flippant child remarked, "So many the fewer souls to bother to save, then," to which he replied sternly, "I would not even want to see a Baptist go to hell by way of an automobile!" He was thinking of the one-eyed missionary.

But then China was his heart's home. He gave up any thought of other lands, knowing that here he would live out his life and here die. That autumn he traveled over the roads and stopped at cities and towns and the welcoming calls of the people warmed his heart. They made a sort of gala occasion of that tour of his, feeling him safely returned. He passed his sixty-ninth birthday, which made him seventy according to the Chinese reckoning, whereby a child at birth is already a year old, and they prepared feasts for him, gave him scrolls gilded and inscribed with words of praise and wide banners of red satin embroidered with letters of black velvet, and last, the insignia of an honored official, a huge red satin panoply borne aloft on a tall pole. He was much embarrassed with it and pleased, too, and came triumphantly home with all his gifts. Carie was put to it to know what to do with so much magnificence of scarlet satin in the plain little mission house, and at last she put everything away in the little round-backed trunk in the attic. There was no place for honor and glory in that self-sacrificing house. Later the trunk fell into the hands of revolutionary soldiers, who divided the shining stuff among them, snatching at it with dirty claws of hands and screeching at each other in quarreling over it. Andrew was relieved to have it gone, and Carie was in the grave by then, and the only one of us all who was safe.

Andrew came home after his three months' tour in a high serenity of happiness. He had always been happy and zestful for his life. His rare fits of melancholy were always cured by work, and his work could never be done. All through the years his soul had been borne along on the lift of his ever enlarging plan, and again and again his own spirit was refreshed by the ecstasy of the knowledge that some other soul had found that source of reason for life which he found in God.

There is no way to explain that ecstasy in Andrew. The only thing I have seen like it is the ecstasy of a father beholding his child for the first time. There was a paternal tenderness in Andrew over every soul who came up to him for baptism. There was a look upon his face, a brooding joy when he lifted his hand to bless the newborn soul, which the children of his flesh never saw when he looked upon them. For Andrew's kin were not those of the blood, but those of the spirit, and he was knit in some mystic fashion to every soul he felt he had brought to salvation. By such ecstasies was he renewed.

But even we had never seen him in the exaltation of that autumn. It had not occurred to him that he was growing old or could ever be old. He never had looked at his face in a mirror to see what it was—Mrs. Pettibrew had settled that long ago when he was a boy in West Virginia. His hair had grown gray late and was not yet white, and his face was as ruddy and his eyes as clearly blue as ever. He was almost jocular with youth, cracking his dry jokes, laughing easily his "haw!" of laughter, because he was so happy. He measured happiness by the success of his work, by the eagerness of souls crowding to be saved—else why should they want to become members of the church?—and his work was growing and there were souls by the hundred.

"What are you thinking?" we asked him one Sunday morning at breakfast when he put down his cup and seemed to be listening, his eyes shining, his whole face alight.

"It came to me suddenly that in thousands of homes today those who were heathen are preparing, young and old, to worship God, and in hundreds of churches and chapels they will sit and listen and pray." It was the top of his life.

10

A little while before this there had come to the station which Andrew made his home a younger missionary and then two others. Indeed, after years of wanting to be alone in his field, Andrew decided it would be well to have a young man or two. He liked young men and had always had a half-joking, half-paternal way with these three, not taking them very seriously, teasing them sometimes about their mistakes in Chinese. There was that time, for instance, when one of them, thinking to use a festival day for the glory of God, brought it into his sermon. It was the birthday of the Flower God, or Hwa Shen, as the people called the god, and the young missionary preached eloquently against the god, adjuring the people not to worship him. But he used the wrong tones in the two syllables, and thereby all unconsciously transformed them into two others, meaning peanuts. The people sat in solemn bewilderment, not understanding why this American became so excited in pleading with them not to worship peanuts, which they never had worshiped, and Andrew sat choking with silent laughter. It was too good a joke not to tell, and he told it perhaps a

trifle too often. And it was not a joke easy for a proud young missionary to bear. And there were others. Andrew knew a great deal and he was an acknowledged scholar in Chinese, and he had spent most of his life in China. It is a little cruel to laugh at the young, but Andrew did not think of that.

Then there was his stubbornness. He had been used to his own way for so many years. When the three young men voted against him in the solemn station meetings of four voting men and four non-voting women, Andrew was only amused. What—let these young fellows with the milk of their mother seminary still wet on their lips tell him what to do? They quoted mission rules to him concerning majority votes, but he pshawed and gave his haw of laughter and did as he pleased.

It was Carie who fought for him, really—Carie with her French shrewdness which perceived that even the prophets plotted against each other. She used to say, troubled, "They are going to oust you one of these days, Andrew—see if they don't!"

"Oh, pshaw, they can't!" he would reply absently, his mind on his plans. He never knew how often when he was not there she defended him and by the very energy of her tongue, kept them quiet. There is that enmity between young and old.

It was when Andrew came home in such triumph, in such fullness of strength and success, that they came one day and told him of the new rule the mission had made while he was away.

"What rule?" he asked amiably. The mission was always making rules—a man would be busy just keeping up with them.

"A new retirement rule has been passed," said the eldest of the three. He had once been a clerk in a department store and God called him out of it to go to China and save souls, but he had never quite got over his feeling about rules. They came down from above. He went on solemnly. "The rule is that a missionary retires at the age of seventy."

They waited for Andrew to grasp it, these righteous young priests before an old son of God who had grown uncouth with his years of hardship and rough travel and living far from the cities. Andrew was no drawing-room figure, for all the distinction he had of a high bearing and a learned serenity and fastidious neatness. He never troubled himself to be thoughtful of anyone in small ways. No one ever saw him pick up a woman's handkerchief, for instance, or rise to give her his seat. And tact he scorned utterly as a subterfuge and a weakness. He stared from one to the other. Striplings— that's what they were!

"Pshaw!" he said loudly. It had just occurred to him that he was practically seventy years old. He grew very calm— even kind. What could these young men understand? They were so young. Why, there were a great many things which he himself was only just now beginning to know and to be able to do! China was a land where age added influence and benefit. The people respected him for being old—that is, older.

But it was Carie who fought his battle, Carie with her quick tongue and fiery sense of justice and flying temper. She had been sitting unseen in the next room. They were afraid of her and had told Andrew at the door they wanted to see him alone.

"I didn't trust them the instant I heard them say that," she exclaimed, telling of it. She rose, overturning her enormous sewing box in her haste. We found buttons and spools of thread under things for days. She swept into the other room, her eyes fairly crackling, her very hair electric. We knew how she looked—had we not seen Carie in battle?

"What are you saying?" she cried. She

never bothered about soft speaking at such times. "You will get out of my house! There's not one of you fit to—to wear his old shoes! You soft-living, ease-loving— He works harder than any of you! Seventy, is he? Get out!" They had gone.

So much she told us she said—"and a good deal more," said Andrew drily. He did not appreciate Carie's battles for his sake—after all, a woman—"I can really look out for myself," he said to her gently, but with firmness.

"You think you can, but you can't," she retorted. "They get ahead of you."

"They don't," he replied.

Their conversations were always made up largely of contradictions.

"They do," she said. He rose abruptly and went out.

"Andrew has no notion of the way people really are," she said when the door was shut. "He's so far above plotting himself that he doesn't know it's in the world. And somehow being Christians doesn't cure them of it." Carie was somewhat of a pessimist about human nature. But it was true that Andrew was guileless and blind.

Andrew said he would not worry about that retirement rule. Nobody could retire him—not until God called him to death.

"They could stop your salary and drive you out of this house," Carie said.

"They wouldn't do that," he said peaceably, and added, "If they did, there would be Chinese who would give us shelter and food."

It was the Chinese who saved him, though. When they heard of the new rule there was such consternation as never was. The Old Teacher! Because he was old! But in China the old were to be honored, to be humored and given their way, not put aside for the very thing that gave them dignity and meaning. Besides, who wanted these young Americans?

They were used to the Old Teacher and he understood them and they would have no one else to be their superior. Delegations of courteous but determined Chinese appeared and presented documents signed by long lists of names. In the end Andrew went on unretired and more triumphant than ever.

Looking back, I can understand how these young priests did not savor such an uproar about an old man whose ways of working were not their ways. It could not have been pleasant to hear that they were not loved as he was loved, nor welcomed as he was. Nor did they realize how many years it had taken him to win that love—how much persecution he had borne and how steadfastly he had visited the sick and stayed by the dying and how often upheld a struggling soul. None of us know how often he did these things, for he never told us. They were simply part of his work. Most of all the Chinese loved him because he knew no color to a man's soul and he took the part of the yellow man again and again against the white man—the lonely convert's side, the poorly paid native preacher's side, against the arrogant priest, the superior missionary.

But those young men were quite sincere. They thought that Andrew was a hindrance to the work, to the sound development of the church. He received members into the church without adequate preparation and examination, they said, visiting him again and again to remonstrate with him.

"I receive, by the authority of my office under God alone, such souls as profess repentance and accept Jesus Christ as their savior," he said with his high look.

It was not enough, they said. These professions were often hypocritical. It meant there were many on the church rolls who should not be there. It made for an unsound organization.

"God will purge them out," Andrew said with confidence.

It was not enough, they said. There were hypocrites even among the leaders. The native preachers themselves were not all true—perhaps most of them under Andrew's loose supervision were guilty of much. There were hints of corruption, of fees accepted, of mishandling church funds, of secret concubinage.

They sat, the three righteous young men, before Andrew and Carie and made their charges. For Andrew let Carie come in now. He was beginning to grow bewildered. The young priests sat facing these two white-haired old people—Andrew's hair seemed to whiten in a week, and Carie's hair had for years been a heap of feathery snow. They had all their facts and figures and Andrew had never been good at keeping figures. He knew roughly how many souls had been saved and how many churches and schools he had and in general how much money he could spend. But these young men knew everything about his field. They had toured it all while he was in America, examining, asking questions, making notes. They had hirelings of their own go and seek out enemies of the church in each town and ask questions about the personal lives of those whom Andrew trusted. When they accused Ma, his close friend, he rose up trembling. "Now I know you're—you're absolutely wrong," he stammered. "I would trust Ma before I'd trust you—or myself."

They smiled. "Perhaps that's been your chief mistake—you seem to have trusted everybody."

The little thin one spoke. "You can't trust the Chinese."

Andrew came to life with a roar. A few times in his life he lost his gentleness and his voice came out of him like a great trumpet.

"If you believe that, why have you come to save them?" he shouted. "How can you save souls if you despise them? Shame on a follower of Jesus Christ who despises any man, however sinful!" He was on his feet, shouting. Carie sat by, silent for once, because he did not need her. He sat down again, suddenly—those moments of his were short, and terrible. He was silent an instant and began again more quietly, "It is necessary to believe in those to whom we have been sent. A soul cannot be won except through belief and patient understanding. I had rather accept some souls who are insincere than refuse one who is true. God will discern, He who sends rain upon just and unjust."

But there were the facts and the figures, they were proofs. They produced certain absolute proofs.

It went on for days, for weeks, for months, the steady undermining of all his work, the devaluation of all which he had so labored to build up. He stoutly refused to believe any of it, but he began to be distressed. He and Carie argued endlessly. Some of what they said was true, she said—it was better to acknowledge what was true and try to correct what wrong there was. But he would acknowledge nothing. Her arguments always strengthened him to opposition, and on opposition his energies blazed freshly. He held everything exactly as it was, went on receiving new members, refused to dismiss anyone—no, not Lin whom they accused of opium smoking, nor Chang who they said was running a big tea house with sing-song girls on the proceeds of the church. He had to have more proofs than he had been shown before he would dismiss a man. Besides, there was Ma, steadily denying everything. He had always believed Ma.

What would have happened if Carie had lived I do not know. She was always beside him, defending him in public, and in private moving him to decisions, to energies, to defenses and fresh determinations by her restless mind, approving and criticizing together.

But Carie died that next autumn. He knew she had not been well, but then she had not been well for years and he had scarcely known it because her will was so large and so indomitable, her body so negligible. She took no consideration of herself and expected none from others. He had an idea that women were often ill—it seemed so in this climate. Besides, Carie never wanted him near when she was ill. It was inconvenient to have her ill, but he did not see anything he could do for her, and anyway there were two daughters in his house. She had been in bed a good deal, but he had been so harassed in his work, so worried—and then one day he saw she was very ill indeed.

At once the trouble with the young missionaries was less important. Carie begged him to go on, but he felt it his duty to delay going away from home until the doctor had made his examination. When the doctor made his report there was no question of going away. She was mortally ill.

When Andrew knew that unless God wrought a miracle Carie's life was soon to end, his first thought was of her soul. For once he asked no miracle and seemed to expect none. He was restless with anxiety over her soul. He felt he ought to speak to her.

"I have never felt entirely certain about your mother's soul," he said to Carie's daughter one morning.

Carie's daughter replied with a touch of sharpness, "Her soul is all right!"

Andrew did not answer. He went slowly upstairs to Carie's room. But when he tried to speak to her, she suddenly was impatient and flouted him in a way she had not been able to do for days.

"You go along and save your heathen," she said, and her eyes flashed for a moment. So he gave it up, after all, and Carie went on dying as she was.

When the end was very near, the nurse they had got from Shanghai came running into his study where he was working on a revision of the Testament—by some strange coincidence he was working on the crucifixion scene and the solemnity of death had already filled him.

"There's a change," the nurse cried, and he rose and followed her upstairs. He could not hurry—he was strangely afraid. Carie dying! It brought death too near. He had stood at many deathbeds, and some of his children had died, but death had not seemed near to him until now.

He went into the room he and Carie had shared for many years, where she now lay in the big double bed alone.

She was unconscious. He was almost glad, for he would not have known what to say to her. It was strange he could think of nothing he would have said. So he stood gravely at the foot of the bed, waiting. The room was full of an awful solemnity as her breath came, caught in her breast, and went out of her with a great sigh, to come no more. In the endless silence he turned and went downstairs, back to his study, and shut the door.

He did not speak of her again, and none of us saw him weep. Whether he was widowed or not, none of us knew. He took no part in any of the last preparations and when we called him to her funeral he dressed himself carefully and went with us. He stood tearless beside her grave, his face set in utter gravity, his eyes sealed in gravity. But he said nothing, and after it was all over he went back to his study again and shut the door. Carie's daughter, yearning over him, passed by the window, to see if he were grieving there alone. But he was working over the pages of the Testament, the Chinese brush in his hand, painting the characters one by one down the page. It was impossible to go in, and she went on upstairs into the bedroom, now his alone, to straighten it for him. Upon the bed lay the frock coat. He had taken it down, pondering whether he would wear it for Carie's sake. But he had not worn it, after all, and it lay there upon the bed, and Carie's daughter took it and hung it up again.

He never mentioned Carie's name again as long as he lived unless a direct question were asked of him, and no one could tell if he grieved. And he never once visited her grave. But something broke in him, some strength of stubbornness. There was no one at home to contradict him, praise him, blame and scold him into energy. The house was very still with only one daughter left, and the other married and gone up the river to live. He had lived always in a routine and it did not occur to him to change it, but sometimes he wanted to change it and could not. Carie had always protested against routine; she loved change and different days. Opposing her volatility, routine had seemed important to him, and valuable, and the only way to accomplish anything—now it seemed less valuable, when there was no one to disturb it.

In the midst of his bewilderment the righteous young men were at him again, and Carie could not rise from her grave to battle for him. In the silent house he listened to their certainties, and for the first time in his life doubt began to creep in. Perhaps they were right—perhaps nothing he had done was any use. He put his hand to his forehead in his old gesture of bewilderment, and Carie was not there to cry out, "Not one of you is fit to step into his old shoes!" And they had proofs of everything now—bills for opium stamped with the church seal, signed confessions, sworn statements.

Everything was shaking and tumbling about him. Carie was gone and the daughter was a young girl, filled with her own loneliness. There was no one to guide him by telling him to do something he did not want to do and would not; to make him believe in himself again. In this one moment of fumbling amd mistrust, the righteous young men put before him something to sign—some sort of promise to turn over his field to them, so that for the sake of the honor of the church they could purify the work. Without knowing what he did, he signed the paper and gave away his work.

All during the winter he stayed at home in a sort of stupor of dismay. He was growing old—they had made him believe it now. He grew very white and, if possible, thinner. He worked a while each day on his translation, and when the weather was fine enough he went to a street chapel to preach. But when before had Andrew stopped for weather? The source in him was failing. Even when some of his faithful converts came to beg him not to give them up, he shook his head helplessly. "I signed something or other," he said with a heavy sigh. He never was sure just what the paper had said, but he knew it took everything away from him. And Ma, who might have helped him, was low that winter with a fresh attack of tuberculosis.

Then spring came. Carie had said to her daughters, "Look out for spring. About the first of April he gets hard to manage. It won't matter if he's eighty, he'll want to get away over the country and behind the hills preaching." When the willows budded in early April and the peach trees bloomed and the wheat was green and farmers were busy about their land, one day he lifted up his head. He smelled the new air. Suddenly he put down his brush and got up and went out of his study to find his youngest daughter, who was now the woman in his house.

"Get my things ready," he commanded her.

"Something came over me," he said, telling of it years later. "I saw I had been a fool."

In a few hours he was on his way on his ancient white horse, riding over the old familiar cobbled roads, over the smooth paths into the hills. And with every mile strength came back to him. "An amazement filled me," he wrote in that story of his. "I saw that I had been in a sinful despair. I dismounted from my beast and going away a little into the privacy of a bamboo grove, I tied the beast and knelt and besought God for forgiveness for the sin of despair. And God heard me and I was delivered and never again did He suffer me to so lose Him."

By the time he reached his first village church he was in a fine anger at the three righteous young men and beyond weariness.

But it was a sad business. He found as he went from place to place that the young men had been very busy. Everything was reorganized. The Chinese preachers whom he had trained and trusted were for the most part gone—"dismissed," he used to say over and over again, "without a particle of real proof and only on rumor. Rumor! Christ was crucified on a rumor and by those who called themselves righteous!"

A fury of hatred filled him as he went about his ruined field. Some of the churches he found shut and the doors sealed, the schools closed. When he came home he went to the young men to demand an explanation. "We found such corruption," they said, "that the only hope was to close everything, scatter the members, and wait and begin again."

And the members were scattered indeed. New, unknown voices were preaching and a few strangers sat and listened half-heartedly. Everything was gone—his whole life's work swept away.

But anger was a strength to him and a healing. He gathered himself together. He would begin again. God would give him years. He would search out his old converts and build new churches out of them—not Presbyterian churches, not organizations subject to the dominations and whims of white men, but native independent churches, using no money but their own, self-supporting, self-governing. He began to plan and with planning despair was gone and after a while anger was gone, and once more he was happy.

And so the search began for the souls he had saved and lost and now was seeking again. He went about in village and town and countryside all that spring and summer, and Ma was better once more in the heat, and the two of them went together searching. Some souls they never found. They had disappeared in the purging. Others they found returned to their old gods, and some they found wavering and not knowing what to do and these were glad to come back to their Old Teacher and were joyful to see him again. And there were others, enough to comfort and reassure him, who had remained true, worshiping God in their homes when the doors of churches were sealed. These were the nucleus of the new church Andrew was to build, the church independent of the foolishness of denominations and the vagaries of men. These were they who were to look straightly to God. They met together in the poorest places, in the tiny living-room of a farmhouse, in the earth-floored room of a country inn. But Andrew fired them to independence. He was very happy.

The three young men found out what he was doing. They had hirelings of their own who brought them stories. Andrew, they said, was dividing the church. He

was causing dissension. An independent native church! It was heresy.

When he came home they waited on him in a body and put before him the paper he had signed. But he was strong by now. He only pshawed, and refused to look at it.

"I signed it under compulsion," he declared. "It's not even legal. I'll swear to that before the consul, if you like."

He was free of them all once more, free of everything.

But he was old and they were young, and there were things they could do to him, though he forgot them in his old high humor. God's work was yet to be done. God would triumph—but meanwhile he was working his body as fiercely as he had in his youth. He pshawed aside every remonstrance from his daughter. And the young men were about to put on him the pressure of mission authority. He could be removed completely, sent back to America not to return, retired to die. His young daughter grew afraid.

There was not one of Carie's children into whom she had not poured her blood. Not one of them was her equal, but they were all fighters and afraid of no man. And her blood stirred in them now to fight for Andrew. He must be rescued and kept happy. He must never feel old again or set aside and useless. There must always be work for him to do—some sort of God's work, because he would not consider anything else worth doing.

They cast about to find salvation for Andrew in such a way that he could never find out that he had been saved, or ever indeed know he needed saving, proud son of God that he was. Where in the world of young men could he fit? There seemed no place for him. He must be taken away and allowed to work somewhere freely as he always had, for freedom was the only air in which his spirit could live and be.

It happened that part of the fruit of Andrew's life had been helping to build a theological seminary. That passion of his for a literate and educated clergy had gone beyond his training class for his own helpers into the planning and building of a school where young men might go and be trained. It had begun humbly enough many years before, but it had grown through donations, allotments and bequests into a group of brick buildings, sponsored by several denominations of the Protestant church into an institution of some dignity, although its traditions were always conservative. At that they were not narrow enough for Andrew's denomination, and it was for this seminary he had fought for many years with his reiterated slogan. "It's better to stay in and fight than get out and lose all hope of winning." Andrew was not afraid of modernism any more than he was of the devil. It made a good foe, and a good foe always whetted him.

To this institution, then, one of Carie's children turned speculative eyes. It would make a good place for Andrew to work in his old age. He would be doing the sort of thing he loved—teaching young men and associated with them daily, and they would learn from his experience. He would be taken out of the jurisdiction of the righteous three, and if they came near him she could be watchful. Best of all, he would be under her own roof where she could take care of him, for she lived in Nanking where the seminary was. He had grown too thin and his ruddiness had gone and left a sort of transparent whiteness out of which his eyes looked too blue and unearthly. But first she must get the place for him.

It was a task she loathed. She would never have begged for herself—Carie was in her. But she was put to it for Andrew. So she went, in as matter-of-fact a way as she could, to the church dignitary then at the head of the seminary and told the case plainly to him, and when she had finished she made no bones, having planned everything before. "And so you must find something for him to do here where I can look after him and keep him happy and not knowing anything about my coming to you."

The dignitary knew Andrew and knew the redoubtable family and the seven sons. And in his time he had had a passage or two with Carie herself over Andrew. He hesitated and fiddled with a paperweight on his desk. It was, Carie's daughter remembers, a little clay boy on a clay buffalo. "We have no vacancies," he murmured, and added something about wanting younger men.

"Not in China," Carie's daughter said decidedly. "Age won't matter here. Besides, surely there is something he can teach them out of all his years."

It appears there was not. Carie's daughter went away, refused but undefeated. It was not for nothing that she had been brought up in a denomination where women were given no recognized voice. They got what they wanted in other ways.

She returned again and again, until a look of terror came into the dignitary's eyes, and she learned to follow immediately upon the heels of an announcing servant before there were opportunities for any nonsense about being busy.

And the time-worn method of women had its reward. In a moment of extreme weariness he said, toying with the clay buffalo, "Of course we have planned a sort of correspondence course—"

She seized on it. "The very thing!"

"He could be given a couple of able assistants who could do the real work," the dignitary went on.

She laughed secretly. As if Andrew could be kept from real work!

"It wouldn't cost you anything—his salary from home would go on," she said diplomatically.

"It might work," he agreed without fervor.

It was enough to build upon, and she built. She built at both ends. She told Andrew he was going to be invited to the seminary and she saw to it that the letter of invitation was something more than half-hearted and that there were a title and a position as well as work for him to do. He was to be Dean of the Correspondence School—a school that did not exist. "But it will be the more exciting to make it," she tempted Andrew.

And she followed the invitation promptly herself, and Carie in her told her how to persuade Andrew.

"You can run all your independent churches just as easily as ever from my house and there won't be anybody to interfere with you, and you can be teaching at the same time, and you'll have plenty of time to work on your Testament."

It was an alluring picture of freedom, and he could not resist it. It was, he said, an enlargement of his usefulness, and therefore it was doubtless God's will.

"I'm sure it is," Carie's daughter said thankfully.

So the mission bungalow which Carie had made into a home for so long was dismantled. There was a pathetic little sale—there was nothing worth much money, and a few precious things were saved—Carie's desk and her organ, the rocking chair in which she had rocked all her babies, Andrew's books and desk, and a picture or two. They were put on a junk and sent up the river, and the house was empty and the lovely garden left to loneliness. A strange life was to come into it—the wastrel life of the new revolution then rising. When Carie's daughter next saw that house, the last time she was to see it, the house that was so filled with childish memories of hot summer afternoons and Christmas mornings and Carie's voice singing and Andrew coming

home, it was a tenement filled with the ruin and waste of revolution. Twenty families of refugees crowded into the rooms Carie had kept so dainty and the plaster was stripped to the laths, and the floors were inches deep in human filth, and the starving people looked out of the holes of windows like desperate dogs. And the garden, where Carie had grown her roses and where lilies had bloomed under the bamboos, had been beaten back to barrenness by the incessant tread of plodding feet. But Carie's eyes were safely shut in her grave, and I am glad for that.

Andrew was to have ten more years to live. He began them happily by disliking at once the room Carie's daughter had given him in her house. She had gone to great pains about that room. First she had chosen the biggest and best room, the one that faced the mountain and the pagoda, into which the sunshine poured cheer. She had furnished it with home things—the rug from Carie's living-room, his own chair, the clock he had wound regularly for forty years, his books in the bookcase—and she made curtains for the windows, very simple white ones, knowing Andrew. She was proud of that room. She ushered him into it.

"The whole house is yours, Father, but this is your own special room."

But it soon appeared that Andrew was uncomfortable. He ranged about the house, looking at various rooms.

"That room of mine," he complained, "it's too big—too much stuff in it—it looks too luxurious."

"You shall have any room you want," she said.

He chose a small room over the kitchen and his things were moved into it. Once more Carie's daughter hung curtains and pictures and spread the rug. Andrew was out when the moving was done, and he made no comment when he came back. But that evening after he had gone up to bed they heard noises prolonged into the night. Carie's daughter went to the door.

"Are you all right?" she called through it.

"Yes," he answered serenely.

She tried the door handle, but it was locked, so after a moment there seemed nothing to do but go away.

The next morning when she went in after he was gone to his day's work she could not believe what she saw. The floor was bare and the curtains were gone and there were no pictures—not even the picture of Carie she had hung upon the wall. And the cushion she had put in the back of his chair to soften its wooden hardness was gone, and the extra mattress she had put to soften the hardness of the single iron bed he had insisted upon buying for himself was gone. She looked under the bed and found the rug and the mattress and in the closet were the curtains and the pictures. The room was a cell, and the sunshine streamed into it mercilessly to show it bare and hideous. But Andrew had arranged it to suit his own heart. A few times in after years Carie's daughter, suffering for its ugliness in a home she tried to make beautiful on what little she had, put curtains at the windows again, small unobtrusive ones, or she slipped in a surreptitious cushion, and any number of times she tried to soften that rigid bed of his with a secret quilt. But Andrew never suffered such things for a day. She always found them put sternly away, folded under the bed or in the closet, and Andrew had his own monastic way to the end.

He took his new work very much for granted and was completely happy. No one crossed him and he lived tremendously. He was busy from early morning until late night. There was constant con-

ference with the men he had chosen to lead the new independent movement. Living cost him nothing these days. He had two good enough suits and saw no need for buying anything for years, if ever, for himself, and he could spend his whole salary on the independent movement. For of course there had to be someone to visit the churches, teach the people and encourage them in plans for expansion. Expansion! It was the old energy of Andrew's life.

I confess that those men from the independent churches who came so regularly to take Andrew's money were not reassuring in their looks. But Andrew could bear no criticism of them. This was the salvaging of his life's work.

"Pshaw, he can't help the way he looks!" he would say when Carie's daughter expressed distaste for a man. "I don't like a pretty man, myself. He's a soundly converted soul and that's the chief thing."

But the soundly converted souls did disconcertingly often look out of amazingly shifty eyes, eyes that would not meet the direct gaze of Carie's daughter, and the hands they put out of their long sleeves were repulsively dirty and eager for money. It is very probable that the three righteous young men were at least partly right, and that Andrew's wheat was badly sown with tares. He was so guileless and hopeful a soul! But he was happy, and Carie's daughter was satisfied.

He was perfectly happy. He came home in the evening exultant with the day, for he loved his work in the seminary. The sight of the young Chinese men who were fitting themselves to go out and preach the Gospel was unfailingly thrilling to his heart. He liked the men set to work with him and went to passionate planning for making a correspondence school of the best sort. He sent all over the world for correspondence school curriculums and took from each what he thought was its best. His New Testament found a new reason for being, too, for without any conceit whatever, Andrew considered his the best and only really intelligible translation into Chinese of the New Testament and in the fullest sense of duty, he put it among the required texts in his new curriculum. When he had everything ready the new school was announced and immediately met with remarkable success. In the course of the ten years Andrew was to see the student roll mount into hundreds and upon it were men from every country in the Orient and some of the South Sea Islands and a few were among Chinese in the United States. Andrew was especially proud of that. All the time he was working for the independent churches, and twice a year he hired a junk—for he had sold his own boat to get money for the new movement—and went out to visit all the members.

So Andrew would not grow old. But it could be seen that his body, in spite of him, was becoming increasingly insufficient for his soul's reach. He came home from every journey spent with exhaustion and white with a whiteness that made his flesh opaque. No sun could make him ruddy in these days. He took on a frosty whiteness that made him seem more unearthly than ever. Carie's daughter begged him to give up the long journeys to the churches, at least, but he would not.

But the day came when he must. He came home unexpectedly one sunny October afternoon, and his daughter saw at once that he was desperately ill. He staggered up the stone steps to the front door, and the sunlight seemed to shine straight through him as though he were a ghost already.

He would answer no questions and she asked none, for she knew him. She put him to bed and sent for the doctor who came and said he was desperately ill with dysentery. Bit by bit as she sat with him through the night she got the story. He had felt he ought to eat the feasts his old and faithful converts prepared for him.

"They're poor people," he gasped; "there must have been something they got cheap—but they meant well."

He had returned to his junk and lain there violently ill for three days and two nights.

"Three days!" cried Carie's daughter. "Why didn't you come home or send a messenger to tell us?"

He could not, it appeared. The captain of the junk was a rascal and when he had an old man at his mercy he would not move without money. He took all Andrew had, his watch and pen and all his goods, and only on Andrew's promise that he would never try to punish him in any way did he at last bring him home, nearly dead.

But we were glad the man had not murdered him and thrown his body into the river—glad he had not quite let him die.

For a few days he came very near death, and then came the long difficult turn. The doctor had said Andrew must go to the hospital, but Andrew had refused with what seemed his last breath. He had never been in a hospital and he had no confidence whatever in trained nurses and their morals, he said. He was too weak to cross then, but when he was a very little better the doctor, by means of vast threats, prevailed on him to go to the hospital. But it was no good. Once there, he insisted on watching his schedule continually, half delirious as he was with fever, and he rang his bell every few minutes to remind the nurse he was a very sick man and that his medicine was due at such and such a time—he kept his watch in his hand. As soon as he was fully conscious he insisted on being taken home. That was the time he said, "I have a daughter who has nothing to do but take care of me," and he raised such a storm that he had to be sent home then and there, though he was too sick to sit up.

So Carie's daughter took care of him and he grew well again at last. But he was never quite so well. The illness had frightened him. He sat in an easy chair in a sunny corner of the garden one day with a blanket over his knees and Carie's daughter came to bring him a cup of broth.

He raised solemn blue eyes to hers and said suddenly, "I'm nearly seventy-five years old!"

She looked at him and saw a childlike terror in his eyes. Her heart flew to him, but she resisted the impulse to gather him up like a child in her arms for comfort. He would have been miserably embarrassed at such a demonstration. Instead she tucked in his blanket and said, "What's seventy-five? Your family is long lived on both sides. Besides, you're well again, and it's a glorious morning and I've been thinking you ought to revise your book on Chinese idioms. There isn't anything to take its place if you let it go out of print."

"That's true," he exclaimed, pleased. "I've been thinking I ought to do it."

But it was the first fear. He never went out on another tour and the movement for independent churches was never completed. Certain men came and went as long as he lived, and his money went out to them, but Carie's daughter asked him no questions. If independent churches made him happier, let him have them, though they were filled with rascals.

The work at the seminary, however, was the ideal work of his old age. Every morning he was up early and impatient for his breakfast and immediately after he was tucked into his comfortable private rickshaw—a victory Carie's daughter had over him—and in his office by eight o'clock. He loved the seminary life, the assemblies where he took his turn at preaching, the coming and going of young men to classes, his own stacks of letters and papers. He felt busy and needed. And young men came to him for advice and confidences, and he listened to their stories of poverty and somehow or other pinched himself yet more to give them aid. Carie's daughter had to watch him or he would have had nothing left. Every week or two she went to his closet and looked over his few garments.

"Where's that knit vest you had for Christmas?" she would demand of him, or she would say, "I can't find but two pair of your woolen socks."

She knew very well that guilty look of his. "One of the young fellows looked awfully cold yesterday—the buildings have no heat and he is too poor to buy a padded coat. Besides, I have my old sweater. I didn't need that fancy vest."

"I can wear but one pair of socks," he said with impatience. "I'm no centipede, I hope!"

And his rickshaw coolie proudly wore the frock coat which had been such cause for arguments between Carie and Andrew. Andrew sat behind it now with peculiar satisfaction. "The wretched thing is doing somebody some good at last," he said. "The man very sensibly sewed up the tails—I don't know why I didn't think of it long ago."

There was no use in giving him things. We tried to enlarge his meager wardrobe at Christmas and on his birthdays and on any occasion we could use for pretext, but he gave everything away he did not wear at the moment, and it was no pleasure to see a new suit just given him hanging on the small obliterated frame of a divinity student. Andrew was an exasperatingly literal Christian. He even gave away his precious clock to a street chapel on the grounds that he did not need it since he had his watch, although he reserved the right to go and wind it once a week.

But he was not entirely content with his seminary work. His correspondence course did not keep him busy, he said, and so he was touchingly pleased when they gave him a small class or two. No student ever spent such time in preparation as he did. For he considered the work of training men to preach as holy work. It was an extension of his own opportunity to save souls. Through these young men he could reach many another soul.

Even so, he was not content unless he was preaching directly to souls unsaved. So two or three times a week, much to his rickshaw puller's rue, he went into the most crowded parts of the city where in two places he had rented small rooms opening full on the busy street, and there he stood and preached to the people who strayed in to sit a while on a free bench. "He has a hot heart for such an old man," his rickshaw puller used to say, and trudged back and forth with a sigh.

11

But he was not yet to have peace for his work. While he had been living out his zestful days, another storm was rising out of the south, the storm of China's last and greatest revolution.

He had not paid much heed to it. There had been so many wars and revolutions in his day and he had long since refused to go away because he heard a war was threatening. Nobody would hurt him, he always declared. So he had stayed when others fled, coming and going in his usual routine, waiting, perhaps, on the side of a street for an army to march by, but granting no further concession to the eternal upset of China's political life.

And the sight of his tall, white-haired figure coming and going as usual gave the common people comfort and a sense of stability.

"Has the Old Teacher gone?" they asked each other.

"No, he has not gone," was the answer, and they settled themselves again. "If the Old Teacher should go, we would not know where to hide ourselves," they used to say.

But then he never went. And he pshawed the idea that this revolution was different from any other. When people talked of the new Bolshevik influence he refused to grant it importance. Bolsheviks were only people, after all. Besides, "the Chinese will never put up with them," he used to say with confidence. It was one of the secrets of his immense serenity that he always firmly believed anything he said himself.

So as the new revolution swept up from the south and knotted itself into central China and expanded again down the Yangtze River, Andrew regarded it without fear and indeed this time with something of indifference. He had seen so many revolutions come and go, leaving nothing but waste behind, that he had no great optimism. Besides, his mind was turning more and more away from the affairs of men to the one great central meaning of his life, his own work. He had a full sense now of the few years left him, and nothing must turn him aside from that work. He did not hear then the rising of any storm. When news filtered through the countryside of a murdered Catholic priest, he remarked calmly, "Well, he was a Catholic, and they don't like Catholics, I suppose."

When the foreign consuls began to send out warnings, urging women and children and old people to go to Shanghai, since no one could foresee exactly what turn the approaching revolutionary armies would take, it did not occur to him that he could possibly be included among them. What! He run with the women and children?

But then the white people were all sharply divided. Some of them felt no good could possibly come of the new movement, led as it was by the young Western-trained Chinese and aided by the Bolshevists. There were others who believed in it and still more who did not know what to think or do. The news of the treatment the white people were receiving in the revolutionary territory was disconcerting, but one could get no proofs or confirmation and mad rumor is at its maddest in China, the land of many tongues and boundless prejudices among men of all colors.

Carie's daughter took sides with the revolutionists. Sun Yat-sen she had admired since her childhood. Carie had taught her that. "Something will come from him," Carie used to say in her tones of confident prophecy, although he was a fugitive most of her life. So when Andrew said he would not go away as the revolutionary armies approached, Carie's daughter made no demur.

Then there came that morning when the consular advice was very strong indeed, amounting as nearly to a command as the representative of a democratic nation may go, that all Americans, women and children and those who were aged, must go away, because of reports of serious anti-foreign action on the part of the revolutionists. They were very near then, those armies. One could, if one listened, hear the sound of distant cannon. And the final contingent of those white people who had decided to leave were going that day. It was the last chance, and if it were refused, there would be no other. All who stayed must stay through to whatever the end would be, because the crisis of battle was near,

and the great city gates would be locked, and none could go out or come in until it was known who were the victors.

Carie's daughter took thought that morning. She believed in the revolutionists, but there might be a rabble after the battle. She thought of her small children, of her sister who had taken refuge with her from a city in the far interior already held by the revolutionists—that narrow escape had not been very promising. And there was her sister's child, too. Well, they could manage with the children, but what of Andrew? He could not walk far or endure hardship any more now. She begged him to go to certain safety.

But Andrew when compelled against his will had a trick of falling ill. It was not conscious pretense—it was an actual disturbance caused by the distress of not having his own way. When she went upstairs to call him to get ready to go he lay there on that narrow iron bed of his, the sheet pulled up to his chin.

"I'm ill," he said very faintly. "I couldn't possibly go."

She looked at him, knowing him, and that there was no persuading him.

"Then we all stay together," she said, and went away and closed the door.

Through that whole day the sound of the guns grew louder and the echo more hard against the rocks of the mountain. By afternoon the city gates were already locked, and there was a strange tense stillness everywhere. Shops were closed, and the streets were empty. People sat behind closed doors, waiting for no one knew what. They had done the same thing many times before, and even the children had been through wars. But this time it was different. One heard such things—the laborers, servants, apprentices, the poor who lived in the mud huts—they were all full of a strange excitement. No one knew what to expect.

In the empty streets Andrew's rickshaw passed as usual, his puller trotting along in the old frock coat. It was March and the air was still keen. Andrew preached that night in one of his street chapels, but almost no one was there to hear him and those who were hurried away quickly into the darkness. He came home to find the whole house alight and a steady stream of Chinese neighbors pouring into the gates. The cellars were full of unknown and poor people taking refuge. It had always been safe in the foreigners' houses before. In no war since 1900 had the foreigners been attacked— the foreigners had gunboats and treaties to take care of them. It was all familiar enough to Andrew. He sat in the living-room with the family and their Chinese friends. Only the unknowing children were asleep.

"This floor seems to seethe," he said. "The cellars are so full." Then he said, "I'm glad I stayed. One must share the life of those one has chosen to be one's own people."

Midnight came on and still there was no news and nothing could be seen in the darkness, and there was only the constant roaring of cannon to be heard. He was very tired. "Since I can't settle any of the fighting, I think I'll go to bed," he said at last with his dry smile. And so he went upstairs to lie and listen to the cracking guns. Near dawn there was a sudden silence and before he could wonder what it was he fell asleep.

It seemed no different from other days, that revolutionary dawn. He woke and the March sun filled his room, and from downstairs came the clatter of breakfast dishes and the smell of bacon and coffee. There were no more guns. Everything was over. He did not need to miss a single day of work. He got up, bathed in the shower he had rigged up for himself out of a small tin tub and the nozzle of a flower sprinkler, and dressed carefully and went downstairs, very cheerful and triumphant, to the usual seven o'clock breakfast. They were all waiting for him, children and grandchildren, and Carie's daughter was gay over the first daffodils of spring from her garden. She had run out before breakfast and cut them and they were on the table.

"Prophetic daffodils!" he said. "I'm glad they waited to open until today."

Everything was all right, they said. The revolutionists had won, the city gates were open, the city had surrendered and was quiet. The Chinese had all gone home to breakfast, and the house was normal again.

"How silly to have gone away!" they told each other over bacon and eggs.

"Wars are all about the same in my experience," said Andrew in great content.

It was a cheerful meal, and afterwards the men hurried off to eight o'clock classes, and Carie's daughter tucked Andrew's lap robe about him in his rickshaw and put a small red rosebud she had grown in a window pot into his buttonhole. Red was for the new day.

He could choose the road through the city or the back road through the hills. This morning he chose the hill road. The air was fresh and sharp and sweet, and the sunshine was warming.

But he had scarcely set himself to enjoy it when he heard his name shouted loudly, over and over. He looked about, but no one was near. Indeed, when he came to think of it, he had seen no one upon the road. Usually it was busy with farmers carrying their baskets of early fresh vegetables on their shoulders to the city markets, or the road was dusty with the feet of donkeys, carrying bags of rice crossed upon their backs. There had been no one.

Then he saw one of the servants from the house running after him, shouting to him. The rickshaw puller halted and the man came up panting. He was the color of cheese and his mouth was so dry he could scarcely speak.

"Old Teacher—Old Teacher—come back!" he panted. "They are killing the foreigners!"

"I don't believe it," said Andrew.

"It is true. One of them is dead already. They shot him in the street. Your elder daughter beseeches you to return."

"I won't," said Andrew. "I have work waiting for me. Go on!" he said to the puller, but the servant laid hands on the shafts.

"She said if you would not come I was to lift you and carry you back, though you struck me for it."

"As for me," said the puller, "I will not pull you on and have your blood on my body."

They had him helpless.

"Go back, then," said Andrew grimly.

It was not the first time he had to think of being killed. The sunshine was gray to him. No one knew what this day would be—perhaps the end—and his work was not done.

When he reached the house they were gathered on the doorstep waiting for him. They had run out of the house just as they were, without coats and hats. In ten minutes the whole world had changed. The gayety of the breakfast table, the warm security of the house, were now as though they never had been.

"Here he is!" the servant shouted, and the puller lowered the shafts and he stepped out.

"What does all this mean?" he demanded.

"We must hide!" Carie's daughter cried to him.

Hide! All these little children! Besides, he hated the thought of it.

"We'd better go decently into the house and pray," he said.

"We can't delay," she replied. "The revolutionary armies are against us. They've killed the two Catholic fathers already, and Jack Williams!"

Before he could argue with her the servants came wailing and running toward them, and there were neighbors slipping in at the gate secretly.

"Hide—hide!" they begged him. "The foreigners' houses are no safety today."

"Where can we hide?" Carie's daughter cried.

The Chinese looked at each other. Who indeed dared to take the burden of these white people? If they were found in a man's house he would be killed and all his children. There was no use to die foolishly.

All the time a strange horrible uproar had been gathering out on the streets. It was the sound of a mob. There was no time to be lost. But there was nowhere to go. The white people looked at each other. This land had been home to them, for Andrew since his youth, for his children and their children since they were born. But suddenly, in an hour, it was home no more. Their house could not shelter them, no gates, no walls could make them safe.

A small stumpy blue-clad figure came running in the back gate as fast as her bound feet would let her. It was only a woman, a common peasant woman to whom Carie's daughter had given food in a famine in the north country, and who in another famine had come south to find her again. Carie's daughter had not rejoiced to see the woman, penniless, half-starved and pregnant. But she took her in because she had a silly soft heart, and she let the baby boy be born there and took care of him to keep him from the tetanus by which the woman had lost every other child she had, and took care of him again when the woman once let him get nearly burned to death. She had not been at all pleased to do it, and had scolded the stupid grateful mother for her stupidity, and when the woman's husband wandered down from the north to hunt this wife she had been thankful to find him a job as a farm laborer and so get them all off her hands. But the baby grew into a chubby brown little boy, and it was nice to see him alive.

This woman, then, came running in. Her husband was away all day, and her little room empty, she said, and Carie's daughter and all her family were to come and hide there. It was only half a tiny hut, really, and no one would think of looking among mud huts. She was tugging at them, she had Carie's daughter's hand, and she pulled Andrew's sleeve, and picked up the smallest yellow-haired child, and started out of the gate and across the fields, and so they followed her.

In the packed silence of the tiny hut they sat down, some on the board bed, some on a bench, and she shut the door silently.

"This is a safe place," she whispered through the cracks. "There are so many children in these huts that if a little foreign child cries it will not be known."

But none of the little foreign children cried that live-long day. There were two little girls and a little boy, none of them yet five years old, a lively, noisy trio on other days. Today, in the darkness, in the strange howling roar outside, they sat perfectly still upon their elders' knees, knowing somehow in what peril they were.

As for Andrew, he could not believe this was the end. All day he sat without a word, among his children and grandchildren. But not one spoke. Each of them was busy in himself. Andrew was thinking back over the years. "Not so much thinking," he wrote afterwards, "as letting the pictures of what had gone drift across my mind. Often I thought I was

somewhere else." And one of Carie's daughters sat thinking of her unborn child and wondering if he would now live to be born. And the other sat looking at her two little girls and thought steadfastly how when the hour came she must be strong and before she died herself she must see them dead first, though she did it herself, and not leave them in the hands of the soldiers.

The strange hours passed. The servants stole across the fields with loaves of bread under their coats and a bottle of boiled water and a tin of milk for the children. Every now and again the door opened and the face of a Chinese friend would appear. Only there was always that moment of fear—was he a friend? Who could tell in this day? But they were friends, and they came in to knock their heads before us, and to beg us to take heart because they were doing all they could with the revolutionary leaders to intercede with them for our lives. And at noon the door opened again and a kind unknown motherly Chinese woman came in with bowls of hot rice gruel and told us to eat and not fear—that no one in all the cluster of huts would tell that we were there. They had threatened even their children, she said. "I told my little devil I would beat him to death if he told," she said to comfort us. And the day mounted to noon.

The noise outside the hut increased. Andrew had heard that noise before—the noise not of angry people but of people in greed, of poor people who see what they have coveted now within reach. There was the sound of thudding upon wood, of a gate being crashed in, the sounds of feet running across ground, of wooden doors splintering, and then the howling of greed again.

"They've got in the house," said Andrew suddenly.

The hut door opened as he spoke and the two Chinese came in who had been

interceding with the revolutionary leaders. They fell on the earthen floor before Andrew.

"Forgive us," they said, "we cannot save your lives. We have done all we can, but there is no longer hope."

And rising and bowing, they went away, their faces the color of clay.

For two hours Andrew and his children sat waiting, expecting every instant to see the door open and soldiers rush in. But it did not open. And outside the din went on, the shouting and the howling. The hut was lit with firelight now—they were burning the foreigners' houses. There could be only a few minutes left. Each in his own fashion took leave of life and earth and thought of how to die proudly before an enemy race, and Andrew bowed his head. The children were asleep in our arms, heartbreakingly precious because it was the last time. The next moment—in an hour at most—it would be finished for us all.

Then across the horror and the din there came a terrific thunder. The hut shook and the children woke. Again it came, again and again, such thunder as none of us had ever heard before. Our ears were stopped with the noise. We stared at each other, asking—it was not thunder from heaven—not this regular repeated roar.

"Cannon!" cried one of the men.

Andrew shook his head. "The Chinese have no such cannon," he shouted above the din.

"American—British cannon," the other shouted back.

Then we remembered what we had all forgotten—there were American, English and Japanese gunboats in the river seven miles away. They had opened fire on the city. We were in a fresh danger. We might be blown to pieces by our own guns. But instantly we were all relieved—it would at least be a clean death, quick

and clean—no torture at the hands of Chinese soldiers.

Suddenly it was over. All noise ceased. The guns stopped, and there was silence, a strange, sudden complete silence. There was no more sound of shouting, no more howling, no more screeching of wrenched and breaking wood. Only the sound of crackling flames went on and the dark little hut was brighter than any day could light it.

Andrew stood up and looked through the tiny window and across the hills. He pressed his face against the hole, staring at something.

"They are burning the seminary buildings!" he whispered. And he sat down and covered his eyes with his hand. His work was gone again. . . .

There was nothing to do but wait now. Someone would come and tell us what to do. It was a long and dreary waiting, the hardest of the day. None of us could guess what the bombardment meant or what the silence. Was the city laid waste under those mighty guns and were we only left alive? No one came near.

Late that night the door opened. There stood two of our Chinese friends, with a guard of soldiers.

"We have come to take you to a safe place," they said gladly.

But the soldiers made us halt. They were in a strange uniform and surely there never was so villainous a guard. Their faces were jeering and flushed, and their features swollen as though they were drunken. They stood there, leaning on their guns, the light of the torches on their wicked, mocking faces. We shrank back. Commit the children and Andrew to these?

"But these are the same soldiers who have been attacking us all day," Carie's daughter protested.

But there was no other way.

"It is your only chance," our friends

urged us. "All the white people are gathered in the big laboratory in the university. We will take you there."

So one by one, Andrew first, we filed out of the tiny hut, eight feet by ten, where we had lived for thirteen hours, three men, two women and the three little children. Those three great tall men! Carie's daughter never thought them so huge before that day.

Across the dark fields we went, past smoking and charred ruins of what only that morning had been cheerful American homes, to the black pile of the university buildings. Once a little weary child, stumbling, fell against a soldier and he turned with a snarl that made the heart stop. But the child's mother cried out, "She did not mean to push you—she is only three years old!" and the soldier went on with a grunt.

So at last we reached the gate of the university. There stood another guard of revolutionary soldiers, the same dark, jeering, evil-looking men. They laughed as we came by and seized their guns and shook them to frighten us. But not even a child cried—they only looked, wondering, having been taught all their small lives to like the Chinese and call them friends. So the dreary little procession entered the building and filed upstairs in the darkness.

There in the big laboratory we found gathered over a hundred white people, men, women, and children, nearly all Americans. Seven had been killed since dawn, but all these others had hidden somehow and been hidden by Chinese friends, and had been rescued after much hideous experience at the hands of mobs and soldiers. We had been very fortunate, we found afterwards. Few of the other white people had not had to face their enemies in one way or another. But the dreadful day was over, and now the darkness covered them and they were trying to rest. Yet at every fresh entrance

they cried out to know who was there and if they were safe. One by one, all through the restless night, the white people came in, some wounded, some beaten, but no more dead. But no one knew what the dawn would be, for the city belonged to the revolution now.

All through the next day we waited, gathered together in the big room. It was not a sad day, though no one knew what its end might be. We organized ourselves, distributed what food there was, and attended to those who were ill and wounded or had newborn babies. And there were those Chinese working for us. They came and went, bringing food and clothes and bedding. They came weeping and begging forgiveness, and telling us that the dead were decently buried. They brought us toothbrushes and towels and coats, for the March wind was piercingly cold and the buildings were unheated, and the soldiers had robbed us of our warm outer garments.

All of us were homeless and penniless, and we did not know whether or not we were yet to be massacred, and there were among us the widowed and those young mothers of newly born babies and women who had suffered such indignity at the hands of mad soldiery as cannot be told. But somehow the day was not sad. We were not friendless. There was not one of us who had not friends among the Chinese and these risked their lives to bring us comfort. For after we went, if ever we were to go, their names would be upon a proscribed list of those who had helped foreigners, and who were "running dogs of the imperialists."

In the afternoon the order came from the guard for us to move out, and go down to the bund seven miles away and get on the American and English battleships in the harbor. We were hurried out by the same wicked-looking soldiers into the street and in broken-down carriages, or on foot or however we could, the march began. At dusk we rounded the road to the river and there, alight from stem to stern, the battleships lay waiting. American marines, American sailor boys, were standing on the bund and they hurried forward and helped old men and women and children into the dories, and then there was the rush of the dark water about the boats, the heave and sweep of the swelling current, the black precipice of the ship's side and the swinging ladder-way, and at last the firm deck beneath the feet. Hearty voices cried out, "You're on American territory now—cheer up!" "Supper's waitin'!"

But it was all a daze—the crowded cabins, the small saloon, the pots of hot food on the table, soup and baked beans and stew, ladled out by shouting, joking sailors. Food and sleep—and oh, the heaven of safety! Women who had not wept once, who had stood up to pillage and cruelty and death, could not keep from weeping, and brave little children, who had stood straight and defiant beside their parents before the guns of the soldiers, cried endlessly about nothing.

As for Andrew, he disappeared from the table and Carie's daughter went out to find him and see how he did. He was standing by the ship's side, staring across the water to the dark city. There was not a light in it, but he knew where it lay, for dim against the sky he could see the crest of the mountain, and the city walls curled about the mountain's foot.

"What are you thinking?" she asked.

"I was just planning about going back," he said quietly. He did not turn or say anything more, and she left him there, gazing into the dark city. Going back! Of course he would be thinking of nothing else.

It is hard to separate one thing from another now. It is all a jumble of faces and stories, tears and laughter. Everyone on the ships had a story, a miracle to tell, now that all were safe. An old American whose hobby was honey-making told of a greedy soldier who thought his hives held treasure and opened one rudely and was set upon by furious bees and ran howling across the garden. A doctor, caught in his hospital, covered his face and hands with scarlet mercurochrome and pretended to be mad when the soldiers came and they ran from him. Another, a doctor from a southern state, hid in his own coal cellar all day, and when he was rescued, marched into the laboratory, his face black with soot, declaring grimly to his fellows, "I'm going home—this is no country for a white man!" and wondered why the others laughed, starving and desperate as they were. There was the wife who swallowed her wedding ring to save it from the greedy clutching hands of the soldiers, and wore it again, triumphantly, the last day upon the battleship.

But there were other stories not for laughter—an old lady who stood immobile while the soldiers jerked at her wedding ring and diamond solitaire, and when one pulled his sword to cut off her finger, remarked in calm English, "You'll not get it off otherwise, my man—it's been on for fifty years." And there was the story of a Chinese professor at his watch at the telephone in the university just before dawn who might have saved us all. The night before the battle had been divided into watches, for it had been arranged that when the revolutionary armies entered the south gate outside which the battle was fought, it should be telephoned to the university, at the north side, what their temper was. There was no other telephone in that end of the city, and the news was then to be taken by foot to each house. But the Chinese professor, though trained at the best American schools of agriculture and forestry, was fat and lazy, and he laid himself down and slept, not believing, to do him justice, that anything would happen. The telephone rang and rang, but he slept. Had he waked or been at his post, some would have been alive today who are dead, and many would have been spared hours which they dare not remember.

Into Shanghai they poured, these worn creatures, to find what shelter they could. Most of them were too sad and disheartened to do anything else than buy tickets on the first boat home, never to return to China.

But Andrew had his plans all made. He said briskly, "I've always heard that the mission work in Korea is so much more successful than in China, and I've always wanted to see why. I'm going to Korea."

"Not by yourself!" Carie's daughter exclaimed.

"All by myself," he said firmly, and went.

What he did in Korea could only be gathered from his scanty letters. He managed somehow to get about a great deal. He discovered colonies of Chinese in Korea who had no churches, since the missionaries in Korea spoke no Chinese, and so immediately he began preaching to them, holding services in their homes, and working to organize them into a church. His letters grew buoyant at once and enthusiastic as though nothing had happened to him. "It's extraordinary," he wrote, "how the work lies waiting to be done."

"The Chinese," he wrote again, "are worth much more than these Koreans. Even here it is the Chinese who do the work and carry on the business. So far as I can see the Korean men do nothing but sit about in their white dresses and get dirty, and the women do nothing but wash the dresses."

He grew immensely scornful of the Korean dress. "No people can amount to anything who wear such silly clothes," he wrote. "The men wear white linen skirts and little tall hats tied under their chins. Their souls seem scarcely worth saving."

"If the Japanese were not here," he wrote again, "I do not believe the Koreans would trouble even to feed themselves."

He came back after six months, in good health and perfectly complacent.

"It is no wonder the missionaries in Korea have such an easy time," he declared. "Anybody can convert a Korean. It's as hard to convert one Chinese as it is twenty Koreans, but you have more in the end. Now I'm going back to real work."

None of us could dissuade him, not even a threatening consul. No one of the Americans had been allowed to return to Nanking except a few young men on occasional visits of supervision. There were no decent places to live. Such foreign houses as had not been destroyed were filled with soldiers. Everything was disorganized and the anti-foreign feeling was still high.

But Andrew pshawed at everything. His trip to the cooler climate of Korea had done him good, and he was full of his high serene obstinacy.

"I don't want a house," he said. "I'll get a room somewhere, and a boy to cook rice and eggs. I don't need any more."

There was nothing to be done with him—there never had been. Carie's daughter, scolding him heartily, packed his small bag and slipped in all the extras she could, without any hope that he would ever use them. And she sent for a faithful servant and bade him go with the old son of God and serve him and watch over him, and so they went off, she half believing she would never see Andrew again. There were terrible tales of cholera and typhus and dysentery that year. And only the very poor were eating the crabs that dug into the banks of the river and canals. Crabs were usually dear and a delicacy for the rich, but this year, though they had never been so fat, the rich were too dainty to eat them because there had been so many dead thrown into the waters, so the poor feasted for once.

But nothing stopped Andrew from what he wanted to do. His man found him a wretched little room in a half-ruined school building and bought a clay charcoal stove the size of a bucket and an earthen pot, and Andrew bought an old iron cot and a chair and a table—foreign stuff sold cheap these days, and second-hand shops were full of loot—and so he was at work again. The seminary buildings were nearly all burned, and what was left of them was occupied by some war lord general or other who had for the time being thrown in his lot with the revolution. It was years before they were given back.

But Andrew never believed much in buildings anyway. He began looking about for the students and he found them here and there. People told him tales about these divinity students. There had been communists among them, and these had led mobs against the foreigners. But Andrew was not troubled.

"I don't believe it," he said serenely, and would not.

He liked being the only white man back. "It's perfectly safe—all nonsense those consuls talk," he wrote to Carie's daughter. He enjoyed his life in those days. And the people along the streets, small shopkeepers and the lords of little inns, and poor people of all sorts called out after him and laughed to see him and were glad to have him back. "Well, it is the Old Teacher back again!" "The Old Teacher has more courage than any of them!" "Stop and drink a bowl of tea, Old Teacher!" they shouted as he passed in his rickshaw.

He loved their welcome and their admiration, and he was living the life of poverty he liked to live. He promptly began to preach on the streets and in the tea shops, and at a time when no other white man could find a house or a room, because no one wanted to rent to foreigners, Andrew somehow rented two different rooms opening on busy streets, bought some benches and two pulpits looted from other churches before the revolution, and was preaching every day and again at night. One of the pulpits was out of the Methodist church and Andrew took a satisfaction in that. "Sound doctrine coming from behind it now!" he said with his dry smile.

And people came to hear him, people who were already beginning to be disillusioned with the revolutionists and their vast promises never redeemed. Disgruntled laborers muttered, "They said we would all have good jobs in factories and they gave us little tickets to prove we were to have a job. 'Show the ticket at the gate,' they said. What gate—what factory? They were dreams!"

Now and again a young student communist would break up a meeting, but Andrew only said mildly to the dispersing crowd, "We will meet again tomorrow as usual at the same hour," and no one could outdo that immense determination. So at a time when no one else could work among the people, he worked in his usual way, without fear or haste.

The outward circumstances of life, indeed, meant nothing to him—a house, a home, food, comfort, all were nothing. His home was in his work, his heart to do God's business. There was no other happiness for him.

When Carie's daughter came back after a year away and set herself to the making again of a home out of a ruined house, defiled by filth and used as a cholera base for months, she found Andrew very serene and quiet. Indeed he seemed scarcely of earth at all any more, so bodiless had he grown, living alone, speaking little except to preach, eating his too frugal food. The faithful man-servant grieved and complained to Carie's daughter that Andrew ate almost nothing.

"His heart is too hot for an old man," the servant mourned. "He burns from within."

She prepared his room first as she knew he liked it and moved him into it without disturbance to him, and he scarcely realized the change. He seemed to have forgotten there had ever been a revolution.

12

He grew very gentle as months went on into a year. All the old high energy went away from him, and he was always gen-tle. He was not so critical, either, as once he was, nor did he distinguish so hardly as once he had between other creeds and his own. He disliked denominationalism more than ever, but in these days he even could forgive a man for believing in im-mersion, and he did not argue any more over anything. His own belief was un-shakable. He believed word for word in the Apostles' Creed, and he lived happily in the full confidence of the second coming of Jesus Christ. One day Christ would appear in the sky, it was sure to him, and the bodies of the righteous would rise from the dead and be caught up with Christ. But Andrew did not wait in anxiety for this coming. He hoped not to die—at the word death that terror crept into his eyes and caught at the heart of Carie's daughter—but he said quite tranquilly, "We are not told when Christ shall appear—it may be tomor-row, it may be in a thousand years."

But he rather thought it would not be a thousand years. He used to tell Carie's

daughter there were certain signs—wars and famines and distress, and especially the rising of what he called "anti-Christ" in Russia. Carie's daughter listened and never argued with him, or ever showed her unbelief. Not for her life would she have robbed Andrew of one atom of that faith which had made life so worth living to him, not now when he was old and needed the faith by which to die. And he never thought to ask her what her own faith was, being so full of his own.

So he lived his last few mellow golden years, never crossed, and humored in all ways, both large and small. So unhin-dered, he seemed to turn before our eyes into a gentle spirit, more frugal of food and drink than ever, more quiet in speech, more transcendent, more remote from earth.

When the perception of the dissolution of his life came to him it is hard to tell. But to him, as to all old, there came gradually the knowledge that there were not many more days in which to work, not many nights left in which to lie down to sleep, and there would soon be a dawn to which he would not wake. Sometimes at twilight he would seem timorous of being alone, as though he remembered the old ghost stories he had heard as a child. He wanted the lights early, and he wanted to hear human voices, to have people about him. Carie's daughter stayed near then, and spoke to him cheerfully of small things, and sat by him with everyday sewing in her hands, and encouraged the children to run in and out. He was comforted by such small ways, and warmed, though he never knew how to share in the life of home or children. But he sat and watched and the look of fear went out of his eyes and after a while he could go up to bed. And Carie's daughter always made a pretext to go up to his room on such nights and see that his blanket was tucked in about him warmly and that the light was ready for his touch and she put on the table by him a little bell to call her in the night, and she left the door open a crack so that he could hear the footsteps in the house and not lie alone thinking of the past gone and death soon ahead.

When dawn came and brought his work he was himself again. Nothing could keep him from his work, nor would Carie's daughter hold him back, knowing that to let him go was life and strength to him.

But in the spring of his eightieth year even his work began to be too much. There was a change that year. His flesh grew almost transparent, until his body looked like a pale mist, like a pure wraith, out of which his eyes shone luminous with disembodied goodness. Everything human had gone from him, all appetite, all anger, all impetuosity. Even the old stubbornness was gone. Much of the time after he had come slowly home from work he spent lying down, his eyes closed. But he liked to lie in the room where Carie's daughter was. Sometimes when she looked up from her work he would be lying there on the sofa, so white, so still, that she would cry out. Then he would open his eyes.

"I'm quite all right," he would say. "I've had a good day's work and I'm resting now."

Yes, there was a change that spring. The early April warmth did not stir him, and for the first time he did not look with longing to the hills. Carie's daughter grew afraid and called a doctor, and the doctor said, "Nothing wrong—just worn out—let him have his way in everything." He always had.

The end came happily and quickly that summer. The heat had made him very faint, and so quite willingly he agreed to go up the river to the Lu Shan mountains to his other daughter. He went off happily with his son-in-law, who came to fetch him. He was feeling well that day

and he made small jokes as he went. And they wrote back that the journey seemed to revive him, and in the mountain air he was more himself than he had been for a long time.

All that summer he was happy. He met old friends, and enemies so old that they seemed friends at last, and they forgot old quarrels and made much of him, and his daughter planned little pleasures for him. The summer passed quickly and suddenly he was, he said, ready for work again. He was better—he had played too long—he had not had such a holiday in years. So he wrote to Carie's daughter and she prepared his room and made it all fresh and ready, and waited for him.

That was the summer of the torrential Yangtze flood. The telegraph poles along the river were torn out by the roots and swirled down to the ocean, and steamers with mails were delayed for days. When Andrew, too, was delayed, she did not worry greatly. No one was getting through. Then, after a week, a letter came through and a telegram, relayed somehow by devious lines. Andrew was gone. There on the mountain top he had been taken ill one night with his old dysentery and in a few short hours it was over. There had been not much pain, not much suffering, only a deep bodily weakness, out of which his spirit broke with a great groan, gladly, into its own freedom.

But the body was so little a part of him that its final stillness seemed nothing of importance. He was half out of it anyway and death was only a slipping out of it altogether and being at last what he always was, a spirit. We buried the pearly shell upon the mountain top. There is nothing between that spot and the sky—no tree, no human habitation. The rocks are beneath, the swirling mists about it, and the winds blow and the sun and stars shine down, and there is no human voice to be heard anywhere.

It is the unfathomed irony of all life, now, to think, years past, that Carie who loved the height of clean high mountains and longed to live up and upon them, body and soul, should lie forever buried in a hot dark place, in a parcel of ground walled about in the heart of a Chinese city to hold a few foreign dead. The very air where she lies is full of human miasma, and about her is the ceaseless roar of human shouting and quarreling and laughter and wailing. The high walls and the locked gates cannot hold them from her even now. And Andrew, who sought men for their souls, lies lonely and free upon his mountain top, as far from her in death as life had made him. She longed all her life to be out of human hold and heat, and all her life humanity held her prisoner, her own humanity and that of all the world, and death was a battle with life and she lost. But Andrew never touched the fringe of human life, he never knew its stuff, he never felt its doubt nor shared its pain.

And so he lived, a happy soul, and never knew he died.

THE LIFE AND WORKS OF PEARL BUCK

By ROBERT A. WIGGINS

PEARL BUCK was born Pearl Comfort Sydenstricker on June 26, 1892, in the home of her mother's family in Hillsboro, West Virginia. Andrew and Carie, Pearl's parents, were missionaries stationed in China under the direction of the Presbyterian Board of Foreign Missions, and at the time of Pearl's birth they were on a leave after many years of service. Of four children born before Pearl only her brother, Edwin, born eleven years before her, survived early childhood.

The family heritage was important for Pearl. Her parents were Southerners who had personally experienced the Civil War and Reconstruction. In addition, they came from a strongly fundamentalist background, and were motivated by idealistic and humanitarian impulses in their careers as missionaries in a vast country far from home. They both valued education and imbued their children with a love of learning.

When Pearl was only a few months old the family returned to their station in the small town of Chinkiang in the province of Kiangsu. During the Boxer Rebellion the family returned to West Virginia for a year. Otherwise Chinkiang was to be Pearl's home until she went to college in the United States.

For Pearl these years were generally placid, busy ones of learning. Except for two intervals of school in Shanghai, Pearl was educated at home. She was taught by her parents, reciting her Latin to her father, and studying the rest of her lessons with her mother. There were books at home, and Pearl read avidly; very few American books reached them, but she knew Shakespeare and the nineteenth-century English novelists well.

Though she knew little about America, Pearl was exposed at an early age to the culture of China. She played with Chinese children, and many lifelong friendships among the Chinese date from her childhood. She was welcome in their homes and conducted herself with the decorum of a properly brought up Chinese girl. She absorbed much of the culture of the people from the servants, particularly from her nurse, Wang Amah, and she spoke the local dialect without an accent. She also received a classical Chinese education from a tutor, learning Mandarin and reading widely in the classics. For years Pearl Buck thought of Chinese as her first language and English as her second.

In 1910, the family returned to America on leave to place Pearl in college. Instead of sailing across the Pacific, they took the long route across Siberia, Russia, Europe, and the Atlantic. That autumn she entered Randolph-Macon College for women in Lynchburg, Virginia. The curriculum at Randolph-Macon appealed to her mother because no concession was made to the sex of the students. Instead of the finishing-school sort of curriculum thought proper for young ladies in the South, this college pioneered in giving the same education to girls as was then standard for boys.

By her third year Pearl was a popular student. She was elected president of her class, joined a sorority, and contributed stories to the school magazine. During her final year at Randolph-Macon, Pearl learned that her mother was ill. She was being torn between an ambition to go on into graduate work and her obligation to her parents when a letter arrived telling of her mother's worsened condition. This resolved her indecision, and she returned to help nurse her mother.

Back in Chinkiang Pearl found many changes. Her mother had become a frail semi-invalid suffering from heart trouble and a tropical disease called sprue. Pearl set about caring for her. She ran the household, supervising the servants and in addition took over her mother's mission duties.

China also had changed. The revolution had come while Pearl was in college, and Sun Yat-sen had been proclaimed first president of a Chinese republic. But conditions were not stable. Conservative and liberal forces were fighting for power, and the provinces were dominated by independent warlords. Furthermore, Japan was beginning to emerge as the leading industrial force of the Orient, and her influence was increasingly felt in the commercial life of China. There was also something of a literary revolution taking place. With the overthrow of the monarchy, the old-style classical scholar no longer dominated intellectual life. Young liberals with Western educations rose to influential positions. They attacked the traditional *wen-li* literary language and promoted the use of the vernacular *pai-hua*. As a consequence, the Chinese novel achieved a stature and appeal it had never before enjoyed.

In 1917 Pearl married John Lossing Buck, an agricultural specialist employed by the Presbyterian Board. The young couple went north to settle in Anhwei province. As a young married woman Pearl now had more freedom to move about among the people and could talk on more intimate terms with the women. In 1919 Pearl went to Nanking for the birth of her first child. There were postpartum complications and she had to journey to the United States for a serious operation. The surgery was successful, but she learned that she could not have any more children. The news came as a shock to her, for she loved children and had planned a large family. Shortly thereafter, her mother's condition worsened, and Pearl spent much of her time caring for her until she died a few months later. She then persuaded her father to give up his home in Chinkiang and come to live with her in Nanking, where he could continue his work.

It was at this time that Pearl Buck began to write seriously. With the help of her mother's diary, she wrote a memoir that was in effect a biography. Pearl had originally intended the book to be a private family record, but it was to be published a decade later as *The Exile*. Her first published work was a short article "In China, Too," that appeared in the *Atlantic Monthly* in January 1923. It was a nostalgic essay about her own remote section of China. Soon after, *Forum* magazine asked her for a similar piece. She called it "Beauty in China."

In 1924 Pearl returned with her husband and daughter to the United States. Her husband took a course at Cornell

University, and Pearl entered the university as a graduate student in English literature. To earn some extra money, she revised a piece of fiction she had written on the boat coming to the U.S., and submitted it to the magazine *Asia*, where it was accepted. In addition, she wrote a long monograph on the impact of the West upon China which won a two-hundred-dollar prize at the university. Another story, a sequel to her first, was accepted by *Asia*.

At the end of that year, Pearl Buck learned that her daughter was hopelessly handicapped and would not respond to medical treatment. She adopted an infant daughter, and after completing work for her M.A. degree, she returned with her two children to her home in China.

In Nanking Pearl Buck settled back into her normal routine of managing a large household and teaching at the city's two universities. She devoted all the time she could spare to writing, and set to work on a novel. It was almost complete when the revolution of 1927 swept into Nanking. The Communist forces seized the town, and began to hunt down foreigners and loot their homes. Pearl Buck's family was saved by a poor peasant woman, who hid them until the American authorities could arrange to evacuate the survivors to Shanghai by gun-boat. But Shanghai was crowded with refugees, so Pearl's family crossed over to Japan and found a small house in a valley near Unzen, where they remained for several months.

It was a year before they could return to Nanking, and their house required much repair before it was habitable. A few things had been saved by servants and friends, among them the manuscript of the biography of Pearl's mother, but the almost completed manuscript of her first novel had been destroyed. Soon, however, Pearl was at work on a new one based on the first short stories she had

published. She sent the completed manuscript to a literary agent she had met in New York.

In 1929, she made a hurried trip to the United States to leave her older child where she might receive better medical care. While on this trip she learned that a publisher was interested in her manuscript, and she called at his offices in New York to arrange publication details.

Back home in Nanking, she resumed her busy life. She was delighted to learn that her book, *East Wind; West Wind*, was selling fairly well. Most of her spare time was now taken up with a project she had been working on for some years—the translation of *Shui Hu Chuan*, a monumental Chinese novel. She also continued to write fiction, and finished the manuscript of *The Good Earth* in about three months. Following this, she completed another manuscript, *The Mother*.

In 1931 her father died in his eightieth year. A short time later Pearl Buck went to Peking for some months to use the resources of the library there for her translation of *Shui Hu Chuan*. Peking was the intellectual center of China, and she quickly became acquainted with the literary life of the city. She also learned that life would become increasingly difficult for white residents in China. Reluctantly, she concluded that she would soon have to leave the country and make a new life in the United States.

In the meantime, she heard that *The Good Earth* had been accepted for publication. Her publisher enthusiastically informed her that the novel had been chosen by the Book-of-the-Month Club. Knowing little of the United States, Pearl had no idea that the news meant a guaranteed sale in the thousands, and would make her book a best-seller. By the time it came out, she was already at work on a sequel called *Sons*.

It is not difficult to account for the

popular success of *The Good Earth.* With the United States in the midst of the most severe economic depression the country had ever known, her book reaffirmed the common man's faith in his power to endure and ultimately to prevail. The homely virtues of thrift, hard work and closeness to the soil struck a deeply responsive chord in the hearts of American readers. In China many people were proud that a book about their country had become so well-known, but some young intellectuals deplored its unflattering description of the Chinese peasants' lot.

In 1932 Pearl Buck's family began a year's leave in the United States. She had completed the manuscript of her translation of *Shui Hu Chuan.* Her growing income now made it possible for her to have her father's translation of the New Testament published, and to arrange for permanent care for her handicapped daughter.

In New York, she was introduced to the literary world of the city at a dinner given by her publisher, and that autumn the novel *Sons,* a sequel to *The Good Earth,* was published. In the spring of 1933, *The First Wife and Other Stories* appeared. Later that year *Shui Hu Chuan* was published under the title *All Men Are Brothers.*

In June 1933 Pearl returned to China by way of a lengthy tour of Europe and Asia. She was now a celebrity and could not avoid a certain amount of ceremony during her travels, but she wanted to meet not only intellectuals but also the ordinary people of each land. She toured England, Sweden, the Low Countries, France, and Italy. She sailed from Italy through the Red Sea to Shanghai, where she was entertained by the staff of the *China Critic.* It was on this occasion that she first met Lin Yutang. When she learned he was writing a book she recommended it to her publisher. It was *My Country and My People.*

She returned to Nanking and for some months tried to settle back into her life there. She wrote *The House Divided,* which completed the trilogy begun with *The Good Earth.* In the meantime, her novel *The Mother,* regarded by some as Pearl Buck's best novel, was published.

But her restless and troubled spirit would not allow her to remain long in Nanking, and once more she traveled, this time to India, Indochina, and Indonesia. It was a trip that strongly confirmed her anticolonial sympathies. No matter how enlightened colonial rule might be, she felt it was inconsistent with the best aspirations of the human spirit and was therefore doomed in the modern world. She returned, dejected by the course of events in Asia and concerned about the continent's uncertain future. In Nanking she found a personal crisis. For many years her marriage had been marred by an unbridgeable gulf between the partners; now she finally accepted the fact that it had failed. In 1934, she left China permanently to make her home in the United States.

She accepted a position on the staff of the John Day Publishing Company and rented an apartment in New York. Soon, however, she found a stone farmhouse and forty-eight acres of land near Perkasie, Pennsylvania. It was close enough for her to commute to New York and yet remote enough for her to find quiet there for her work.

In 1935, Pearl Buck married Richard J. Walsh, the president of John Day Publishing Company and the editor of *Asia.* They divided their time between a home in New York and the farm in Pennsylvania. Not long after her remarriage she adopted two baby boys, and when they were a year old two more infants, a boy and a girl.

In the same year she was awarded the William Dean Howells Medal by the American Academy of Arts and Letters for *The Good Earth.*

The biography of her mother, *The Exile,* was also published in 1935, together with *Fighting Angel,* a biography of her father. The following year Pearl Buck was elected to membership in the National Institute of Arts and Letters.

It was at this time that Pearl Buck began to write about America. She also came to a far-reaching decision about her writing. She decided to address herself to a mass audience rather than to try to win the favor of a limited circle of critics and literati. In 1938 she defended her new approach to writing—and her growing contributions to large-circulation magazines—in an address before the National Education Association.

It would be easy for me to do what many others have done—simply shrug my shoulders at the mass of popular writing and say that it was nothing to do with literature. But I cannot. I keep going back to it. It is what most people read—then it must have its importance somewhere in relation to literature. One cannot dismiss lightly a magazine bought and read by three million people. . . . It is important. It is a serious thing for literature if three million read—not literature, but something which gives them greater satisfaction.

Literary critics up to this time had been generally kind in their treatment of Pearl Buck's work, though there were some dissenting voices who felt that her books had been overpraised. But her stories of American life were not so generously received. Her novel *This Proud Heart* appeared in 1938, and the reviewers felt that it did not match her previous work.

The year 1938 was an eventful one for Pearl Buck. She continued her exploration of America by taking a long motor tour into the western states, to experience as much of the variety of America as she could at first hand. Of course, the most exciting event of the year was the news that she had been awarded the Nobel Prize for Literature.

A few weeks after the announcement Pearl Buck embarked for Sweden to attend the presentation ceremonies. She later wrote of the event in *My Several Worlds:* "I have had much happiness in my life and splendid events have come my way, but, aside from the continuing joys of home, the four days in Stockholm in the year 1938 remain my most perfect single recollection. . . . The warmth of the Swedish people, combined with their dignity and their calm, restored my soul. It was good to be received, not with adulation, but with respect and affection. I cherish that memory."

She went first to London and learned there that Europe was closer to war than Americans imagined. In Denmark she was interviewed by the press and asked to comment on an invitation to visit Germany. "I don't want to visit a country where I am not allowed to think and speak freely as I am doing here," she replied with accustomed candor. "I am an individualist and a democrat." Just as forthrightly she criticized the Nationalist regime in China because it could not win the loyalty of the people. Offended, the Chinese representatives in Sweden did not appear at the Nobel Prize ceremony.

Pearl Buck's apprehension about China's future was not without foundation. In 1936 Chiang Kai-shek had been compelled to ally with the Chinese Communists to resist the Japanese invasion in the north. Pearl Buck was disturbed by these events and interrupted her writing on American themes to return to her old style in a novel that dealt with the theme of Sino-Japanese relations. *The Patriot,* published in 1939, optimistically concluded that the unity of peoples ultimately transcends the discord of governments.

From the time she settled in the United States, she had established a work schedule that allowed her to accomplish an enormous amount without sacrificing time with her growing family. She had the capacity to organize her activities efficiently and the discipline to accomplish what she set out to do. Until *Asia* ceased publication, she spent one day a week in New York as advisory editor to the publisher. The rest of the week she spent at home, devoting each morning to her own writing. She usually wrote short articles, speeches, and stories on the typewriter, but longer works were often handwritten in large notebooks. Her usual daily quota was about 2,500 words, and she rarely found it necessary to rewrite or revise.

In addition to her voluminous writing for magazines, Pearl Buck continued her exploration of American life in her novels. In *Other Gods* (1940) she examined the common American phenomenon of hero worship and the fate of the hero himself. An essentially good and simple man is made a hero by the public, responds to the adulation, and is ultimately destroyed by the necessity to satisfy that public. This year also saw the beginning of a new literary activity with the publication of a collection of stories called *Stories for Little Children.* Since then she has written a dozen volumes for children of various ages; about half of them concern life in China.

As the war clouds gathered, Pearl Buck intensified her activities on behalf of racial understanding. In 1941, she founded the East and West Association, to advance "mutual understanding between peoples." One of its major activities was providing Asian speakers whenever they were needed. She also loaned her name and efforts to various organizations having to do with the Negro in America; she was on the Advisory Board of the Common Council for American Unity and a member of the National Committee of the National Urban League. In addition she has also supported such liberal organizations as the American Civil Liberties Union and the Japanese-American Committee for Democracy.

In 1941, she turned once again to China for the theme of a novel. *Dragon Seed* told how the Chinese peasant had met the Japanese conqueror. It was published early in 1942 and was the sixth of her books to be chosen by the Book-of-the-Month Club. It was followed in 1943 by a sequel, *The Promise.* That year also saw publication of a piece of patriotic nonfiction entitled *What America Means to Me.* In it she asserted her faith in the American dream of political freedom.

During World War II, Pearl Buck bought some extra land around her home and began to operate it as a cattle farm for milk production. She wanted to teach her adopted children the values of a life lived close to the soil. After the war she became involved, through her own experience, in the social problems of adoption. She was touched by the plight of many orphans of Asiatic and mixed ancestry who, because of their race, were classified as unadoptable. Pearl Buck refused to believe that such children were really unwanted in America, and set about finding them homes. In 1949 she founded Welcome House, a nonprofit organization devoted to the care and adoption of American-born children of Asian ancestry.

In 1945 Pearl Buck published a novel, *Townsman,* under the pseudonym of John Sedges. She felt that her novels on American themes were not being received on their own merits, and that her readers expected her novels to deal only with China. Three others were published under the name John Sedges before the real author was revealed. They are *Angry Wife* (1947), *Long Love* (1949), and *Bright Procession* (1952).

During the 1950s her literary reputation somewhat declined, and none of her books has since approached the enormous popularity that she commanded during the prewar years. The personal respect that she inspires, however, is undiminished. In 1951, she was elected to the American Academy of Arts and Letters, only one of two women in that august body of fifty. She also served as president of the Authors' Guild and worked through that organization to improve the economic position of professional writers.

Pearl S. Buck celebrated her seventieth birthday in June 1962. Full of years and honors and the material rewards that her writing had brought her, she might understandably have retired. But her interest in the world about her remained high, and the year 1962 saw the publication of a short novel, *Satan Never Sleeps*, set in contemporary China. It tells of the conflict between Christianity and atheism in Communist China. It was produced as a motion picture in the same year. And in 1962 she was also entertained by the President at a White House dinner given for American winners of the Nobel Prize. Now nearing eighty, Pearl Buck still continues to write; hardly a year has passed without a book published.

Any account of Pearl Buck as a writer must take account of her many nonliterary pursuits. More than most writers she has had an unusual background of education and experience to draw upon, and she has always managed to make time for all she wanted to do. The title of her 1954 autobiography, *My Several Worlds*, was not a reference, but aptly described the several careers that she has successfully followed. The full record of her philanthropic activities probably will never be known; apart from her private charities, she has given generously of her time and talent to numerous organizations working for the values in which she believed. She has a remarkable talent for friendship and has extended her hospitality to a flood of visitors as well as kept up a voluminous correspondence with her friends. She has raised a large family that never lacked her attention and affection. She found time to operate a dairy farm, and for many years was an editorial advisor, reading many manuscripts and books each week. At the same time, she has been one of the most prolific of writers—an incomplete bibliography, compiled in 1957, listed fifty books and nearly three hundred pamphlets, stories, and articles, all produced in fewer than thirty years. A decade later, the number had grown to over sixty books and over three hundred shorter pieces.

Robert A. Wiggins is professor of literature at the University of California at Davis.

THE 1938 PRIZE

By KJELL STRÖMBERG

In 1938 the award of the Nobel Prize for Literature to Pearl Buck caused considerable astonishment throughout the world. Few people had thought of this best-selling American novelist in connection with the award. For three years running, the Swedish Academy had crowned writers of an unquestionably superior quality, men who were true revolutionaries of contemporary literature—Luigi Pirandello, Eugene O'Neill, and Roger Martin du Gard. There was no lack of candidates who were perfectly worthy of inclusion in this constellation of first-magnitude stars. Recommendations arrived from every corner of the world, but the Academy remained deaf to them. The hue and cry aroused by the award to Mrs. Buck quieted down quickly, however, because, after all, in the year 1938 the world did have more serious things to worry about.

This was the year of Munich, when the specter of a new world war came into sharper focus. In the autumn of that crucial year, the various Nobel committees set about the business of awarding their Prizes. The debates were characterized by confusion and dispute.

The most hotly disputed Nobel Prize was of course the award for peace. An intense surge of public opinion—not only in the great nations which were directly concerned, such as France and England, but also in the smaller, "neu-tral" countries—favored the British Prime Minister, Neville Chamberlain, the "savior of the peace." Edouard Daladier, the French Prime Minister, also had strong backing. An equally vigorous campaign was waged in the same countries for Eduard Beneš, the former President of Czechoslovakia, the nation at whose expense the frail peace had been safeguarded for the moment. In France, Léon Blum, the former Prime Minister and leader of the socialists, became an eloquent pleader for Beneš, who also found valiant supporters in the Scandinavian countries. Unfortunately (or fortunately!) neither had been proposed to the Nobel Committee of the Norwegian Parliament before the February 1 deadline.

The Norwegian and Swedish press set up a cry for an ad hoc change of the rules in favor of Chamberlain, who—it was said—had done more for peace than all the previous winners put together. The Academy's reply was a categorical statement that it simply could not change the rules, and very wisely, a spokesman for the Nobel Foundation let it be known through the press that it might be better to wait on the course of events, as had so often been done; that is, to think it over for a year. Finally the Nansen International Office for Refugees in Geneva received the Nobel Peace Prize for 1938.

It goes without saying that political

[279]

considerations also had a certain influence on the debates concerning the literature Prize. Karel Capek, whose name had been submitted, had many warm supporters, and the idea of awarding the Prize to the greatest living Czech writer would at the same time seem a well-deserved homage to his martyred country. (His works, incidentally, included *The War of the Newts,* that apocalyptic vision of the future war which was to explode much sooner than anyone then imagined.) Among his most fervent supporters, Capek could count Jules Romains, the French novelist and playwright who was at the time president of the International P.E.N. Club. Romains, author of *Men of Good Will,* had also joined Albert Einstein, Thomas Mann, H. G. Wells, and Romain Rolland in signing an open letter addressed to the Nobel Institute of Medicine submitting the name of Sigmund Freud for the Prize in Medicine. Freud was then in London, a Jewish refugee driven from his university chair in Vienna, deprived of his possessions, and relieved of his Austrian nationality following the Nazi occupation of his country which had taken place without a shot being fired in the spring of that disastrous year. The founder of psychoanalysis, who had also proven himself a true poet in his interpretations of dreams, had already been proposed once before, in 1936, for the Nobel Prize for Literature. Another possible "political" candidate was Carl J. Burckhardt, former professor at the University of Zurich, who was later to be the Swiss minister to France. At that time he had great responsibilities as High Commissioner of the League of Nations in Danzig, a prime nerve center in a Europe writhing in convulsions.

At any rate, for the Prize in Literature, the Swedish Academy could choose from among some thirty candidates, all of them more or less eligible from a purely literary point of view. The list of talents included three who were subsequently to win the Prize—the Finn, F. E. Sillanpää, Johannes V. Jensen of Denmark, and the German novelist Hermann Hesse, who had recently become Swiss by naturalization. All three names had often appeared on the list of candidates, together with those of the philosopher and historian, Benedetto Croce, the Greek poet Costes Palamas, and the English novelist Aldous Huxley. The winner, however, proved to be Pearl Buck Walsh, née Sydenstricker, whose name had been proposed at the last minute by four members of the Swedish Academy.

How can her victory be explained? No doubt the embarrassing political situation in Europe was a factor, for very few writers of importance had been able or had wanted to steer completely clear of the events which at that time were upsetting the minds of all men. This worthy American novelist of Dutch origin doubtless seemed to offer a most tempting escape to anyone who didn't want to get too involved with European events or to risk attracting the fire of the powerful men of the world.

It was not, however, exclusively for her first great story of Chinese life, *The Good Earth* (1931), that Pearl Buck was awarded the Prize, although this novel did have an immediate success rivaling that of her fellow American, Margaret Mitchell (who had also been proposed for the Nobel Prize after the publication of *Gone with the Wind*). Both novels had been translated into virtually every language in the world, and both had enjoyed worldwide success as motion pictures. In the report he drew up for his colleagues, Per Hallström, the permanent secretary of the Swedish Academy, emphasized the importance which two biographical novels devoted to her parents should take in the final consideration of this daughter of Presbyterian missionaries in the Far East. For these two novels, *The Exile* and *Fighting Angel,* Per Hallström concluded, "the distinction of the Nobel Prize might be more solidly deserved than in many other cases." In the citation we learn that the Prize was awarded to Pearl Buck "for her rich and truly epic descriptions of peasant life in China and for her biographical masterpieces."

Caught quite unawares by the honor, Pearl Buck herself was certainly surprised when she heard the good news from journalists who invaded her New York apartment even before she had received the official cable from the Swedish Academy. With a touching modesty which did her honor, she preferred to believe, until confirmation arrived, that it was a mistake or a joke in bad taste, and that if indeed, for the third time the Prize had gone to an American, the real winner would prove to be Theodore Dreiser. When she was finally convinced that the Prize was actually hers, she decided at once to go to Stockholm, accompanied by her publisher and second husband, Richard J. Walsh. In Sweden, she charmed everybody, including her distinguished sister-novelist Selma Lagerlöf, winner of the 1909 Prize, whom Mrs. Buck was particularly eager to meet.

Translated by Dale McAdoo.

Ivan Bunin

1933

"For the strict artistry with which

he has carried on the classical Russian

traditions in prose writing"

Illustrated by TERECHKOVITCH

PRESENTATION ADDRESS

By PER HALLSTRÖM

PERMANENT SECRETARY
OF THE SWEDISH ACADEMY

Ivan bunin's literary career has been clear and uncomplicated. He came from a family of country squires and grew up in the literary tradition of the times in which that social class dominated Russian culture, created a literature occupying a place of honor in contemporary Europe, and led to fatal political movements. "The lords of the scrupulous consciences" is what the following generation ironically called these men who, full of indignation and pity, set themselves up against the humiliation of the serfs. They deserved a better name, for they would soon have to pay with their own prosperity for the upheaval that they were going to cause.

Only the debris of the family possessions remained about the young Bunin; it was in the world of poetry that he could feel a strong rapport with the past generations. He lived in a world of illusions without any energy, rather than of national sentiment and hope for the future. Nonetheless he did not escape the influence of the reform movement; as a student, he was deeply struck by the appeal of Tolstoy's proclaiming fraternity with the humble and poor. Thus he learned like others to live by the toil of his hands, and for his part he chose the craft of cooper in the home of a co-religionist who greatly loved discussion. (He might well have tried a less difficult craft—the staves come apart easily, and it takes much skill to make a vessel that will hold its content.)

For a guide in more spiritual doctrines he had a man who fought with wavering energy against the temptations of the flesh in a very literal sense, and here vegetarianism entered his doctrine. During a voyage with him—to Tolstoy's home to be presented to the master—Bunin was able to observe his victories and defeats. He was victorious over several refreshment stands in railroad stations but finally the temptation of the meat pâtés was too strong. Having finished chewing, he found ingenious excuses for his particular fall: "I know, however, that it is not the pâté that holds me in its power but I who hold it. I am not its slave; I eat when I want to; when I don't want to, I don't eat." It goes without saying that the young student did not want to stay long in his company.

Tolstoy himself did not attach great importance to Bunin's religious zeal. "You wish to live a simple and industrious life? That is good, but don't be priggish about it. One can be an excellent man in all kinds of lives." And of the profession of poet he said, "Oh well, write if you have a great fancy for it, but remember well that it can never be the goal of your life." This warning was lost on Bunin; he was already a poet with all his being.

He quickly attracted attention for verses that followed austere classical models; their subject was often descriptions of melancholic beauty of past life in the old manors. At the same time he developed in prose poems his power to render nature with all the fullness and richness of his impressions, having exercised his faculties with an extraordinary subtlety to reproduce them faithfully. Thus he continued the art of the great realists while his contemporaries devoted themselves to the adventures of literary programs: symbolism, neo-naturalism, Adamism, futurism, and other names of such passing phenomena. He remained an isolated man in an extremely agitated era.

When Bunin was forty, his novel *Derévnya* (*The Village,* 1910) made him famous and indeed notorious, for the book provoked a violent discussion. He attacked the essential point of the Russian faith in the future, the Slavophiles' dream of the virtuous and able peasant, through whom the nation must someday cover the world with its shadow. Bunin replied to this thesis with an objective description of the real nature of the peasants' virtues. The result was one of the most somber and cruel works even in Russian literature, where such works are by no means rare.

The author gives no historical explanation of the decadence of the *muzhikí,* except for the brief information that the grandfather of the two principal characters in the novel was deliberately tracked to death by his master's greyhounds. This deed expresses well, in fact, the imprint borne by the spirit of the suppressed. But Bunin shows them just as they are without hesitating before any horror, and it was easy for him to prove the truthfulness of his severe judgment. Violence of the most cruel kind had recently swept the province in the wake of the first revolution—a foreshadowing of a later one.

For lack of another name, the book is called a novel in the translations, but it really bears little resemblance to that genre. It consists of a series of immensely tumultuous episodes from lower life; truth of detail has meant everything to the author. The critic questioned not so much the details but their disinterested selection—the foreigner cannot judge the validity of the criticism. Now the book has had a strong revival because of events since then, and it remains a classic work, the model of a solid, concentrated, and sure art, in the eyes of the Russian émigrés as well as of those in the homeland.

The descriptions of villages were continued in many shorter essays, sometimes devoted to the religious elements which, in the eyes of the enthusiastic national generation, made the *muzhikí* the people of promise. In the writer's pitiless analysis the redemptive piety of the world is reduced to anarchic instincts and to the taste for self-humiliation, essential traits of the Russian spirit according to him. He was indeed far from his youthful Tolstoyian faith. But he had retained one thing from it: his love of the Russian land. He has hardly ever painted his marvelous countryside with such great art as in some of these novellas. It is as if he had done it to preserve himself, to be able to breathe freely once more after all he had seen of the ugly and the false.

In a quite different spirit *Sukhodól* (1911–1912), the short novel of a manor, was written as a counterpart to *The Village*. The book is not a portrayal of the present times, but of the heyday of the landed proprietors, as remembered by an old servant in the house where Bunin grew up. The author is not an optimist in this book, either; these masters have little vital force, they are as unworthy of being responsible for their own destinies and those of their subordinates as the severest accuser could have desired. In effect one finds here in large measure the materials for that defense of the people which Bunin silently passed over in *The Village*.

But nonetheless the picture appears now in a totally different light; it is filled with poetry. This is due in part to the kind of reconciliation that the past possesses, having paid its debt by death; but also to the sweet vision of the servant who gives charm to the confused and changing world in which, however, her youth was ruined. But the chief source of poetry is the author's imaginative power, his faculty for giving this book, with an intense concentration, the richness of life. *Sukhodól* is a literary work of *very* high order.

During the years which remained before the World War, Bunin made long trips through the Mediterranean countries and to the Far East. They provided him with the subjects of a series of exotic novellas, sometimes inspired by the world of Hindu ideas, with its peace in the abnegation of life, but more often by the strongly accentuated contrast between the dreaming Orient and the harsh and avid materialism of the West. When the war came, these studies in the spirit of the modern globetrotters with the imprint created by the world tragedy were to result in the novella that came to be his most famous work: *Gospodín iz San Francisco* (*The Gentleman from San Francisco,* 1916).

As often elsewhere, Bunin here simplifies the subject extremely by restricting himself to developing the principal idea with types rather than complex characters. Here he seems to have a special reason for this method: it is as if the author were afraid to come too close to his figures because they awaken his indignation and his hate. The American multimillionaire, who after a life of ceaseless thirst for money, sets out as an old man into the world to refresh the dry consciousness of his power, his blindness of soul, and his avidity for senile pleasure, interests the author only in so far as he can show in what a pitiable manner he succumbs, like a bursting bubble. It is as if a judgment of the pitiless world were pronounced against his character. In place of a portrait of this pitifully insignificant man, the novella gives by its singularly resolute art a portrait of destiny, the enemy of this man, without any mysticism but only with strictly objective description of the game of the forces of nature with human vanity. The mystical feeling, however, is awakened in the reader and becomes stronger and greater through the perfect command of language and tone. *The Gentleman from San Francisco* was immediately accepted as a literary masterpiece; but it was also something else: the portent of an increasing world twilight; the condemnation of the essential guilt in the tragedy; the distortion of human culture which pushed the world to the same fate.

[288]

The consequences of the war expelled the author from his country, so dear to him despite everything, and it seemed a duty to remain silent under the severe pressure of what he had suffered. But his lost country lived again doubly dear in his memory, and regret gave him more pity for men. Still, he sometimes, with stronger reason, painted his particular enemy, the *muzhík,* with a somber clear-sightedness of all his vices and faults; but sometimes he looked forward. Under all repellent things, he saw something of indestructible humanity, which he represented not with moral stress but as a force of nature, full of the immense possibilities of life. "A tree of God," one of them calls himself, "I see thus that God provides it; where the wind goes, there I follow." In this manner he has taken leave of them for the present.

From the inexhaustible treasures of his memories of the Russian nature, Bunin was later able to draw anew the joy and the desire to create. He gave color and brilliance to new Russian destinies, conceived in the same austerity as in the era when he lived among them. In *Mítina lyubóv (Mitya's Love,* 1924–1925), he analyzed young feelings with all the mastery of a psychology in which sense impressions and states of mind, marvelously rendered, are particularly essential. The book was very successful in his country, although it signaled the return to literary traditions which, with many other things, had seemed condemned to death. In what has been published of *Zhizn Arsénieva*—Part I, *Istóki dnéy (The Well of Days,* 1930)—partially an autobiography, he has reproduced Russian life in a manner broader than ever before. His old superiority as the incomparable painter of the vast and rich beauty of the Russian land remains fully confirmed here.

In the literary history of his country, the place of Ivan Bunin has been clearly defined and his importance recognized for a long time and almost without divergence of opinions. He has followed the great tradition of the brilliant era of the nineteenth century in stressing the line of development which can be continued. He perfected concentration and richness of expression—of a description of real life based on an almost unique precision of observation. With the most rigorous art he has well resisted all temptations to forget things for the charm of words; although by nature a lyric poet, he has never embellished what he has seen but has rendered it with the most exact fidelity. To his simple language he has added a charm which, according to the testimonies of his compatriots, has made of it a precious drink that one can often sense in the translations. This ability is his eminent and secret talent, and it gives the imprint of the masterpiece to his literary work.

Mr. Bunin—I have tried to present a picture of your work and of that austere art which characterizes it, a picture doubtlessly quite incomplete because of the little time at my disposal for a task so demanding. Please receive now, sir, from the hands of His Majesty the King, those marks of distinction which the Swedish Academy is conferring on you, together with its heartfelt congratulations.

ACCEPTANCE SPEECH

By *IVAN BUNIN*

O N NOVEMBER NINTH, very far from here in a poor country house in an old Provençal town, I received the telephone call that informed me of the choice of the Swedish Academy. I would not be honest if I told you, as one does in such cases, that it was the profoundest emotional moment of my life. A great philosopher has said that even the most vehement feelings of joy hardly count in comparison with those which provoke sorrow. I do not wish to strike a note of sadness at this dinner, which I shall forever remember, but let me say nonetheless that in the course of the past fifteen years my sorrows have far exceeded my joys. And not all of those sorrows have been personal—far from it. But I can certainly say that in my entire literary life no other event has given me so much legitimate satisfaction as that little technical miracle, the telephone call from Stockholm to Grasse. The prize established by your great countryman, Alfred Nobel, is still the highest reward that can crown the work of a writer. Ambitious like most men and all writers, I was extremely proud to receive that reward at the hands of the most competent and impartial of juries, and be assured, gentlemen of the Academy, I was also extremely grateful. But I should have proved a paltry egotist if on that ninth of November I had thought only of myself. Overwhelmed by the congratulations and telegrams that began to flood me, I thought in the solitude and silence of night about the profound meaning in the choice of the Swedish Academy.

For the first time since the founding of the Nobel Prize you have awarded it to an exile. Who am I in truth? An exile enjoying the hospitality of France, to whom I likewise owe an eternal debt of gratitude. But, gentlemen of the Academy, let me say that irrespective of my person and my work your choice in itself is a gesture of great beauty. It is necessary that there should be centers of absolute independence in the world. No doubt, all differences of opinion, of philosophical and religious creeds, are represented around this table. But we are united by one truth, the freedom of thought and conscience; to this freedom we owe civilization. For us writers, especially, freedom is a dogma and an axiom. Your choice, gentlemen of the Academy, has proved once more that in Sweden the love of liberty is truly a national cult.

Finally, a few words to end this short speech: my admiration for your royal family, your country, your people, your literature, does not date from this day alone. Love of letters and learning has been a tradition with the royal house of Sweden as with your entire noble nation. Founded by an illustrious soldier, the Swedish dynasty is one of the most glorious in the world. May His Majesty the King, the chivalrous King of a chivalrous people, permit a stranger, a free writer honored by the Swedish Academy, to express to him these sentiments of profound respect and deep emotion.

THE GENTLEMAN
FROM SAN FRANCISCO

By IVAN BUNIN

Translated by Bernard Guilbert Guerney

"Alas, alas, that great city Babylon, that mighty city!"—
—Revelation of St. John

The Gentleman from San Francisco—neither at Naples nor on Capri could any one recall his name—with his wife and daughter, was on his way to Europe, where he intended to stay for two whole years, solely for the pleasure of it.

He was firmly convinced that he had a full right to a rest, enjoyment, a long comfortable trip, and what not. This conviction had a two-fold reason: first he was rich, and second, despite his fifty-eight years, he was just about to enter the stream of life's pleasures. Until now he had not really lived, but simply existed, to be sure—fairly well, yet putting off his fondest hopes for the future. He toiled unweariedly—the Chinese, whom he imported by thousands for his works, knew full well what it meant,—and finally he saw that he had made much, and that he had nearly come up to the level of those whom he had once taken as a model, and he decided to catch his breath. The class of people to which he belonged was in the habit of beginning its enjoyment of life with a trip to Europe, India, Egypt. He made up his mind to do the same. Of course, it was first of all himself that he desired to reward for the years of toil, but he was also glad for his wife and daughter's sake. His wife was never distinguished by any extraordinary impressionability, but then, all elderly American women are ardent travelers. As for his daughter, a girl of marriageable age, and somewhat sickly,—travel was the very thing she needed. Not to speak of the benefit to her health, do not happy meetings occur during travels? Abroad, one may chance to sit at the same table with a prince, or examine frescoes side by side with a multi-millionaire.

The itinerary the Gentleman from San Francisco planned out was an extensive one. In December and January he expected to relish the sun of southern Italy, monuments of antiquity, the tarantella, serenades of wandering minstrels, and that which at his age is felt most keenly—the love, not entirely disinterested though, of young Neapolitan girls. The Carnival days he planned to spend at Nice and Monte-Carlo, which at that time of the year is the meeting-place of the choicest society, the society upon which depend all the blessings of civilization: the cut of dress suits, the stability of thrones, the declaration of wars, the prosperity of hotels. Some of these people passionately give themselves over to automobile and boat races, others to roulette, others, again, busy themselves with what is called flirtation, and others shoot pigeons, which soar so beautifully from the dove-cote, hover a while over the emerald lawn, on the background of the forget-me-not colored sea, and then suddenly hit the ground, like little white lumps. Early March he wanted to devote to Florence, and at Easter, to hear the Miserere in Paris. His plans also included Venice, Paris, bull-baiting at Seville, bathing on the British Islands, also Athens, Constantinople, Palestine, Egypt, and even Japan, of course, on the way back. . . . And at first things went very well indeed.

It was the end of November, and all the way to Gibraltar the ship sailed across seas which were either clad by icy darkness or swept by storms carrying wet snow. But there were no accidents, and the vessel did not even roll. The passengers,—all people of consequence—were numerous, and the steamer, the famous "Atlantis," resembled the most expensive European hotel with all improvements; a night refreshment-bar, Oriental baths, even a newspaper of its own. The manner of living was a most aristocratic one; passengers rose early, awakened by the shrill voice of a bugle, filling the corridors at the gloomy hour when the day broke slowly and sulkily over the grayish-green watery desert, which rolled heavily in the fog. After putting on their flannel pajamas, they took coffee, chocolate, cocoa; they seated themselves in marble baths, went through their exercises, whetting their appetites and increasing their sense of well-being, dressed for the day, and had their breakfast. Till eleven o'clock they were supposed to stroll on the deck, breathing in the chill freshness of the ocean, or they played table-tennis, or other games which arouse the appe-

tite. At eleven o'clock a collation was served consisting of sandwiches and bouillon, after which people read their newspapers, quietly waiting for luncheon, which was more nourishing and varied than the breakfast. The next two hours were given to rest; all the decks were crowded then with steamer chairs, on which the passengers, wrapped in plaids, lay stretched, dozing lazily, or watching the cloudy sky and the foamy-fringed water hillocks flashing beyond the sides of the vessel. At five o'clock, refreshed and gay, they drank strong, fragrant tea; at seven the sound of the bugle announced a dinner of nine courses. . . . Then the Gentleman from San Francisco, rubbing his hands in an onrush of vital energy, hastened to his luxurious state-room to dress.

In the evening, all the decks of the "Atlantis" yawned in the darkness, shone with their innumerable fiery eyes, and a multitude of servants worked with increased feverishness in the kitchens, dish-washing compartments, and wine-cellars. The ocean, which heaved about the sides of the ship, was dreadful, but no one thought of it. All had faith in the controlling power of the captain, a red-headed giant, heavy and very sleepy, who, clad in a uniform with broad golden stripes, looked like a huge idol, and but rarely emerged, for the benefit of the public, from his mysterious retreat. On the forecastle, the siren gloomily roared or screeched in a fit of mad rage, but few of the diners heard the siren: its hellish voice was covered by the sounds of an excellent string orchestra, which played ceaselessly and exquisitely in a vast hall, decorated with marble and spread with velvety carpets. The hall was flooded with torrents of light, radiated by crystal lusters and gilt chandeliers; it was filled with a throng of bejeweled ladies in low-necked dresses, of men in dinner-coats, graceful waiters, and deferential maîtres-d'hôtel. One of these,—who accepted wine orders exclusively—wore a chain on his neck like some lord-mayor. The evening dress, and the ideal linen made the Gentleman from San Francisco look very young. Dry-skinned, of average height, strongly, though irregularly built, glossy with thorough washing and cleaning, and moderately animated, he sat in the golden splendor of this palace. Near him stood a bottle of amber-colored Johannisberg, and goblets of most delicate glass and of varied sizes, surmounted by a frizzled bunch of fresh hyacinths. There was something Mongolian in his yellowish face with its trimmed silvery moustache; his large teeth glimmered with gold fillings, and his strong, bald head had a dull glow, like old ivory. His wife, a big, broad and placid woman, was dressed richly, but in keeping with her age. Complicated, but light, transparent, and innocently immodest was the dress of his daughter, tall and slender, with magnificent hair gracefully combed; her breath was sweet with violet-scented tablets, and she had a number of tiny and most delicate pink dimples near her lips and between her slightly-powdered shoulder blades. . . .

The dinner lasted two whole hours, and was followed by dances in the dancing hall, while the men—the Gentleman from San Francisco among them—made their way to the refreshment bar, where Negroes in red jackets and with eyeballs like shelled hard-boiled eggs, waited on them. There, with their feet on tables, smoking Havana cigars, and drinking themselves purple in the face, they settled the destinies of nations on the basis of the latest political and stock-exchange news. Outside, the ocean tossed up black mountains with a thud; and the snowstorm hissed furiously in the rigging grown heavy with slush; the ship trembled in every limb, struggling with the storm and plowing with difficulty the shifting and seething mountainous masses that threw far and high their foaming tails; the siren groaned in agony, choked by storm and fog; the watchmen in their towers froze and almost went out of their minds under the superhuman stress of attention. Like the gloomy and sultry mass of the inferno, like its last, ninth circle, was the submersed womb of the steamer, where monstrous furnaces yawned with red-hot open jaws, and emitted deep, hooting sounds, and where the stokers, stripped to the waist, and purple with reflected flames, bathed in their own dirty, acid sweat. And here, in the refreshment-bar, carefree men, with their feet, encased in dancing shoes, on the table, sipped cognac and liqueurs, swam in waves of spiced smoke, and exchanged subtle remarks, while in the dancing-hall everything sparkled and radiated light, warmth and joy. The couples now turned around in a waltz, now swayed in the tango; and the music, sweetly shameless and sad, persisted in its ceaseless entreaties. . . . There were many persons of note in this magnificent crowd; an ambassador, a dry, modest old man; a great millionaire, shaved, tall, of an indefinite age, who, in his old-fashioned dress-coat, looked like a prelate; also a famous Spanish writer, and an international belle, already slightly faded and of dubious morals. There was also among them a loving pair, exquisite and refined, whom everybody watched with curiosity and who did not conceal their bliss; he danced only with her, sang—with great skill—only to her accompaniment, and they were so charming, so graceful. The captain alone knew that they had been hired by the company at a good salary to play at love, and that they had been sailing now on one, now on another steamer, for quite a long time.

In Gibraltar everybody was gladdened by the sun, and by the weather which was like early Spring. A new passenger appeared aboard the "Atlantis" and aroused everybody's interest. It was the crown-prince of an Asiatic state, who traveled incognito, a small man, very nimble, though looking as if made of wood, broad-faced, narrow-eyed, in gold-rimmed glasses, somewhat disagreeable because of his long moustache, which was sparse like that of a corpse, but otherwise—charming, plain, modest. In the Mediterranean the breath of winter was again felt. The seas were heavy and motley like a peacock's tail and the waves stirred up by the gay gusts of the tramontane, tossed their white crests under a sparkling and perfectly clear sky. Next morning, the sky grew paler, and the skyline misty. Land was near. Then Ischia and Capri came in sight, and one could descry, through an opera-glass, Naples, looking like pieces of sugar strewn at the foot of an indistinct dove-colored mass, and above them, a snow-covered chain of distant mountains. The decks were crowded, many ladies and gentlemen put on light-fur-coats; Chinese servants, bandy-legged youths—with pitch black braids down to the heels and with girlish, thick eyelashes,—always quiet and speaking in a whisper, were carrying to the foot of the staircases, plaid wraps, canes, and crocodile-leather valises and handbags. The daughter of the Gentleman from San Francisco stood near the prince, who, by a happy chance, had been introduced to her the evening before, and feigned to be looking steadily at something far-off, which he was pointing out to her, while he was, at the same time, explaining something, saying something rapidly and quietly. He was so small that he looked like a boy among other men, and he was not handsome at all. And then there was something strange about him; his glasses, derby and coat were most commonplace, but there was something horse-like in the hair of his sparse moustache, and the thin, tanned skin of his flat face looked as though it were somewhat stretched and varnished. But the girl listened to him, and so great was her excitement that she could hardly grasp the meaning of his words, her heart palpitated with incomprehensible rapture and with pride that he was standing and speaking with her and nobody else. Everything about him was different; his dry hands, his clean skin, under which flowed ancient kingly blood, even his light shoes and his European dress, plain, but singularly tidy—everything hid an inexplicable fascination and engendered thoughts of love. And the Gentleman from San Francisco, himself, in a silk-hat, gray leggings, patent leather shoes, kept eyeing the famous beauty who was standing near him, a tall, stately blonde, with eyes painted according to the latest Parisian fashion, and a tiny, bent peeled-off pet-dog, to whom she addressed herself. And the daughter, in a kind of vague perplexity, tried not to notice him.

Like all wealthy Americans he was very liberal when traveling, and believed in the complete sincerity and good-will of those who so painstakingly fed him, served him day and night, anticipating his slightest desire, protected him from dirt and disturbance, hauled things for him, hailed carriers, and delivered his luggage to hotels. So it was everywhere, and it had to be so at Naples. Meanwhile, Naples grew and came nearer. The musicians, with their shining brass instruments had already formed a group on the deck, and all of a sudden deafened everybody with the triumphant sounds of a ragtime march. The giant captain, in his full uniform appeared on the bridge and like a gracious Pagan idol, waved his hands to the passengers,—and it seemed to the Gentleman from San Francisco,—as it did to all the rest,—that for him alone thundered the march, so greatly loved by proud America, and that him alone did the captain congratulate on the safe arrival. And when the "Atlantis" had finally entered the port and all its many-decked mass leaned against the quay, and the gangplank began to rattle heavily,—what a crowd of porters, with their assistants, in caps with golden galloons, what a crowd of various boys and husky ragamuffins with pads of colored postal cards attacked the Gentleman from San Francisco, offering their services! With kindly contempt he grinned at these beggars, and, walking towards the automobile of the hotel where the prince might stop, muttered between his teeth, now in English, now in Italian—"Go away! Via . . ."

Immediately, life at Naples began to follow a set routine. Early in the morning breakfast was served in the gloomy dining room, swept by a wet draft from the open windows looking upon a stony garden, while outside the sky was cloudy and cheerless, and a crowd of guides swarmed at the door of the vestibule. Then came the first smiles of the warm roseate sun, and from the high suspended balcony, a broad vista unfolded itself: Vesuvius, wrapped to its base in radiant morning vapors; the pearly ripple, touched to silver, of the bay, the delicate outline of Capri in the skyline; tiny asses dragging two-wheeled buggies along the soft, sticky embankment, and detachments of little soldiers marching somewhere to the tune of cheerful and defiant music.

Next on the day's program was a slow automobile ride along crowded, narrow, and damp corridors of streets, between high, many-windowed buildings. It was followed by visits to museums, lifelessly clean and lighted evenly and pleasantly, but as though with the dull light cast by snow;—then to churches, cold, smelling of wax, always alike; a majestic entrance, closed by a ponderous, leather curtain, and inside—a vast void, silence, quiet

flames of seven-branched candlesticks, sending forth a red glow from where they stood at the farther end, on the bedecked altar,—a lonely, old woman lost among the dark wooden benches, slippery gravestones under the feet, and somebody's "Descent from the Cross," infallibly famous. At one o'clock—luncheon, on the mountain of San-Martius, where at noon the choicest people gathered, and where the daughter of the Gentleman from San Francisco once almost fainted with joy, because it seemed to her that she saw the prince in the hall, although she had learned from the newspapers that he had temporarily left for Rome. At five o'clock it was customary to take tea at the hotel, in a smart *salon*, where it was far too warm because of the carpets and the blazing fireplaces; and then came dinner-time—and again did the mighty, commanding voice of the gong resound throughout the building, again did silk rustle and the mirrors reflect files of ladies in low-necked dresses ascending the staircases, and again the splendid palatial dining hall opened with broad hospitality, and again the musicians' jackets formed red patches on the estrade, and the black figures of the waiters swarmed around the maître-d'hôtel, who, with extraordinary skill, poured a thick pink soup into plates. . . . As everywhere, the dinner was the crown of the day. People dressed for it as for a wedding, and so abundant was it in food, wines, mineral waters, sweets and fruits, that about eleven o'clock in the evening chamber-maids would carry to all the rooms hot-water bags.

That year, however, December did not happen to be a very propitious one. The doormen were abashed when people spoke to them about the weather, and shrugged their shoulders guiltily, mumbling that they could not recollect such a year, although, to tell the truth, that it was not the first year they mumbled those words, usually adding that "things are terrible everywhere"; that unprecedented showers and storms had broken out on the Riviera, that it was snowing in Athens, that Aetna, too, was all blocked up with snow, and glowed brightly at night, and that tourists were fleeing from Palermo to save themselves from the cold spell. . . .

That winter, the morning sun daily deceived Naples; toward noon the sky would invariably grow gray, and a light rain would begin to fall, growing thicker and duller. Then the palms at the hotel-porch glistened disagreeably like wet tin, the town appeared exceptionally dirty and congested, the museums too monotonous, the cigars of the drivers in their rubber raincoats, which flattened in the wind like wings, intolerably stinking, and the energetic flapping of their whips over their thin-necked nags—obviously false. The shoes of the signors, who cleaned the street-car tracks, were in a frightful state, the women who splashed in the mud, with black hair unprotected from the rain, were ugly and short legged, and the humidity mingled with the foul smell of rotting fish, that came from the foaming sea, was simply disheartening. And so, early-morning quarrels began to break out between the Gentleman from San Francisco and his wife; and their daughter now grew pale and suffered from headaches, and now became animated, enthusiastic over everything, and at such times was lovely and beautiful. Beautiful were the tender, complex feelings which her meeting with the ungainly man aroused in her,—the man in whose veins flowed unusual blood, for, after all, it does not matter what in particular stirs up a maiden's soul: money, or fame, or nobility of birth. . . . Everybody assured the tourists that it was quite different at Sorrento and on Capri, that lemon-trees were blossoming there, that it was warmer and sunnier there, the morals

purer, and the wine less adulterated. And the family from San Francisco decided to set out with all their luggage for Capri. They planned to settle down at Sorrento, but first to visit the island, tread the stones where stood Tiberius's palaces, examine the fabulous wonders of the Blue Grotto, and listen to the bagpipes of Abruzzi, who roam about the island during the whole month preceding Christmas and sing the praises of the Madonna.

On the day of departure—a very memorable day for the family from San Francisco—the sun did not appear even in the morning. A heavy winter fog covered Vesuvius down to its very base and hung like a gray curtain low over the leaden surge of the sea, hiding it completely at a distance of half a mile. Capri was completely out of sight, as though it had never existed on this earth. And the little steamboat which was making for the island tossed and pitched so fiercely that the family lay prostrated on the sofas in the miserable cabin of the little steamer, with their feet wrapped in plaids and their eyes shut because of their nausea. The older lady suffered, as she thought, most; several times she was overcome with sea-sickness, and it seemed to her then she was dying, but the chambermaid, who repeatedly brought her the basin, and who for many years, in heat and in cold, had been tossing on these waves, ever on the alert, ever kindly to all,—the chambermaid only laughed. The lady's daughter was frightfully pale and kept a slice of lemon between her teeth. Not even the hope of an unexpected meeting with the prince at Sorrento, where he planned to arrive on Christmas, served to cheer her. The Gentleman from San Francisco, who was lying on his back, dressed in a large overcoat and a big cap, did not loosen his jaws throughout the voyage. His face grew dark, his moustache white, and his head ached heavily; for the last few days, because of the bad weather, he had drunk far too much in the evenings.

And the rain kept on beating against the rattling window panes, and water dripped down from them on the sofas; the howling wind attacked the masts, and sometimes, aided by a heavy sea, it laid the little steamer on its side, and then something below rolled about with a rattle.

While the steamer was anchored at Castellamare and Sorrento, the situation was more cheerful; but even here the ship rolled terribly, and the coast with all its precipices, gardens and pines, with its pink and white hotels and hazy mountains clad in curling verdure, flew up and down as if it were on swings. The row boats hit against the sides of the steamer, the sailors and the deck passengers shouted at the top of their voices, and somewhere a baby screamed as if it were being crushed to pieces. A wet wind blew through the door, and from a wavering barge flying the flag of the Hotel Royal, an urchin kept on unwearyingly shouting "Kgoyal-al! Hotel Kgoyal-al! . . ." inviting tourists. And the Gentleman from San Francisco felt like the old man that he was,—and it was with weariness and animosity that he thought of all these "Royals," "Splendids," "Excelsiors," and of all those greedy bugs, reeking with garlic, who are called Italians. Once, during a stop, having opened his eyes and half-risen from the sofa, he noticed in the shadow of the rock beach a heap of stone huts, miserable, mildewed through and through, huddled close by the water, near boats, rags, tin-boxes, and brown fishing nets,—and as he remembered that this was the very Italy he had come to enjoy, he felt a great despair. . . . Finally, in twilight, the black mass of the island began to grow nearer, as though burrowed through at the base by red fires, the wind grew softer, warmer, more fragrant; from the dock-lanterns huge golden serpents flowed down the tame waves which undulated like black oil. . . . Then, suddenly, the anchor rumbled and fell with a splash into the water, the fierce yells of the boatman filled the air,—and at once everyone's heart grew easy. The electric lights in the cabin grew more brilliant, and there came a desire to eat, drink, smoke, move. . . . Ten minutes later the family from San Francisco found themselves in a large ferry-boat; fifteen minutes later they trod the stones of the quay, and then seated themselves in a small lighted car, which, with a buzz, started to ascend the slope, while vineyard stakes, half-ruined stone fences, and wet, crooked lemon-trees, in spots shielded by straw sheds, with their glimmering orange-colored fruit and thick glossy foliage, were sliding down past the open car windows. . . . After rain, the earth smells sweetly in Italy, and each of her islands has a fragrance of its own.

The Island of Capri was dark and damp on that evening. But for a while it grew animated and let up, in spots, as always in the hour of the steamer's arrival. On the top of the hill, at the station of the *funiculaire,* there stood already the crowd of those whose duty it was to receive properly the Gentleman from San Francisco. The rest of the tourists hardly deserved any attention. There were a few Russians, who had settled on Capri, untidy, absentminded people, absorbed in their bookish thoughts, spectacled, bearded, with the collars of their cloth overcoats raised. There was also a company of long-legged, long-necked, round-headed German youths in Tyrolean costume, and with linen bags on their backs, who need no one's services, are everywhere at home, and are by no means liberal in their expenses. The Gentleman from San Francisco, who kept quietly aloof from both the Russians and the Germans, was noticed at once. He and his ladies were hurriedly helped from the car, a man ran before them to show them the way, and they were again surrounded by boys and those thickset Caprean peasant women, who carry on their heads the trunks and valises of wealthy travelers. Their tiny, wooden, foot-stools rapped against the pavement of the small square, which looked almost like an opera square, and over which an electric lantern swung in the damp wind; the gang of urchins whistled like birds and turned somersaults, and as the Gentleman from San Francisco passed among them, it all looked like a stage scene; he went first under some kind of medieval archway, beneath houses huddled close together, and then along a steep echoing lane which led to the hotel entrance, flooded with light. At the left, a palm tree raised its tuft above the flat roofs, and higher up, blue stars burned in the black sky. And again things looked as though it was in honor of the guests from San Francisco that the stony damp little town had awakened on its rocky island in the Mediterranean, that it was they who had made the owner of the hotel so happy and beaming, and that the Chinese gong, which had sounded the call to dinner through all the floors as soon as they entered the lobby, had been waiting only for them.

The owner, an elegant young man, who met the guests with a polite and exquisite bow, for a moment startled the Gentleman from San Francisco. Having caught sight of him, the Gentleman from San Francisco suddenly recollected that on the previous night, among other confused images which disturbed his sleep, he had seen this very man. His vision resembled the hotel keeper to a dot, had the same head, the same hair, shining and scrupulously combed, and wore the same frock-coat with rounded skirts. Amazed, he almost stopped for a while. But as there was not a mustard-seed of

what is called mysticism in his heart, his surprise subsided at once; in passing the corridor of the hotel he jestingly told his wife and daughter about this strange coincidence of dream and reality. His daughter alone glanced at him with alarm, longing suddenly compressed her heart, and such a strong feeling of solitude on this strange, dark island seized her that she almost began to cry. But, as usual, she said nothing about her feeling to her father.

A person of high dignity, Rex XVII, who had spent three entire weeks on Capri, had just left the island, and the guests from San Francisco were given the apartments he had occupied. At their disposal was put the most handsome and skillful chambermaid, a Belgian, with a figure rendered slim and firm by her corset, and with a starched cap, shaped like a small, indented crown; and they had the privilege of being served by the most well-appearing and portly footman, a black, fiery-eyed Sicilian, and by the quickest waiter, the small, stout Luigi, who was a fiend at cracking jokes and had changed many places in his life. Then the maître-d'hôtel, a Frenchman, gently rapped at the door of the American gentleman's room. He came to ask whether the gentleman and the ladies would dine, and in case they would, which he did not doubt, to report that there was to be had that day lobsters, roast beef, asparagus, pheasants, etc., etc.

The floor was still rocking under the Gentleman from San Francisco—so seasick had the wretched Italian steamer made him—yet, he slowly, though awkwardly, shut the window which had banged when the maître-d'hôtel entered, and which let in the smell of the distant kitchen and wet flowers in the garden, and answered with slow distinctiveness, that they would dine, that their table must be placed farther away from the door, in the depth of the hall, that they would have local wine and champagne, moderately dry and but slightly cooled. The maître-d'hôtel approved the words of the guest in various intonations, which all meant, however, only one thing; there is and can be no doubt that the desires of the Gentleman from San Francisco are right, and that everything would be carried out, in exact conformity with his words. At last he inclined his head and asked delicately:

"Is that all, sir?"

And having received in reply a slow "Yes," he added that today they were going to have the tarantella danced in the vestibule by Carmella and Giuseppe, known to all Italy and to "the entire world of tourists."

"I saw her on post-card pictures," said the Gentleman from San Francisco in a tone of voice which expressed nothing. "And this Giuseppe, is he her husband?"

"Her cousin, sir," answered the maître-d'hôtel.

The Gentleman from San Francisco tarried a little, evidently musing on something, but said nothing, then dismissed him with a nod of his head.

Then he started making preparations, as though for a wedding: he turned on all the electric lamps, and filled the mirrors with reflections of light and the sheen of furniture, and opened trunks; he began to shave and to wash himself, and the sound of his bell was heard every minute in the corridor, crossing with other impatient calls which came from the rooms of his wife and daughter. Luigi, in his red apron, with the ease characteristic of stout people, made funny faces at the chambermaids, who were dashing by with tile buckets in their hands, making them laugh until the tears came. He rolled head over heels to the door, and, tapping with his knuckles, asked with feigned timidity and with an obsequiousness which he knew how to render idiotic:

"Ha sonata, Signore?" (Did you ring, sir?)

And from behind the door a slow, grating, insultingly polite voice, answered:

"Yes, come in."

What did the Gentleman from San Francisco think and feel on that evening forever memorable to him? It must be said frankly; absolutely nothing exceptional. The trouble is that everything on this earth appears too simple. Even had he felt anything deep in his heart, a premonition that something was going to happen, he would have imagined that it was not going to happen so soon, at least not at once. Besides, as is usually the case just after sea-sickness is over, he was very hungry, and he anticipated with real delight the first spoonful of soup, and the first gulp of wine; therefore, he was performing the habitual process of dressing, in a state of excitement which left no time for reflection.

Having shaved and washed himself, and dexterously put in place a few false teeth, he then, standing before the mirror, moistened and vigorously plastered what was left of his thick pearly-colored hair, close to his tawny-yellow skull. Then he put on, with some effort, a tight-fitting undershirt of cream-colored silk, fitted tight to his strong, aged body with its waist swelling out because of an abundant diet; and he pulled black silk socks and patent-leather dancing shoes on his dry feet with their fallen arches. Squatting down, he set right his black trousers, drawn high by means of silk suspenders, adjusted his snow-white shirt with its bulging front, put the buttons into the shining cuffs, and began the painful process of hunting up the front button under the hard collar. The floor was still swaying under him, the tips of his fingers hurt terribly, the button at times painfully pinched the flabby skin in the depression under his Adam's apple, but he persevered, and finally, with his eyes shining from the effort, his face blue because of the narrow collar which squeezed his neck, he triumphed over the difficulties—and all exhausted, he sat down before the pier-glass, his reflected image repeating itself in all the mirrors.

"It's terrible!" he muttered, lowering his strong, bald head and making no effort to understand what was terrible; then, with a careful and habitual gesture, he examined his short fingers with gouty callosities in the joints, and their large, convex, almond-colored nails, and repeated with conviction, "It's terrible!"

But here the stentorian voice of the second gong sounded throughout the house, as in a heathen temple. And having risen hurriedly, the Gentleman from San Francisco drew his tie more taut and firm around his collar, and pulled together his abdomen by means of a tight waistcoat, put on a dinner-coat, set to rights the cuffs, and for the last time he examined himself in the mirror. . . . This Carmella, tawny as a mulatto, with fiery eyes, in a dazzling dress in which orange-color predominated, must be an extraordinary dancer,—it occurred to him. And cheerfully leaving his room, he walked on the carpet, to his wife's chamber, and asked in a loud tone of voice if they would be long.

"In five minutes, papa!" answered cheerfully and gaily a girlish voice. "I am combing my hair."

"Very well," said the Gentleman from San Francisco.

And thinking of her wonderful hair, streaming on her shoulders, he slowly walked down along corridors and staircases, spread with red velvet carpets,—looking for the library. The servants he met hugged the walls, and he walked by as if not noticing them. An old lady, late for dinner, already bowed with years, with milk-white hair, yet bare-necked, in a light-gray silk dress, hurried at top speed, but she walked in a mincing, funny, hen-like manner, and he easily overtook her. At the glass door of the dining hall where the guests had already gathered and started eating, he stopped before the table crowded with boxes of matches and Egyptian cigarettes, took a great Manilla cigar, and threw three liras on the table. On the winter veranda he glanced into the open window; a stream of soft air came to him from the darkness, the top of the old palm loomed up before him afar-off, with its boughs spread among the stars and looking gigantic, and the distant even noise of the sea reached his ear. In the library-room, snug, quiet, a German in round silver-bowed glasses and with crazy, wondering eyes—stood turning the rustling pages of a newspaper. Having coldly eyed him, the Gentleman from San Francisco seated himself in a deep leather arm-chair near a lamp under a green hood, put on his pince-nez and twitching his head because of the collar which choked him, hid himself from view behind a newspaper. He glanced at a few headlines, read a few lines about the interminable Balkan war, and turned over the page with an habitual gesture. Suddenly, the lines bulged out, the pince-nez fell from his nose. . . . He dashed forward, wanted to swallow air—and made a wild, rattling noise; his lower jaw dropped, dropped on his shoulder and began to shake, the shirt-front bulged out,—and the whole body, writhing, the heels catching in the carpet, slowly fell to the floor in a desperate struggle with an invisible foe. . . .

Had not the German been in the library, this frightful accident would have been quickly and adroitly hushed up. The body of the Gentleman from San Francisco would have been rushed away to some far corner—and none of the guests would have known of the occurrence. But the German dashed out of the library with outcries and spread the alarm all over the house. And many rose from their meal, upsetting chairs, others growing pale, ran along the corridors to the library, and the question, asked in many languages, was heard: "What is it? What has happened?" And no one was able to answer it clearly, no one understood anything, for until this very day men still wonder most at death and most absolutely refuse to believe in it. The owner rushed from one guest to another, trying to keep back those who were running and soothe them with hasty assurances, that this was nothing, a mere trifle, a little fainting-spell by which a Gentleman from San Francisco, had been overcome. But no one listened to him, many saw how the footman and waiters tore from the gentleman his tie, collar, waistcoat, the rumpled evening coat, and even—for no visible reason—the dancing shoes from his black silk-covered feet. And he kept on writhing. He obstinately struggled with death, he did not want to yield to the foe that attacked him so unexpectedly and grossly. He shook his head, emitted rattling sounds like one throttled, and turned up his eye-balls like one drunk with wine. When he was hastily brought into Number Forty-three,—the smallest, worst, dampest, and coldest room at the end of the lower corridor,—and stretched on the bed,—his daughter came running, her hair falling over her shoulders, the skirts of her dressing-gown thrown open, with bare breasts raised by the corset. Then came his wife, big, heavy, almost completely dressed for dinner, her mouth round with terror.

In a quarter of an hour all was again in good trim at the hotel. But the evening was irreparably spoiled. Some tourists returned to the dining-hall and finished their dinner, but they kept silent, and it was obvious that they took the accident as a personal insult, while the owner went from one guest to another, shrugging his shoulders in impotent and appropriate irritation, feeling like one innocently victimized, assuring everyone that he understood perfectly well "how disagreeable this is," and giving his word that he would take all "the measures that are within his power" to do away with the trouble. Yet it was found necessary to cancel the tarantella. The unnecessary electric lamps were put out, most of the guests left for the beer-hall, and it grew so quiet in the hotel that one could distinctly hear the tick-tock of the clock in the lobby, where a lonely parrot babbled something in its expressionless manner, stirring in its cage, and trying to fall asleep with its paw clutching the upper perch in a most absurd manner. The Gentleman from San Francisco lay stretched in a cheap iron bed, under coarse woolen blankets, dimly lighted by a single gas-burner fastened in the ceiling. An ice-bag slid down on his wet, cold forehead. His blue, already lifeless face grew gradually cold; the hoarse, rattling noise which came from his mouth, lighted by the glimmer of the golden fillings, gradually weakened. It was not the Gentleman from San Francisco that was emitting those weird sounds; he was no more,—someone else did it. His wife and daughter, the doctor, the servants were standing and watching him apathetically. Suddenly, that which they expected and feared happened. The rattling sound ceased. And slowly, slowly, in everybody's sight a pallor stole over the face of the dead man, and his features began to grow thinner and more luminous, beautiful with the beauty that he had long shunned and that became him well. . . .

The proprietor entered. "Gia e morto," whispered the doctor to him. The proprietor shrugged his shoulders indifferently. The older lady, with tears slowly running down her cheeks, approached him and said timidly that now the deceased must be taken to his room.

"O no, madam," answered the proprietor politely, but without any amiability and not in English, but in French. He was no longer interested in the trifle which the guests from San Francisco could now leave at his cash-office. "This is absolutely impossible," he said, and added in the form of an explanation that he valued this apartment highly, and if he satisfied her desire, this would become known over Capri and the tourists would begin to avoid it.

The girl, who had looked at him strangely, sat down, and with her handkerchief to her mouth, began to cry. Her mother's tears dried up at once, and her face flared up. She raised her tone, began to demand, using her own language and still unable to realize that the respect for her was absolutely gone. The proprietor, with polite dignity, cut her short: "If madam does not like the ways of this hotel, he dare not detain her." And he firmly announced that the corpse must leave the hotel that very day, at dawn, that the police had been informed, that an agent would call immediately and attend to all the necessary formalities. . . . "Is it possible to get on Capri at least a plain coffin?" madam asks. . . . Unfortunately not; by no means, and as for making one, there will be no time. It will be necessary to arrange things some other way. . . . For instance, he gets English soda-water in big, oblong boxes. . . . The partitions could be taken out from such a box. . . .

By night, the whole hotel was asleep. A waiter opened the window in Number 43—it faced a corner of the garden where a consumptive banana-tree grew in the shadow of a high stone wall set with broken glass on the top—turned out the electric light, locked the door, and went away. The deceased remained alone in the darkness. Blue stars looked down at him from the black sky, the cricket in the wall started his melancholy, care-free song. In the dimly lighted corridor two chambermaids were sitting on the windowsill, mending something. Then Luigi came in, in slippered feet, with a heap of clothes on his arm.

"Pronto?"—he asked in a stage whisper, as if greatly concerned, directing his eyes toward the terrible door, at the end of the corridor. And waving his free hand in that direction, "Partenza!" he cried out in a whisper, as if seeing off a train,—and the chambermaids, choking with noiseless laughter, put their heads on each other's shoulders.

Then, stepping softly, he ran to the door, slightly rapped at it, and inclining his ear, asked most obsequiously in a subdued tone of voice:

"Ha sonata, Signore?"

And, squeezing his throat and thrusting his lower jaw forward, he answered himself in a drawling, grating, sad voice, as if from behind the door:

"Yes, come in. . . ."

At dawn, when the window panes in Number Forty-three grew white, and a damp wind rustled in the leaves of the banana-tree, when the pale-blue morning sky rose and stretched over Capri, and the sun, rising from behind the distant mountains of Italy, touched into gold the pure, clearly outlined summit of Monte Solaro, when the masons, who mended the paths for the tourists on the island, went out to their work—an oblong box was brought to room number forty-three. Soon it grew very heavy and painfully pressed against the knees of the assistant doorman who was conveying it in a one-horse carriage along the white highroad which winded on the slopes, among stone fences and vineyards, all the way down to the seacoast. The driver, a sickly man, with red eyes, in an old short-sleeved coat and in worn-out shoes, had a drunken headache; all night long he had played dice at the eatinghouse—and he kept on flogging his vigorous little horse. According to Sicilian custom, the animal was heavily burdened with decorations: all sorts of bells tinkled on the bridle, which was ornamented with colored woolen fringes; there were bells also on the edge of the high saddle; and a bird's feather, two feet long, stuck in the trimmed crest of the horse, nodded up and down. The driver kept silence: he was depressed by his wrongheadedness and vices, by the fact that last night he had lost in gambling all the copper coins with which his pockets had been full,— neither more nor less than four liras and forty centesimi. But on such a morning, when the air is so fresh, and the sea stretches nearby, and the sky is serene with a morning serenity,—a headache passes rapidly and one becomes carefree again. Besides, the driver was also somewhat cheered by the unexpected earnings which the Gentleman from San Francisco, who bumped his dead head against the walls of the box behind his back, had brought him. The little steamer, shaped like a great bug, which lay far down, on the tender and brilliant blue filling to the brim the Neapolitan bay, was blowing the signal of departure,—and the sounds swiftly resounded all over Capri. Every bend of the island, every ridge and stone was seen as distinctly as if there were no air between heaven and earth. Near the quay the driver was overtaken by the head doorman who conducted in an auto the wife and daughter of the Gentleman from San Francisco. Their faces were pale and their eyes sunken with tears and a sleepless night. And in ten minutes the little steamer was again stirring up the water and picking its way toward Sorrento and Castellamare, carrying the American family away from Capri forever. . . . Meanwhile, peace and rest were restored on the island.

Two thousand years ago there had lived on that island a man who became utterly entangled in his own brutal and filthy actions. For some unknown reason he usurped the rule over millions of men and found himself bewildered by the absurdity of this power, while the fear that someone might kill him unawares, made him commit deeds inhuman beyond all measure. And mankind has forever retained his memory, and those who, taken together, now rule the world, as incomprehensibly and, essentially, as cruelly as he did,—come from all the corners of the earth to look at the remnants of the stone house he inhabited, which stands on one of the steepest cliffs of the island. On that wonderful morning the tourists, who had come to Capri for precisely that purpose, were still asleep in the various hotels, but tiny long-eared asses under red saddles were already being led to the hotel entrances. Americans and Germans, men and women, old and young, after having arisen and breakfasted heartily, were to scramble on them, and the old beggar-women of Capri, with sticks in their sinewy hands, were again to run after them along stony, mountainous paths, all the way up to the summit of Monte Tiberia. The dead old man from San Francisco, who had planned to keep the tourists company but who had, instead, only scared them by reminding them of death, was already shipped to Naples, and soothed by this, the travelers slept soundly, and silence reigned over the island. The stores in the little town were still closed, with the exception of the fish and greens market on the tiny square. Among the plain people who filled it, going about their business, stood idly by, as usual, Lorenzo, a tall old boatman, a carefree reveler and once a handsome man, famous all over Italy, who had many times served as a model for painters. He had brought and already sold— for a song—two big sea-crawfish, which he had caught at night and which were rustling in the apron of Don Cataldo, the cook of the hotel where the family from San Francisco had been lodged,—and now Lorenzo could stand calmly until nightfall, wearing princely airs, showing off his rags, his clay pipe with its long reed mouth-piece, and his red woolen cap, tilted on one ear. Meanwhile, among the precipices of Monte Solare, down the ancient Phoenician road, cut in the rocks in the form of a gigantic staircase, two Abruzzi mountaineers were coming from Anacapri. One carried under his leather mantle a bagpipe, a large goat's skin with two pipes; the other, something in the nature of a wooden flute. They walked, and the entire country, joyous, beautiful, sunny, stretched below them; the rocky shoulders of the island, which lay at their feet, the fabulous blue in which it swam, the shining morning vapors over the sea westward, beneath the dazzling sun, and the wavering masses of Italy's mountains, both near and distant, whose beauty human word is powerless to render. . . . Midway they slowed up. Overshadowing the road stood, in a grotto of the rock wall of Monte Solare, the Holy Virgin, all radiant, bathed in the warmth and the splendor of the sun. The rust of her snow-white plaster-of-Paris vestures and queenly crown was touched into gold, and there were meekness and mercy in her eyes raised toward the heavens, toward the eternal and beatific abode of her thrice-blessed Son. They bared their heads, applied the pipes to their lips, and praises flowed on, candid and humbly-joyous, praises to the sun and the morning, to Her, the Immaculate Intercessor for all who suffer in this evil and beautiful world, and to Him who had been born of her womb in the cavern of Bethlehem, in a hut of lowly shepherds in distant Judea.

As for the body of the dead Gentleman from San Francisco, it was on its way home, to the shores of the New World, where a grave awaited it. Having undergone many humiliations and suffered much human neglect, having wandered about a week from one port warehouse to another, it finally got on that same famous ship which had brought the family, such a short while ago and with such a pomp, to the Old World. But now he was concealed from the living: in a tar-coated coffin he was lowered deep into the black hold of the steamer. And again did the ship set out on its far sea journey. At night it sailed by the island of Capri, and, for those who watched it from the island, its lights slowly disappearing in the dark sea, it seemed infinitely sad. But there, on the vast steamer, in its lighted halls shining with brilliance and marble, a noisy dancing party was going on, as usual.

On the second and the third night there was again a ball—this time in mid-ocean, during the furious storm sweeping over the ocean, which roared like a funeral mass and rolled up mountainous seas fringed with mourning silvery foam. The Devil, who from the rocks of Gibraltar, the stony gateway of two worlds, watched the ship vanish into night and storm, could hardly distinguish from behind the snow the innumerable fiery eyes of the ship. The Devil was as huge as a cliff, but the ship was even bigger, a many-storied, many-stacked giant, created by the arrogance of the New Man with the old heart. The blizzard battered the ship's rigging and its broad-necked stacks, whitened with snow, but it remained firm, majestic—and terrible. On its uppermost deck, amidst a snowy whirlwind there loomed up in loneliness the cozy, dimly lighted cabin, where, only half awake, the vessel's ponderous pilot reigned over its entire mass, bearing the semblance of a pagan idol. He heard the wailing moans and the furious screeching of the siren, choked by the storm, but the nearness of that which was behind the wall and which in the last account was incomprehensible to him, removed his fears. He was reassured by the thought of the large, armored cabin, which now and then was filled with mysterious rumbling sounds and with the dry creaking of blue fires, flaring up and exploding around a man with a metallic headpiece, who was eagerly catching the indistinct voices of the vessels that hailed him, hundreds of miles away. At the very bottom, in the under-water womb of the "Atlantis," the huge masses of tanks and various other machines, their steel parts shining dully, wheezed with steam and oozed hot water and oil; here was the gigantic kitchen, heated by hellish furnaces, where the motion of the vessel was being generated; here seethed those forces terrible in their concentration which were transmitted to the keel of the vessel, and into that endless round tunnel, which was lighted by electricity, and looked like a gigantic cannon barrel, where slowly, with a punctuality and certainty that crushes the human soul, a colossal shaft was revolving in its oily nest, like a living monster stretching in its lair. As for the middle part of the "Atlantis," its warm, luxurious cabins, dining-rooms, and halls, they radiated light and joy, were astir with a chattering smartly-dressed crowd, were filled with the fragrance of fresh flowers, and resounded with a string orchestra. And again did the slender supple pair of hired lovers painfully turn and twist and at times clash convulsively amid the splendor of lights, silks, diamonds, and bare feminine shoulders: she—a sinfully modest pretty girl, with lowered eyelashes and an innocent hair-dressing, he—a tall, young man, with black hair, looking as if it were pasted, pale with powder, in most exquisite patent-leather shoes, in a narrow, long-skirted dresscoat,—a beautiful man resembling a leech. And no one knew that this couple had long since been weary of torturing themselves with a feigned beatific torture under the sounds of shamefully-melancholy music; nor did any one know what lay deep, deep, beneath them, on the very bottom of the hold, in the neighborhood of the gloomy and sultry maw of the ship, that heavily struggled with the ocean, the darkness, and the storm. . . .

THE ELAGHIN AFFAIR

By IVAN BUNIN

Translated by Bernard Guilbert Guerney

A horrible affair, this—strange, enigmatic, unsolvable. On the one hand it is very simple; but, on the other, very intricate, resembling a dime novel—which was precisely what everybody in our town called it—and, at the same time, it might be utilized in the creation of a profound and artistic work of literature. On the whole the counsel for the defense spoke justly at the trial:

"In this case," said he at the opening of his speech, "there seems to be no room for disagreement between the prosecuting attorney and myself. Why, the defendant has himself pleaded guilty, while both his crime and his personality, as well as the personality of his victim—whose will he may seem to have violated, as it were—must appear to well-nigh all those present in this court-room unworthy of any special philosophizing, because of their apparently sufficient inanity and drabness. But all this is not at all so; all this is so only in appearance; there is plenty to disagree over—the grounds for dispute and deliberations are very numerous. . . ."

And further on he said:

"Let us suppose that my aim is to attain leniency, at least, for the accused. Were this the case I would have but little to say. No lawmaker has indicated by what, precisely, judges must be guided in cases such as ours; a great latitude has been left for the exercise of their understanding, conscience, and insight—which, in the upshot, are precisely the determining factors in deciding upon this or that framing of the law which fittingly punishes the act. And so my endeavor then would be to influence that understanding, that conscience; my endeavor would be to place in the very foreground all that is best in the accused, and all that mitigates his guilt. I would strive to awaken kindly emotions in the judges, and would do so all the more insistently inasmuch as the defendant denies but one element in his guilt—that of malice pretense.

"However, even if it were a case of such pleading, could I possibly avoid a dispute with the prosecutor, who has classified the prisoner at the bar as nothing more or less than a 'criminal lycanthrope'? In every trial it is possible to regard everything in different ways—everything may be shown in this light or that, or represented just as one wishes, in one way or another. And what do we see in this case of ours? Why, this—that there seems to be not a single trait, not a single detail in it, which the prosecution and I could regard alike, which we could be in agreement upon when it comes to telling about it or throwing light upon it! Every minute I am forced to say to the opposing counsel: 'Everything is so—and yet it isn't so!' But that is just the most important thing: at its very core everything 'isn't so' about this case! . . ."

Here is how this affair began:

It was the 19th of June of last year. The morning was young—between the hours of five and six—but it was already light in the dining-room of Likharev, captain of the Life Guards Hussar regiment; it was also stuffy, dry, and hot from the summer sun over the city. However, things were still quiet—all the more so since the captain's quarters were in one of the buildings of the Hussar barracks, located outside the city. And, making the most of this quiet, as well as of his youth, the captain was sleeping soundly. The table was cluttered with bottles of liqueurs and half-finished cups of coffee. Another officer, Count Koshitz, the staff captain, was sleeping in the adjoining room, the parlor; while still farther off, in the study, slumbered Cornet Sevski. The morning, in a word, was quite a usual one, and the scene simply set; but, as is generally the case when in the middle of what is usual there happens something unusual, that which happened so suddenly in the quarters of Captain Likharev during the early morning of the 19th of June was all the more horrible, amazing, and somehow seemingly more improbable. Unexpectedly, amid the complete stillness of the morning, the bell jangled in the entry; then came the cautious, light, barefoot patter of the orderly running to open the door; after which an intentionally raised voice rang out:

"Is the captain at home?"

And it was with a noisiness just as intentional that the visitor entered, flinging open the door into the dining-room with particular familiarity, clattering with his boots and clinking his spurs with particular audacity. The captain lifted a bewildered and sleep-laden face. Standing before him was one of his messmates, Cornet Elaghin—a diminutive, puny, carroty, and freckled fellow, bandy-legged and unusually spindly-shanked, booted with that dandyism which, as he was fond of saying, was his "chief" weakness. He quickly shed his summer uniform top-coat and, having chucked it on a chair, said loudly: "There y'are—here are my shoulder-straps!" And after that he made his way to the divan placed against the opposite wall, slumped upon it on the flat of his back, and flung his hands behind his head.

"Hold on, hold on!" muttered the captain, following him with goggling eyes. "Where are you coming from—and what's the matter with you?"

"I've killed Manya," said Elaghin.

"Are you drunk? What Manya?" asked the captain.

"Maria Sosnovskaya, the actress."

The captain let his feet drop to the floor.

"Come, now, what are you up to—are you fooling?"

"Alas, not at all, to my regret—or, perhaps, to my good fortune."

"Who's there? What's up?" the count called out from the drawing-room.

Elaghin stretched himself and, with a light kick, threw the door leading into the drawing-room ajar.

"Stop yelling," said he. "It's I, Elaghin. I've shot Manya."

"What's that?" asked the count—and, after an instant's silence, burst into sudden laughter. "Oho, so that's it!" he shouted gaily. "Well, what the devil—it won't count against you this once! It's a good thing you woke us up, or else we'd surely have overslept. We were cutting up again yesterday until three in the morning."

"I give you my word I killed her," Elaghin repeated insistently.

"You're lying, fellow, you're lying,"

the host began shouting as he reached for his socks. "Why, you had me all scared, thinking something had really happened. . . . Ephraim, serve the tea!"

Elaghin reached down into a trouser-pocket, pulled out a small key, and, having deftly tossed it over his shoulder onto the table, said:

"There, go and have a look for yourselves."

During the trial the procureur had a great deal to say about the cynicism and horror of certain incidents comprising the Elaghin drama, and more than once did he stress the above incident as well. He forgot that on this morning it was only during the first minute that Captain Likharev had failed to notice Elaghin's "supernatural" pallor, as he expressed it, and that "not human" something in his eyes; but after that the captain was "simply overwhelmed by both the one and the other. . . ."

II

And so this is what took place on the morning of the 19th of June of last year:

Half an hour later Count Koshitz and Cornet Sevski were already standing at the entrance of the house where Sosnovskaya had lived. Now they were no longer in a mood for jesting.

They had all but made their cabby founder his horse; they had leaped headlong from their light carriage, had thrust the key into the keyhole repeatedly, and had rung the bell desperately—but the key did not fit, and all was silence on the other side of the door. Losing patience, they hastened into the courtyard and started a search for the caretaker. The caretaker hurried into the kitchen through the back entrance and, upon his return, reported that, according to what the maid had said, Sosnovskaya had not passed the night at home—she had gone

away early in the evening, taking some sort of parcel along with her.

The two officers were taken aback—what was to be done in such a case? After due deliberation and shrugging of shoulders they got back into their carriage and went off to the police station, taking the caretaker with them. From there they rang up Captain Likharev.

The captain yelled furiously into the transmitter:

"This damned fool—he's got me almost bawling like a baby over him—forgot to say that you shouldn't have gone to her rooms at all, but to their so-and-so secret love-nest—" and he gave the address. "Did you get that?" —and he repeated it. "Something in the nature of a Parisian *garçonnière* or bachelor apartment, with the entrance directly from the street."

They galloped off to the new address.

The caretaker sat with the driver; the police sergeant, with restrained independence, took a seat in the carriage, opposite the officers. It was hot; the streets were crowded and noisy, and it was hard to believe that on such a sunny and lively morning someone could be lying dead somewhere, and the mind was nonplussed at the thought that that someone had been done to death by the twenty-two-year-old Alec Elaghin. How could he ever have found the heart to do it? What had he killed her for? Why, and how, had he killed her? It was impossible to understand anything; the questions remained without any answer.

When they finally stopped in front of an old and uninviting two-storey house on a street in the old quarter of the town, the two officers "fell in spirits altogether," to use their words. Could it be possible that *this* was here, and could it be possible that *this* had to be seen—even though they were drawn to see it, and drawn irresistibly? The police sergeant, on the other hand, immediately felt himself stern, alert, and self-assured.

"The key, if you please," said he crisply and firmly, and the officers hastened to surrender the key to him with the same timidity that the caretaker would have evinced.

In the central arch of the house were iron gates; beyond the gates could be glimpsed a small patio with a sapling, the verdure of which was somehow preternaturally vivid—or seemed so against the dark-gray stone walls. And to the right of the gates was that same mysterious door, issuing directly on the street, which they had to open. And now the police sergeant, assuming a frown, thrust in the key, and the door opened—and Count Koshitz and Cornet Sevski beheld something that looked like an utterly dark corridor. The police officer, having guessed, as though by scent, where he had to seek for the switch, stretched out his hand, scraped it over the wall, and lit up a dark and somber place, in the dark recesses of which, between two armchairs, stood a small table bearing plates that held remnants of game and fruit.

Yet still more somber was that which met their eyes when they penetrated farther. On the right side of the corridor there proved to be a small entrance into an adjoining room, likewise utterly dark. It was sepulchrally illumined by a small lantern of opalescent glass, hanging close to the ceiling, under black silk draped like an enormous parasol. Some black fabric also draped, from floor to ceiling, the walls of this room—a room devoid of even a single window and, save for the door, without any outlet.

Here, also in the farther recess of the room, stood a large, low Turkish divan —and lying upon it, whitely gleaming, clad only in a night-gown, with eyes and lips half-open, with head drooping on her bosom, with her extremities stretched out and her feet slightly apart, was a very young woman of rare beauty.

III

The beauty of the deceased was rare in that it satisfied to a rare degree those exacting demands which fashionable painters, for example, set themselves when portraying comely women. Here was everything requisite—a superb form, a superb body-tone, a foot tiny and without a single blemish, a childlike, simple-hearted charm about the lips, small and regular features, marvelous hair. And all this was by now dead; all had begun to petrify, to fade, and her beauty made the dead woman still more awesome. Her hair was in perfect order—her coiffure would have graced any ball. Her head was lying on a slightly raised cushion of the divan, while her chin rested lightly on her bosom, which position bestowed upon her fixed, half-open eyes and her entire face an apparently somewhat puzzled expression. And all this was strangely illumined by a small opalescent lantern hanging near the ceiling, at the bottom of an enormous, parasol-shaped black drapery, resembling some bird of prey that had spread its webbed wings over the dead woman.

On the whole the scene overwhelmed even the police sergeant. Next, hesitatingly, they all began a closer inspection.

The superb bare arms of the dead woman were extended straight along her body. Upon her breast, on the lace of her night-gown, were lying two visiting-cards of Elaghin's, while at her feet lay a Hussar saber, looking exceedingly crude by the side of their feminine nakedness. The count was about to pick it up in order to take it out of the scabbard, laboring under the absurd notion that there might be traces of blood on the blade. The police sergeant held him back from committing any such unlawful act.

"Ah, of course, of course," the count mumbled in a whisper. "One must not handle anything yet, of course. I'm struck by the fact that I don't see any blood anywhere, or, in general, any traces of a crime. . . . A case of poisoning, evidently?"

"Have patience," said the police officer sententiously. "Let's wait for the coroner and the doctor. But, beyond a doubt, it does look like poisoning as much as anything else—"

And, really, things did have that look. There was no blood anywhere—neither on the floor, nor on the divan, nor on the body, nor on the dead woman's nightgown. Thrown over the arm-chair near the divan were a pair of step-ins and a *peignoir;* under these was a tiny chemise —blue, with a pearly sheen—a skirt of excellent dark-gray material, and an opera-cloak of gray silk. All these had been tossed down pell-mell, but they, too, were free from any blood-stain—there was not a single drop. The poison theory was also further confirmed by the things which were found on a wall-ledge above the divan: on this ledge, amid champagne bottles and corks, candle-ends and hairpins, and amid scribbled and torn scraps of paper, stood an unfinished tumbler of porter and a small medicine vial, on the long, white, tongue-like tag of which, staring blackly and ominously, was the inscription: *OP. PULV*.

But just at the moment when the police sergeant, Count Koshitz, and Cornet Sevski were by turns examining this tag, they heard out in the street the noise of the carriage with the doctor and the coroner driving up, and in a few minutes it turned out that Elaghin had been telling the truth: Sosnovskaya had really been killed with a revolver. There were no blood-stains on the night-gown. But then a dark-purple spot was revealed under the gown, in the region of the heart—and, in the center of this spot, a small, round wound with scorched edges; dark, watery blood was oozing out of the wound, but this blood had not stained anything, since the wound had been covered with a handkerchief crumpled into a wad.

What else did the expert post-mortem examination establish? Not a great deal: that the dead woman's right lung showed traces of tuberculosis; that the shot had been fired point-blank, and that death had come instantaneously, even though the late Sosnovskaya had still been able to utter a short phrase after the shot; that there had been no struggle between the slayer and his victim; that she had drunk champagne, and that she had taken a small quantity of opium with porter, but not sufficient to poison her; and, finally, that on this fatal night she had had sexual relations with a man. . . .

But why had this man killed her, and what for? In answering these questions Elaghin stubbornly persisted that it was because both of them—he as well as Sosnovskaya—were in a "tragic situation"; that they could see no other way out of it except death; and that in killing his mistress he had merely carried out her own behest. However, all this seemed to be entirely contradicted by the notes the woman had written just before her death. For had there not been found on her breast two of Elaghin's visiting-cards, closely written in her hand in Polish— and that, it must be said by the way, quite wretchedly spelled? One card was addressed to General Konovitzin, chairman of the Board of Directors of her theater, and ran:

Dear Friend:

I thank you for your noble friendship of several years. . . . I send you my last regards, and beg of you to pay to my mother all the sums due me for my recent appearances. . . .

The other read:

This man has acted justly in killing me. . . . Mother—my poor, unfortunate darling! I am not asking for forgiveness, inasmuch as I am dying not of my own will. . . . Mother! We shall see each other again . . . there, above. . . . I feel that this is the last moment. . . .

On just such other cards did Sosnovskaya write her other ante-mortem notes as well. These were strewn over the wall-ledge, in painstakingly torn pieces. When assembled and pasted together they read as follows:

This man demands my death and his own. . . . I am not fated to come out alive. . . .

And so my last hour has struck. . . . My God, forsake me not!— My last thought I dedicate to my mother—and to my art, which I hold sacred—

An abyss . . . abyss. . . . This man is my fate. . . . My God, save me, succor me. . . .

And, finally, came the most enigmatic one:

Quand même pour toujours—

All these notes—those that were found quite intact on the dead woman's bosom, as well as those that had been found in fragments on the wall-ledge—apparently contradicted Elaghin's assertions. But, to be precise, only *apparently.* Why had not those two cards been torn up which had been lying on Sosnovskaya's breast, and one of which bore such fatal words for Elaghin as: "I am dying not of my own will"? Elaghin had not only not torn them up and carried them off with him, but had even put them in the most conspicuous place himself—for who else but he could have done so? Had he not torn them up in his hurry, perhaps? In his hurry he might, of course, have forgotten to do so. But if he had been in a hurry, how could he have put on the dead woman's bosom notes so fraught with danger for him? And then, in general, had he been at all flustered? No; he had put the dead woman to rights, had, after having first protected the wound with a handkerchief, readjusted her night-gown, and then had been dressing and putting himself in order. . . . No, the prosecuting attorney had been right at this point: all this had not been done in a hurry.

IV

The prosecuting attorney said:
"There are two classes of criminals. First, criminals by accident, whose misdeeds are the fruit of an unfortunate conflux of circumstances and of that exasperation which is scientifically designated as a 'raptus of insanity.' And, secondly, criminals who act as they do through malicious and premeditated intent—these are the congenital enemies of society and of the social order; these are the lycanthropes, the criminal wolves. In which division shall we number the man on the prisoner's bench? In the second, of course. He is, indubitably, a criminal wolf; he has committed his crime because he has become bestialized by his idle and unbridled mode of living. . . ."

This tirade was an unusually strange one (even though it did voice the almost universal opinion in our city concerning the Elaghin case), and all the more strange because all through the trial Elaghin sat with his head leaning on his hand, which also served to screen his face from the public, and answered all questions quietly, abruptly, and with a certain heart-rending timidity and sadness. And yet, at the same time, the prosecuting attorney was also right—the criminal sitting on the prisoner's bench was by no means an ordinary one, and not at all one stricken by a "raptus of insanity."

The prosecuting attorney posed two questions: in the first place, of course, whether the crime had been committed in a state of aberration—that is, of excitement; and, in the second, whether Elaghin's had been merely an involuntary complicity in the slaying? And he answered both questions with complete assurance: "No, and no!"

"No!" he had said in answer to his first question. "There cannot even be any idea of any aberration whatsoever—and that, first and foremost, because no state of mental excitement can continue for several hours at a stretch. Then, too, what could have brought on Elaghin's aberration?"

To settle the last question the prosecutor put a great number of minute questions to himself—and immediately rejected them, or even held them up to ridicule and scorn. Said he:

"Hadn't Elaghin been drinking more than usual, perhaps, on this fatal day? No; he generally drank a great deal—but on this day no more than usual.

"Was the accused a man sound of health, and is he so at present? I join in the opinion of the medical men who have had him under observation: he is quite sound, but utterly unused to curbing himself.

"Wasn't the aberration brought on, perhaps, by the impossibility of his marrying the woman he loved—that is, if it be admitted that he really did love her? No—inasmuch as we know that the accused did not entertain the idea of any such marriage or undertake any steps whatsoever to bring it about."

And he said further:

"Wasn't his aberration brought on, perhaps, by Sosnovskaya's proposed departure for abroad? No, inasmuch as he had long known about such a departure. But, in that case, might not his aberra-

tion have been brought on by the idea of breaking off with Sosnovskaya—a breaking-off consequent upon her departure? Again no—for they had discussed this breaking-off a thousand times prior to this night. And, if that be the case, what did, finally, bring on his madness? Their talks about death? The strange setting of the room—its witch's spell, so to say, its depressiveness, even as, in general, the depressiveness of this entire unwholesome, eerie night? But, as far as talks about death are concerned, surely they could not possibly have been a novelty to Elaghin! Such conversations had been carried on between him and his inamorata incessantly, and, of course, he had become utterly fed up with them ever so long ago. As for the unholy obsession of the room—why, it's mirth-provoking even to speak of it! Surely such a spell was quite modified by objects quite prosaic: by the supper, by the scraps of that supper on the table, by the bottles, and even—if you will pardon me—by the chamberpot. . . . Elaghin ate, drank, answered the calls of nature, went into the other room—now after wine, now after a knife to sharpen a pencil. . . ."

And the prosecuting attorney concluded as follows:

"As for whether the murder committed by Elaghin was a fulfillment of the dead woman's will: really, we do not have to deliberate long over this question. For the determination of that point we can take the uncorroborated assertions of Elaghin that Sosnovskaya herself had begged him to kill her—or we can take Sosnovskaya's own note, so utterly fatal to him: 'I am dying not of my own will. . . .'"

V

A good deal could have been objected to in the details of the prosecutor's speech. "The accused is quite sound.

. . ." But where is one to draw the line between health and ill health? "He undertook no steps whatsoever to bring the marriage about." But then, in the first place, he did not undertake any such steps only because he was thoroughly and firmly convinced of their futility; and, in the second place, are love and marriage so very closely bound together? And would Elaghin have found peace and, in general, a complete and satisfactory denouement for the drama of his love by espousing Sosnovskaya? Really, is it not well known that there is about every strong love, and, in general, about every love that is not altogether humdrum, a peculiar tendency apparently to shun wedlock, somehow?

Yet all these, I repeat, are but details. For basically the prosecuting attorney was right—there had been no aberration.

He said:

"The medical experts have arrived at the conclusion that Elaghin had been 'rather in a calm state' than in an aberrant one; whereas I maintain that his state had been not merely calm, but amazingly calm. We are convinced of this by an inspection of the tidied-up room where the crime had been committed and where Elaghin had still remained for a long time after his crime. Then we have the evidence of the witness Yaroshenko, who had seen with what calmness Elaghin left this apartment and how meticulously, how unhurriedly he turned the key in the street-door. Also, there is Elaghin's behavior at Captain Likharev's. What, for instance, did Elaghin say to Cornet Sevski, who pleaded with him 'to come to his senses,' to recollect if Sosnovskaya had not shot herself? Elaghin had said: 'No, brother—I remember everything *very well'*—and immediately proceeded to describe just how he had fired the shot. The witness Budberg was 'even unpleasantly struck by

Elaghin—after his confession he had drunk tea with utter sang-froid!'

"As for the witness Foht, *he* had been struck still more. 'I hope, sir,' Elaghin had said ironically to Staff-Captain Foht, 'that you will excuse me from drill duty today.'—'This was so frightful,' says Foht, 'that Cornet Sevski could not restrain himself and broke into sobs.' True, there was a moment when Elaghin, too, broke into sobs, this was when the captain had come back from the commander of the regiment, to whom he had gone for instructions concerning Elaghin, and when Elaghin had gathered from the faces of Likharev and Foht that he, Elaghin, was in reality no longer an officer. Only at that very moment did he break into sobs," the prosecuting attorney concluded. "Only at that moment!"

The last phrase is likewise a very strange one. Who does not know how frequently such an awakening from the stupor of misfortune occurs suddenly brought about by something utterly insignificant, something which may meet one's eye by chance and in a moment reminds a man of all his former happy life—and of all the hopelessness, all the horror of his present situation? And yet Elaghin had been reminded of all this not at all by something insignificant, casual. Why, he was an officer born, you might say—ten generations of his ancestors had been in the army. And now he was no longer an officer. And, as if that were not enough, he was one no longer because the woman whom he loved truly more than he did his own life was no longer in this world—and because he, he himself, had done this monstrous deed.

However, these, too, are but details. For the main thing is that there really had been no "raptus of insanity." But, in that case, what had there been? The prosecuting attorney admitted that "in this shady affair everything must first of all resolve itself into a consideration of the characters of Elaghin and Sosnovskaya, and into a clearing up of their relations." And he firmly declared:

"We have here the coming together of two individualities having nothing in common."

Was that really so? It is precisely therein that the whole question consists: Was that really so?

VI

Concerning Elaghin I would say, first of all, that he is two-and-twenty—a fatal age, a dreadful period which determines what a man's whole future is to be. Usually during this period a man is living through what is medically known as puberty, or sexual maturing, and, in terms of life, one's first love, which is almost always looked upon merely poetically and, on the whole, quite frivolously. Frequently this "first love" is accompanied by dramas, by tragedies; but nobody at all ever gives a thought to the fact that it is precisely at this time that men and women are living through something far more profound, more complex, than the agitation and torment which are ordinarily styled the "adoration of a beloved being." They are living, without themselves being aware of it, through·the weird blossoming, the excruciating revelation, the first sacred mass, of sex.

And so, had I been Elaghin's counsel, I should have asked the judges to direct their attention to his age precisely from this point of view, and also to the fact that the man sitting before us was not at all an ordinary one in that respect. "A young Hussar, a locoed wastrel, burning the candle of his life at both ends," the prosecutor was saying, echoing the general opinion. And, in proof of the correctness of his words, he cited the story

of one of the witnesses, the actor Lissovski—of how Elaghin had once arrived at the theater in the daytime, as the cast was gathering for rehearsal; and how Sosnovskaya, upon catching sight of him, had jumped aside and hid behind Lissovski's back and quickly said to him: "Screen me from him, Uncle!"—"Screen her I did," Lissovski told his story, and this Hussar youngster, full to the gills with wine, suddenly stopped short, as if he were locoed. He stands there, with his legs wide apart, and gapes in perplexity —where could Sosnovskaya have gone to?

There you have it, precisely—a locoed fellow. But the only thing is—locoed by what? Come, could it really have been by his "idle and unbridled mode of living"?

Elaghin came from a genteel and well-to-do family. He had been at a very early age deprived of his mother (who, mark you, had been of quite an exultant nature). From his father, a man morose and stern, he was estranged, first of all, by that fear in which he, Elaghin, had both grown and reached maturity. The prosecutor, with a cruel effrontery, depicted not only the moral but also the physical image of Elaghin. And it was he who said:

"Such, gentlemen, was our hero in his picturesque raiment of a Hussar. But look at him now! Now nothing any longer prettifies him; before us is a squat and stoop-shouldered young man with a little moustache like an albino's, and with an extremely indeterminate, vacuous expression on his face. In his skimpy black frock-coat he reminds one but very little of Othello. . . . In other words the accused is, in my opinion, an individual with sharply defined degenerate peculiarities; extremely timorous in certain cases, as, for instance, in his attitude toward his father, and extremely arrogant in others, without taking any obstacles into consideration—that is, when he feels himself free from his father's eye, and, in general, hopes to go unpunished. . . ."

Well, there was a great deal of truth in this blunt characterization. But I, as I listened to it, failed to understand, first of all, how anyone could regard lightly all those frightfully intricate and tragic things which frequently mark persons of sharply defined hereditary taint; and, secondly, I saw in that which was true about the characterization only a very small moiety of truth, after all. Yes, Elaghin had grown up in fear and trembling before his father. But fear and trembling do not constitute cowardice, and this holds particularly true when it is one's parents who inspire the fear and trembling, and, to boot, in a man who is endowed with an intensified sensitiveness of all that heredity which binds him to all his sires, grandsires, and great-grandsires. —Yes, Elaghin's outward appearance is not the classical appearance of a Hussar; but in this as well I see one of the proofs of the extraordinariness of his nature. "Look more closely," I would have said to the prosecutor, "at this carroty, stoop-shouldered, and spindly-shanked fellow, and you will perceive, well-nigh with fear, how far removed from insignificance is this freckled face with its small and greenish eyes, whose gaze avoids yours. And, after that, turn your attention to his stamina—the stamina of a degenerate: on the day of the murder he had been drilling (from early morning, as a matter of course), and at breakfast had drunk six ponies of vodka, a bottle of champagne, two ponies of cognac—and, with all that, had remained almost perfectly sober!"

VII

In great contradistinction to the generally prevalent low opinion concerning Elaghin was the testimony of many of his messmates. All of these gave the finest reports about him. Here, for instance, is the squadron commander's opinion of Elaghin:

"Upon entering the regiment Elaghin had placed himself on a remarkably fine footing with the officers, and, when it came to the rank and file, was always exceedingly kind, considerate, and just. His character, to my way of thinking, had but one marked trait—that of nervousness. This, however, found its expression not in anything disagreeable, but merely in frequent and rapid transitions from gaiety to melancholy, from talkativeness to taciturnity, from self-assurance to utter despondency about his merits, and, in general, about his whole destiny. . . ."

Next we have the opinion of Captain Likharev:

"Elaghin had always been a kind and good comrade, only he had his peculiarities—now he would be modest and shyly secretive, then he would get into a certain devil-may-care mood, a mood of bravado. After coming to me with his confession of murdering Sosnovskaya, and after Sevski and Koshitz had gone off to the old quarter of the town, he had kept on, by turns, now weeping passionately, now laughing sardonically and riotously. And when he was arrested and was being carried off to be locked up, he consulted us, with a wild smile, as to what tailor he ought to order his civilian clothes from. . . ."

Then there is Count Koshitz's opinion:

"Elaghin was, on the whole, a fellow of gay and gentle disposition—nervous, impressionable, even inclined to exaltation. He was especially affected by the drama and by music—the latter often brought him to tears; and, besides, he himself had unusual musical ability. . . ."

All the other witnesses as well voiced almost the same views:

"A fellow exceedingly susceptible to

infatuations, but apparently always expecting something genuine, something out of the ordinary. . . ."—"At our little friendly sprees he was, for the most part, gay, and something of a charming pest: he'd call for more champagne than anybody else, treating all comers to it." —"Having entered into a liaison with Sosnovskaya, and trying his utmost to conceal from everybody his feelings toward her, he became very much changed. He was frequently brooding, sad; he used to say that he was becoming confirmed in his intention of doing away with himself. . . ."

Such are the reports concerning Elaghin, emanating from persons who had lived on terms of the greatest intimacy with him. Whence, then (I reflected as I sat through the trial), had the prosecuting attorney taken such black pigments for his portrait of Elaghin? Or has he some other reports? No, he has not. There remains, therefore, only the supposition that he had been induced to use these black pigments by the generally prevalent notions of the *jeunesse dorée,* and by what he had learned from the only letter of Elaghin's at the disposal of the court, written to a friend of his in Kishenev. In this letter Elaghin spoke with great freedom concerning his life: "I've attained, brother, to some sort of indifference: nothing—nothing!—matters. If things are right today—well, glory be to God for that! As for what the morrow may bring—I should worry! Morning brings counsel, and all that sort of thing. I have got me one fine reputation—that of the first drunkard and ninny throughout the whole town, almost. . . ."

Such a self-appraisal seemed to go hand in hand with the eloquence of the prosecutor, who contended that "for the sake of animal enjoyment Elaghin had placed in the pillory of public judgment the woman who had given him her all,

and had deprived her not only of her life but even of the last honor—that of Christian interment—" But *did* these two appraisals really go hand in hand? The prosecuting attorney had taken from this letter only several lines. For in full it ran as follows:

My dear Sergei:

I've received your letter, and, although I've taken my time about answering it, such a delay couldn't be helped. Probably, when you read my letter, you'll be thinking: "These pothooks look as if they had been made by a fly that had just crawled out of an inkwell!" Oh, well, handwriting is (so they say), if not a mirror of one's character, at least an expression of it, to a certain degree. I'm still the same mooncalf I've always been—or, if you like, even a worse one, since two years of independent life and *a thing or two besides* have left their impress upon me. There is a thing or two, brother, which Solomon the Wise himself could not convey. And for that reason don't be surprised if one fine day you find out that I went root-a-toot and bumped myself off. I've attained, brother, to some sort of indifference: nothing—nothing!—matters. If things are right today—well, glory be to God for that! As for what the morrow may bring—I should worry! Morning brings counsel, and all that sort of thing. I have got me one fine reputation—that of the first drunkard and ninny throughout the whole town, almost. And yet, at the same time (would you believe it?), at times I feel within my soul such strength, and torment, and yearning for everything that is good, that is lofty—in general, a yearning for the Devil alone knows what; all I know is that it creates a nagging ache in one's breast.

You'll say that these are still growing pains. How is it, then, that others of my own age do not feel anything of the sort? I've become fearfully nervous. Sometimes, on a winter night, with a blizzard raging and with a hard frost, I jump out of bed, get on horseback, and go flying through the streets, startling even the police, who have got over being startled by anything. And, mark you, at such times I'm as sober as a judge, and not just getting over a terrific jag. I long to seize some ever-elusive melody which, apparently, I have heard somewhere—and yet it never, never comes! Oh, well, I'll confess it to you: I've fallen in love, and that with a woman who is not in the least—not the very least!—like all the others with which this town swarms.—However, enough of this. Write me, please. You know my address. Remember how you used to put it?—"Cornet Elaghin, Russia—"

It is amazing: how could anybody, after having read merely this letter and nothing else, say that "We have here the coming together of two individualities having nothing in common"?

VIII

Sosnovskaya was a pure-blooded Pole. She was older than Elaghin, being eight-and-twenty. Her father had been an insignificant government clerk who had ended his life by suicide when she was only three. Her mother had long remained a widow and then had married again (again a petty government clerk) and had soon become a widow again. As you see, Sosnovskaya's family was rather mediocre. Whence, then, came all those strange psychic traits by which Sosnovskaya was distinguished, and whence that passion for the stage which, as we know, was so early revealed in her? All this, I think, was not at all due to the upbring-ing she received in her family and in the private boarding-school where she had studied. And, apropos, it must be said that she had studied exceedingly well and, in her spare time, had read a great deal. And, in reading, she had at times jotted down excerpts from the books of thoughts and utterances that were to her liking—of course, as always in such cases, connecting them with herself in one way or another. And, as a general thing, she was forever making certain notations, keeping something in the nature of a diary—if only one may call a diary those scraps of paper which she sometimes did not so much as touch for months on end, and upon which she poured out at haphazard her dreams and her views of life—or else simply used for keeping track of her accounts with her laundress, her dressmaker, and of other things of that sort. But just what was it that she excerpted from her reading?

"Not to be born is the foremost happiness of all; the second is to return into non-existence as quickly as possible." A marvelous thought!

The world is wearisome—deathly wearisome—whereas my soul is striving toward something out of the ordinary. . . .

"Men comprehend only those sufferings from which they die."—De Musset

No, I shan't marry—ever! I vow I never shall, by God and Death. . . .

There is naught but Love and Death. But where, in all Creation, a man whom I could fall in love with? There is none such—there cannot be! Yet how can I die—I who love Life like a woman possessed?

There is naught in Heaven or on Earth more fearful, attractive, and enigmatic than Love. . . .

Mother, for instance, says that I ought to marry for money. I—*I!*—to marry for money! What an unearthly word *Love* is; how much hell and charm there is in it—even though I have never loved!

The whole world regards me with millions of carnivorous eyes: it reminds me of my visits to the menagerie when I was a little girl. . . .

"It is not worth while to be a human being. Nor an angel, for that matter. Even the angels murmured and rose up against God. It is only worth while to be either God or a nonentity."—Krassinski

"Who can boast of having penetrated into her soul, when all the efforts of her life are directed toward concealing the depths of her soul?"—De Musset

Having finished boarding-school, Sosnovskaya had immediately informed her mother of her decision to dedicate herself to art. Her mother, a good Roman Catholic, would not at first, of course, even hear of her daughter's becoming an actress. However, her daughter was not at all the sort to submit to anybody whatsoever and had even before succeeded in instilling into her mother that her life, the life of Maria Sosnovskaya, could not possibly be humdrum and inglorious.

At eighteen she had gone to Lvov and had rapidly realized her dreams: not only had she got on the stage without any difficulties, but in a short while had become prominent on it. In a short time she had attained celebrity both before the public and in the theatrical world—a celebrity so considerable that after her third year on the stage she had received an invitation to play in our city. However, in Lvov, too, she had been jotting down in her little note-book much the same things as before:

"Everybody talks about her, everybody weeps and laughs over her—but who knows her?"—De Musset

Were it not for my mother, I would kill myself. This is my constant longing. . . .

Whenever I chance to go beyond the city, and behold the sky, so splendidly beautiful and so bottomless, I don't know what comes over me. I want to scream, to sing, to declaim, to weep . . . to fall in love and to die. . . .

I shall choose a splendidly beautiful death. I shall rent a little bit of a room and order it draped with some funereal material. There will have to be music playing somewhere on the other side of the wall, and I shall lie down in an unpretentious white gown and surround myself with innumerable flowers —and it will be the scent of these very flowers that shall kill me. Oh, how wonder-inspiring that will be!

And, further on, we have:

They all, all demand my body and not my soul.

Were I rich I would go all around the world and make love all over the terrestrial globe.

"Does man know what he wants? Does he feel certain of that which he thinks?"—Krassinski

And, finally:

The scoundrel!

Who was this scoundrel who, of course, had done that which it is not so very hard to surmise? All that is known is that he had existed—and could not but have existed. "Even at the time she was in Lvov," said the witness Zauhse, a fellow-trouper of Sosnovskaya's in that town, "she would undress rather than dress whenever she had to go on to act, and when she received her friends and admirers at home, she did so in a transparent *peignoir* and with her feet bare. Their beauty threw everybody, but the novices especially, into rapturous amazement, whereupon she used to say: 'Don't you be astonished—they're all my own—' and would show her legs up to above her knees. At the same time she never ceased from reiterating to me (often with tears) that there was nobody deserving of her love, and that her sole hope was in death."

And lo, on the scene had appeared this "scoundrel," with whom she took trips to Constantinople, Venice, Paris, and whom she visited in Cracow and Berlin. This had been some Galician landowner or other, a man exceedingly rich. The witness Volsky, who had known Sosnovskaya from her very childhood, said concerning him (and her):

"I've always considered Sosnovskaya a woman of a very low moral plane. She did not know how to conduct herself as befitted an *artiste* and one who came from our locality. All she liked was money—money and men. It was cynical, the way she sold herself, while still almost a little girl, to that old boar from Galicia."

It was about this very "boar" that Sosnovskaya had told Elaghin in the conversation she had had with him just before her death. Letting a word drop here and there, she complained to him:

"I grew up in loneliness; there was no one to look after me. . . . I was altogether a stranger in my family—and even in the whole world. . . . A certain woman (may all her offspring be accursed!) was making me depraved—pure, trusting little girl that I was. . . . And in Lvov I came to love a certain man, sincerely, like a father, who turned out to be such a scoundrel—such a scoundrel!—that I cannot even recall him without horror. And it was he who

taught me to use hashish, to drink wine; he used to take me to Constantinople, where he had a whole harem. He used to loll in this harem of his, eying his naked odalisques, and compelled me to strip as well—the vile, low-down fellow! . . ."

IX

In our town Sosnovskaya soon became a "byword on all tongues."

"While still in Lvov," testified the witness Meshkov, "she had suggested to many a man that he die for one night with her, and was forever repeating that she was seeking a heart capable of love. She was seeking very persistently for this loving heart, but she herself was constantly saying: 'My chief aim is to live and to make use of life. A vintner must try all wines—and not become intoxicated with any single one. And just so must a woman act with men.' And act accordingly she did," said Meshkov. "I am not at all certain whether she tasted all the wines, but I do know that she surrounded herself with an enormous lot of them. However, it may be that she did this, just as she did everything else, in order to create a hubbub around her, to acquire *claqueurs* for her appearances. 'Money,' she used to say, 'is so much rubbish. I'm greedy, at times miserly, as much so as any woman of the bourgeoisie; but, somehow, I don't give money a thought. The main thing is fame; everything else will come!' And, in my opinion, she was forever harping on death also with this object of making people talk about her. . . ."

The same sort of thing that had taken place in Lvov continued in our town as well. And the notes she wrote were almost of the same tenor as before:

God, what ennui, what anguish! If only an earthquake or an eclipse would come along!

Somehow, one evening, I happened to be in a churchyard. It was so splendid there. It seemed to me . . . but no, I am not able to describe this emotion. I felt like remaining the whole night . . . declaiming over the graves . . . and then dying of exhaustion. On the following day I played better than ever before. . . .

And again:

Yesterday I visited the churchyard at ten in the evening. What a depressing spectacle! The moon poured its beams upon the headstones and crosses. It seemed to me that I was surrounded by the dead in their thousands. Yet I felt so happy, so joyous. Mine was an exceedingly fine mood. . . .

And after she had come to know Elaghin and had heard from him of the death of a corporal in his regiment, she had demanded that Elaghin take her to the chapel where the dead man was lying, and had jotted down that the sight of the dead man and the chapel in the light of the moon had made a "staggeringly rapturous impression" upon her.

The thirst for fame, for being noticed by her fellow mortals, had at this time become simply a frenzy with her. Yes, she *was* exceedingly good-looking. Her beauty was not, on the whole, of an original cast, and yet there was about it some sort of a peculiar, rare, unusual charm, some sort of mixture of simple-heartedness and innocence with feral cunning, and also an admixture of constant play-acting and sincerity. Look at her portraits. Note attentively her gaze, a gaze peculiarly her own, a gaze always somewhat from under her brows, with her rosebud lips constantly open just a wee bit; a gaze pensive, but most frequently of all endearing, enticing, holding forth a promise of something—as if

consenting to something secret, something depraved.

And she knew how to make use of her beauty. On the stage she not only snared her adorers through her especial ability, when actually treading the boards, to make herself blossom forth through all her charms, through the sounds of her voice and the loveliness of her movements, by means of her laughter and her tears, but she also snared them by appearing, most frequently of all, in roles that afforded her an opportunity to exhibit her body. And when at home, she wore seductive Oriental and Greek costumes, in which she would receive her multifarious guests.

One of her rooms she had set aside specially for suicide, as she herself put it. Here one could find not only revolvers and dirks, but also swords, scimitar- and creese-shaped, as well as vials with all sorts of poisons. And she made death her constant and favorite subject of conversation. But that did not suffice: frequently, while conversing about all the numerous and diverse devices for doing away with oneself, she would snatch a loaded revolver off the wall and, cocking the trigger and putting the muzzle up to her temple, would say:

"Kiss me, quick, or I'll shoot this very minute!"

Or else would take a capsule of strychnine in her mouth and announce that unless her visitor fell on his knees instantly and kissed her bare foot she would swallow this capsule. And she did and said all this in such a way that her visitor blanched with fear and took his departure doubly bewitched by her, going forth and spreading throughout the town precisely those universally agitating rumors which she so desired.

"On the whole, she was hardly ever her own self," the witness Zalesski, who had known her very intimately and very long, testified at the trial. "Play-acting, teasing —these formed her constant occupation. She was a great hand at driving a man to frenzy with tender, enigmatic glances, smiles fraught with great meaning, or with the sad sigh of a defenseless child. And that's just the way she behaved with Elaghin. Now she would set him in a blaze—now she would douse him with a bucket of cold water.—Did she want to die? Why, she was as fond of life as any carnivorous animal; she was inordinately afraid of death. There was, in general, a great deal of the joy of life and of gaiety in her make-up. I remember how Elaghin had once sent her the skin of a polar bear. She had a great number of visitors just when it arrived, but she became perfectly oblivious of them that very instant, that's how enraptured she was with this rug. She spread it upon the floor, and, paying no attention to anybody, began to turn somersaults on it, to perform feats which would have aroused the envy of any professional acrobat. . . . She was an enchanting woman!"

However, the same Zalesski told of how she had suffered from fits of despair and ennui. Doctor Seroshevski, who had known her for ten years and had treated her even before her departure for Lvov (she had had incipient consumption), likewise testified that of late she had been suffering excruciatingly from serious nervous derangement, loss of memory, and hallucinations, so that he felt apprehensive about her mental faculties. It was because of this same derangement that she was under the care of another physician, by the name of Schumacher, whom she was constantly assuring that she would not die a natural death and from whom she had once borrowed a couple of volumes of Schopenhauer, "which she had read very attentively, and, most surprising of all, had understood splendidly, as it later turned out." And still another physician, Doctor Niedzelski, gave the following evidence:

"She was a strange woman! Whenever she had guests, she was, for the most part, very jolly, very coquettish; but there were times when she would suddenly lapse into silence for no reason on earth, rolling up her eyes and letting her head sink on the table. . . . Or else she'd begin throwing and smashing tumblers and wineglasses against the floor. . . . On such occasions one always had to request her, as quickly as possible: 'There, keep it up, keep it up!'—and she would immediately desist from this pastime."

And it was this very woman whom Cornet Alexander Elaghin eventually encountered.

X

How had this encounter taken place? How had the intimacy between them been born, and what were their feelings, their attitudes, toward each other? Elaghin himself told about this on two occasions: the first time, briefly and fragmentarily, to the coroner, a few hours after the murder; the second time, at the interrogations which took place three weeks after the first.

"Yes," he had said, "I am guilty of having taken Sosnovskaya's life, *but by her own will*. . . .

"I became acquainted with her a year and a half ago in the box-office of her theater, through Lieutenant Budberg. I came to love her ardently, and thought that she shared my feelings. But it wasn't always that I felt certain of this. At times it even seemed to me that she loved me more than I did her, but at other times things seemed quite otherwise. Besides that, she was constantly surrounded by admirers, and playing the coquette, whereas I suffered all the cruel pangs of jealousy. However, in the upshot, it wasn't this at all that constituted our tragic situation, but something else that I'm unable to express. In any event I swear that it was not out of jealousy I killed her. . . .

"As I say, I became acquainted with her in February of last year, at the theater, near the box-office. I called on her shortly after that, but up to October I did not visit her more than twice a month, and then always in the daytime. In October I confessed my love for her, and she allowed me to kiss her. A week after that she and I and a friend of mine named Voloshin took a trip to a suburban restaurant for supper; but she and I returned from there alone, and, although she was feeling gay, kindly, and somewhat tipsy, I felt such timidity before her that I was afraid even to kiss her hand.

"Some time after that she asked me for a volume of Pushkin, and, having finished his *Egyptian Nights,* she said: 'But would *you* have spirit enough to give up your life for a single night with the woman you loved?'—and when I made haste to answer that I would, she smiled enigmatically. I was already very much in love with her and clearly perceived and felt that, for me, this love was a fatal one. As our intimacy increased, I grew bolder: I began to speak to her of my love more and more often; I used to say that I felt myself perishing—if only because my father would never permit me to marry her, or because, as a theatrical star, she would find it impossible to live with me out of wedlock, since Polish society would never have forgiven her anything like an unconcealed liaison with a Russian officer. And she, for her part, complained against her fate, against her strange soul; she avoided, however, any direct response to my confessions of love, to my unvoiced questions as to whether she loved me; rather, she seemed to hold out hope for me, as it were, through these complaints of hers and their intimacy.

"Then, since January of this year, I began to call on her every day. I sent her bouquets to the theater, I sent flowers to her home, I made her presents. . . . I gave her a couple of mandolins, a polar-bear rug, an elaborate diamond ring, and a bracelet, also of diamonds. I had also decided to give her a brooch in the form of a skull. She adored emblems of death, and more than once had said to me that she wished to have just such a brooch from me, with an inscription in French: *Quand même pour toujours!*

"On the twenty-sixth of March of this year I received an invitation to supper from her. After the supper she yielded herself to me for the first time—in what she called her Japanese room. And it was also in this very room that our further assignations took place—she would send her maid off to bed after supper. And then, later on, she gave me a key to her bedroom, the outside door of which led directly to the staircase. . . . To commemorate the twenty-sixth of March we ordered wedding rings for ourselves, on the inside of which rings were engraved, by her wish, our initials and the date of our intimacy. . . .

"During one of our excursions beyond the city, in a village, we walked up to a cross standing near a Roman Catholic church, and I made a vow of my eternal love for her in front of this cross saying that she was my wife in the sight of God, and that I would be true to her to my very grave. She stood there, sad and thoughtful, and kept silent. Then she said, simply and firmly: 'And I love you, too. *Quand même pour toujours. . . .*'

"One day, at the beginning of May, as I was having supper at her place, she took out some opium in powder form and said: 'How easy it is to die! One has but to add a sprinkling of this to one's food, and all is over!' And, having put the powder into a goblet of champagne, she brought the drink up to her mouth. I snatched it out of her hand, dashed the wine into the fireplace, and smashed the goblet against one of my spurs. On the following day she told me: 'Yesterday's tragedy turned out to be a comedy!' And she added: 'Well, what can I do? I can't get up nerve enough to do it myself, while you, too, cannot, dare not do it— what a disgrace!'

"And after that we began to see each other at rarer intervals: she said that she could no longer receive me at home evenings. Why?—I was going crazy and suffering dreadfully. But, besides that, she changed toward me—she became cold and mocking; at times she received me as if we were barely acquainted, and was forever taunting me because of my lack of firmness. . . . And then, suddenly, everything changed once more. She began dropping in on me to take me along driving, she started making playful advances to me—perhaps because I, too, had begun to adopt a cold reserve in my treatment of her. . . . Finally she told me to rent another apartment for our love trysts,—but this apartment would have to be on some little-frequented street, in some somber old house; it would have to be perfectly dark, this apartment, and I would have to decorate it as she would tell me. . . . You know just how this apartment was decorated. . . .

"And so, on the sixteenth of June, I dropped in at her place about four in the afternoon and told her that the apartment was ready, and handed over one of the keys to her. She smiled and, returning the key to me, answered: 'We'll talk of this later.' Just then there was a ring at the door—a certain Shkliarevich had come. I hastily put away the key in my

pocket and began speaking of this and that. But, as Shkliarevich and I were going away, she said to him in the entry, loudly: 'Come Monday,' whereas to me she whispered: 'Come tomorrow, at four' —and she whispered this in such a way that my head began to swim. . . .

"The next day I was at her place on the stroke of four. What, then, was my astonishment when the cook, who opened the door, informed me that Sosnovskaya was not able to receive me —and with that she handed me a letter from her! She wrote that she was not feeling well and that she was going to her mother's country place, that it was 'too late now.' Utterly beside myself I dropped into the first refreshment place I came to and dashed off a dreadful note to her, asking her what she meant by 'too late,' and sent this note off by messenger. But the messenger brought it back to me; it turned out that she was not at home.

"Thereupon I decided that she wanted to break off with me once and for all, and so, on getting home, I wrote her another letter, sharply reproaching her for the whole game she was carrying on with me and requesting her to return to me her wedding ring, which was probably nothing but a joke to her, but was to me the dearest thing in life, that which was to go into the grave with me; by this I wanted to say that everything was at an end between us and to make her understand that death was all that was left for me. Together with this letter I returned to her her photograph, all her letters to me, and all the things of hers which I treasured so—gloves, hairpins, a toque. . . . My orderly came back and told me that she was not at home and that he had left my letter and package with the caretaker. . . .

"In the evening I went to the circus, where I ran into Shkliarevich, whom I was barely acquainted with. Dreading to be alone, however, I drank champagne with him. Suddenly Shkliarevich said to me: 'I say, I can see what you're going through, and I know the why and wherefore. Believe me, she's not worth it. We've all gone through the same thing; she's led all of us around by our noses. . . .' I felt like snatching out my saber and splitting his head open, but I was in such a state that I not only did not do anything of the kind, and did not cut such talk short, but, in secret, even rejoiced at it—rejoiced over the chance of having found a sympathizer in anybody at all. And I don't know what came over me. I didn't drop a single word to him, nor did I say a word concerning Sosnovskaya; but I did bring him to the old quarter of the town and show him the apartment which I had so lovingly picked out for our trysts. I felt so bitter, so humiliated because I had been tricked thus in the matter of this apartment. . . .

"From there I made my cabby drive like blazes to Neviarovski's restaurant. It was drizzling, and the cabby flew along, but even this drizzle and the lights ahead hurt me and terrified me. At one o'clock in the morning I came home from the restaurant with Shkliarevich and had already begun to undress when my orderly handed me a note: Sosnovskaya was waiting for me in the street; she begged me to come down immediately.

"She had come in a carriage with her maid, and told me that she had become so frightened on my account that she had been unable to come alone, even, and had therefore taken the maid along. I bade my orderly see the maid home, while I myself took a seat in Sosnovskaya's carriage and we went off to the old quarter of the town. On the way I upbraided her, accusing her of playing a game with me. She kept silent and, gazing ahead of her, from time to time wiped away her tears. She seemed calm, however. And since she could almost always communicate her mood to me, I began to calm down in my turn.

"When we arrived, she brightened up altogether: the rooms were very much to her liking. I took her hand, begged forgiveness for all my reproaches, also begging her to give me back her photograph —I mean the one I had sent back to her in my exasperation. We had frequent quarrels, and, in the upshot, I always felt myself at fault and always begged forgiveness.

"At three in the morning I escorted her home. On the way our talk again took a sharp turn. She sat staring straight ahead of her. I could not see her face—I was conscious only of the odor of her perfume and the icy, malicious sound of her voice. 'You're no man,' she was saying, 'you haven't any backbone at all! I can, whenever I wish, either drive you crazy or calm you down. Were I a man, I'd make mincemeat of such a woman as myself!' Whereupon I yelled at her: 'If that's so, take your ring back!'—and I put it on her finger by force. She turned to me, and, smiling in confusion, said: 'Come tomorrow.' I answered that I would not come, under any circumstances. Awkwardly, timidly she fell to imploring me, saying: 'No, you will come, you will . . . to our new apartment.' And she added decisively: 'No, I'm imploring you to come! I'm going abroad soon and want to see you for the last time; but, mainly, I must tell you something very important.' And bursting into tears once more, she concluded: 'The only thing that amazes me is that you claim you love me, that you cannot live without me and will shoot yourself— yet you don't want to see me for the last time. . . .' Whereupon I said, trying to be restrained, that if such were the case, I would inform her on the morrow at what hour I would be free. When we parted at the entrance to her house, in the rain, my heart was rending from pity and love for her. On getting back home I was surprised and disgusted to find Shkliarevich sleeping there. . . .

"Monday morning, the eighteenth of June, I sent her a note, saying that I would be free from noon on. She answered: 'At six; the new place.' "

XI

Sosnovskaya's maid, Antonina Kovanco, and her cook, Vanda Linevich, testified that on Saturday, the 16th, their mistress, as she had been lighting a spirit-lamp to heat the curling-iron for her bangs, had through absent-mindedness thrown the match on the front of her light *peignoir,* and the *peignoir* had blazed up, while Sosnovskaya screamed out wildly, tearing and throwing it off herself. She had become so frightened that she took to her bed, sent for the doctor, and kept on repeating:

"There, you'll see: that signifies a great misfortune. . . ."

The charming, unhappy woman! This incident of the *peignoir,* and her childlike terror, agitate and touch me extraordinarily. This trifling detail somehow amazingly connects and illuminates for me all that is fragmentary and contradictory in what we had always heard about her, and what had been dinned into our ears, both in society and all through the trail, ever since she had met her end. But, mainly, it awakens within me, amazingly, a lively sense of the real Sosnovskaya.

In general, I would say once more: Amazing is the poverty of human judgment! It was as though all had agreed to utter nothing but vulgar banalities. "Come, now, what was there to make such a fuss about here? He was a Hussar, a jealous and besotted wastrel, burning

the candle of his life at both ends; she was a play-actress, a stroller, who had got all tangled up in her shiftless and immoral life. . . ."

"Private dining-rooms; wine; cocottes; debauchery," people summed him up. "The clanking of his saber made him deaf to all the loftier feelings. . . ."

Loftier feelings, wine, indeed! But what *is* wine, and especially for such a nature as Elaghin's?—"At times I feel within my soul such torment, and yearning for everything that is good, that is lofty—in general, a yearning for the Devil alone knows what; all I know is that it creates a nagging ache in one's breast. . . . I long to seize some ever-elusive melody, which, apparently, I have heard somewhere—and yet it never, never comes! . . ." But when one is tipsy, one breathes more easily and expansively; when one is tipsy, the elusive refrain sounds more clearly and nearer at hand. . . .

"She did not love him," they said of her, "she was merely afraid of him; why, he was forever making threats to her that he would kill himself—that is, that he not only would burden her soul with his death, but would also make her the sorry heroine of a great scandal. We have testimony to the effect that 'she even experienced a certain aversion for him.' She had belonged to him just the same, you say? But then, does that really alter matters? Whom hadn't she belonged to! However, Elaghin had wanted to turn into a drama one of those numerous comedies of love which she was so fond of performing. . . ."

And people also said:

"She was terrified by that frightful, inordinate jealousy which he began to evince more and more. On one occasion, while he was present, the actor Strakuhn happened to be one of her guests. Elaghin had at first sat on calmly, merely

paling from jealousy. But suddenly he got up and went into an adjoining room. She darted after him and, catching sight of a revolver in his hand, fell on her knees before him, imploring him to take pity on himself and her. And probably not a few such scenes had been played out. Isn't it comprehensible, after this, that she would at last resolve to rid herself of him, to set out for a trip abroad, for which trip she had already made all preparations on the very eve of her death? He had brought her a key to the apartment in the old quarter of the town —an apartment she had thought of only to have a pretext for not receiving him in her own place up to her departure. This key she had not accepted. He began importuning her to accept it. She had declared that now it was 'too late'—as much as to say: 'It's no use my taking the key now—I'm going away.' But he dashed off such a vehement letter to her that, upon receiving it, she galloped off to him at the dead of night, beside herself from fear that she might find him already dead. . . ."

Let us admit that everything is so— even though all these reasonings contradict Elaghin's confession utterly. But still, why was Elaghin so "fearfully," so "inordinately" jealous, and why had he wanted to turn the comedy into a drama? What did he want to do all that for? Why had he not simply shot her during one of his attacks of jealousy? Why had there been "no struggle between the slayer and his victim"? And, furthermore: "She had at times even experienced a certain aversion for him. . . . She had occasionally, in the presence of strangers, made mock of him, had bestowed humiliating nicknames upon him, had called him a 'bowlegged puppy,' for instance. . . ."

But even as far back as her Lvov notes there is an entry concerning the aversion she had experienced toward some un-

known: "So he still loves me! But what about me? What are my feelings toward him?—Both love and aversion!" She used to insult Elaghin, you say? Well, on one occasion, having quarreled with him (quarrels were a quite frequent occurrence with this couple), she had called in the maid and, having chucked her "betrothal" ring on the floor, had shouted: "Take this nasty rubbish for yourself!" Ah, yes—but what had she done just before this? She had run into the kitchen just before and had said to her maid: "I'm going to call you in right away and fling this ring on the floor and tell you to take it for yourself. But remember, I'll only be putting on an act. You must give it back to me this very day, because with this ring I've betrothed myself to him, to this booby—and it is the dearest thing in the world to me."

It was not at all in vain that they called her a "woman of light conduct." Hers was wholly one of those natures with sharply expressed, unsatisfied, insatiable sexuality—a sexuality which it is even impossible to satiate. As a consequence of what? But then, how do I know what it is a consequence of? And notice what always occurs: it is precisely men of that fearfully complex type which is, in a greater or lesser degree, atavistic —persons who are by their very being hypersensitive not only as far as women are concerned, but, generally, in all their consciousness of the world—it is such men who are drawn by all the forces of their souls and bodies to precisely such women. Why? Because of their low taste, because of their dissoluteness, or simply because of the accessibility of such women? Of course no—a thousand times no! No, if only because such men do, after all, excellently perceive and feel to what an extent a liaison or propinquity with such women is always agonizing, and, at times, downright destructive.

They feel, they perceive, they know all this, yet nevertheless are drawn most of all to them, to precisely these women; are irresistibly drawn to their agony and even their destruction. Why?

"Of course, she had been merely putting on an act when she was writing her little farewell ,notes, making herself believe that her last hour had really come. And no diaries whatsoever convince one to the contrary—which diaries, it must be said by the way, are quite banal and naïve; nor, for that matter, do we find any of her churchyard visits convincing—"

No one denies the naïveté of her diaries and the theatricality of her churchyard jaunts, just as no one denies that she was fond of hinting at her resemblance to Marie Bashkirtseva and Marie Vetser. But then, why had she chosen precisely such a sort of diary and not some other, and why had she wanted to be akin to precisely such women? She had everything: beauty, youth, fame, money, hundreds of admirers; and all these she had availed herself of with passion and intoxication, and yet her life was one continuous yearning, a ceaseless craving to get away from this baneful earthly vale, where everything is never, never the thing sought for, longed for. For what reason? This: that she had hypnotized herself through having play-acted all this for so long. But why had she play-acted precisely thus and not in some other way? Was it because all this sort of thing is so customary among women who have dedicated themselves (as they express it) to art? But—why should all this be so customary? Why?

XII

On Sunday morning the tap-bell in Sosnovskaya's bedroom began ringing a little before eight o'clock; she had awakened and had called her maid consider-ably before the usual time. The maid had carried in a tray with a cup of chocolate and then parted the curtains. Her mistress was sitting up in bed, and, as her wont was, watched her pensively and absent-mindedly from under her eyebrows and with lips half-open; then she said:

"But d'you know, Tonia, that I fell asleep yesterday immediately after the doctor left? Oh, Mother o' God, how frightened I was! But no sooner had the doctor come than I began to feel so well, so calm. In the night-time I woke up, got on my knees in bed, and prayed for a whole hour. . . . Just think: what would I have looked like if I had been burned all over? My eyes would have been just a couple of burst blisters, my lips would have puffed up. I'd have been just a fright to look at. . . . My whole face would have been covered over with cotton wool. . . ."

She would not touch the chocolate for a long time and all the while sat brooding over something. Then she drank off the chocolate and, having taken her bath, sat down at her tiny escritoire in her little bath-robe and with her hair down, and wrote several letters on black-bordered stationery—she had ordered it long before. After dressing and breakfasting she went away. She visited her mother in the country and returned only at midnight, together with Strakuhn, the actor, who had "always been one of the family" to her.

"They were both jolly when they arrived," the maid told her story. "I met them in the entry and at once called her aside and handed her the letter and the things which Elaghin had sent in her absence. She whispered to me about the things: 'Hide 'em, quick, so Strakuhn won't see 'em.' Then she hastily opened the letter, and at once turned pale, lost her head, and began shoutin', no longer payin' any attention to Strakuhn, who was sittin' in the drawin'-room: 'For God's sake, run as fast as ever you can for a carriage!' I ran out an' got one an' found her all ready on the front steps when I come back. We dashed along at full speed, an' all the way she kept crossin' herself and repeatin': 'Oh, Mother o' God! If only I might find him alive!' "

On Monday, bright and early in the morning, she went off to the river to bathe. On this day she had invited to dinner Strakuhn and a certain English-woman who generally came to her al-most every day to give her lessons in English, and almost never did. After din-ner the Englishwoman left, while Stra-kuhn stayed on for another hour and a half. He smoked, lying on a divan, with his head on the lap of his hostess, "who had on nothing but a loose, light dressing-gown, and little Japanese slippers, with-out any stockings." Finally Strakuhn left, and, as she was bidding him goodbye, she begged him to come "this very evening, at ten."

"Won't that be rather too often?" Strakuhn had asked, laughing, as he looked for his cane in the entry.

"Oh, no—please come!" she had said. "But if I should happen to be out, don't you be angry at me, now, Luci"—using the familiar diminutive of his first name, Lucian.

And after that, for a long while, she was engaged in burning certain letters and papers in the fireplace. She hummed, and jested with the maid:

"I'm going to burn everything now, since I wasn't burned up myself! Ah, but it would have been fine if I'd been burned up! Only altogether, so's there would be nothing but ashes left of me! . . ."

Then she said: "Tell Vanda to have supper ready by ten tonight. Well, I'm going now."

She left about six, taking along with her "somethin' that was all wrapped up

in paper and that looked like a revolver."

She set out for the old quarter of the town, but on the way ordered her car-riage to turn aside so that she might call on Leshchinskaya, her dressmaker, who was mending and altering the *peignoir* which had caught fire Saturday when she had it on. And, according to Lesh-chinskaya's words, the actress "had been in a gay and charming mood." After she had looked over the *peignoir* and it had been wrapped up in paper together with the parcel she had taken with her from home, she had sat on for a long time in the work-room among the apprentice girls, repeating all the while: "Oh, Mother o' God, how late I am—it's time I was going, my little angels!"—and still would not leave. At last she resolutely got up and with a sigh, but gaily, said:

"Goodbye, Pani Leshchinskaya! Goodbye, my little sisters, my little angels! Thanks for chatting with me. It's such a pleasure for me to sit in your feminine circle, you darlings—for it's al-ways men and men with me!"

And, once more nodding her head with a smile from the threshold, she walked out.

Why had she taken the revolver along with her? This weapon belonged to Elaghin, but she kept it in her place, being apprehensive that he might shoot himself. "But now she intended to return it to its proper owner, inasmuch as in a few days she was going abroad for a long period," the prosecuting attorney had said, and added: "Thus she set out for the fatal assignation—yet not knowing that it was fatal. At seven she was in the ground-floor apartment of that house in the old quarter of the town—and then the door of this flat closed, to open again only on the morning of the nineteenth of June. What had taken place there in the night? There is none to tell us this save Elaghin. Let us hear him once more, then. . . ."

XIII

And once more, amid deep silence, all of us who formed the dense throng in the court-room listened to those pages of the indictment which the prosecuting attorney deemed it necessary to refresh our memory with, and with which Elaghin's story concluded:

" 'Monday morning, the nineteenth of June, I sent her a note, saying that I would be free from noon on. She answered: "At six; the new place." At a quarter to six I was there, bringing with me some cold delicacies, two bottles of champagne and two of porter, two small glasses, and a flacon of eau-de-Cologne. But I had to wait a long while—she came only at seven.

" 'On entering she gave me an absent-minded peck, then passed on into the second room and threw the parcel she had brought down on the divan. "Leave the room," she said to me in French, "I want to undress." I went into the outer room and again sat alone for a long while. I was fully sober and fearfully depressed, vaguely sensing that everything was at an end, that everything was coming to an end. . . . The setting itself was a strange one: I was sitting under artificial light, as if it were night, and yet at the same time I knew and felt that out of doors, beyond the walls of these bottled-up dark rooms, it was still daylight, and that the summer evening was beautiful. . . . She did not call me for a long time, nor do I know what she was doing. It was perfectly quiet on the other side of her door. Finally she called out: "You may come in now. . . ."

" 'She was lying on the divan in nothing but the *peignoir*, without stockings or slippers, and did not say anything, merely staring from under her brows at the ceiling—at the lantern. The parcel she had brought was now unwrapped and

I caught sight of my own revolver. I asked: "What ever did you bring that thing for?" She waited a space before answering: "Oh, just so,— As you know, I'm going away. . . . You'd better keep it here, and not in your place. . . ." A frightful thought flashed through my head: "No, she's not doing this without some reason!"—but I didn't say anything. . . .

" 'And the conversation which began between us after this was constrained and cold for a considerable time. In secret I was frightfully agitated; I was constantly striving to conjecture something, constantly expecting to get my thoughts together at any moment and finally to tell her something important and decisive. For I understood that this was, perhaps, our last time together, or, in any event, a parting for a long period—and yet I still couldn't say anything, feeling my complete impotence. She said: "Smoke, if you like." "But you don't like my smoking," I answered. "No, *now* nothing matters," said she. "And do let me have some champagne!" I became as elated at this as if it were my salvation. In a few minutes we had finished the whole bottle. I sat down near her and started kissing her hands, saying that I would not survive her departure. She rumpled my hair and uttered, as if her thoughts were elsewhere: "Yes, yes. . . . What a misfortune it is that I cannot be your wife! . . . Everything and everybody is against us; only God alone, perhaps, is on our side. I love your soul; I love your *fantasy*." What she meant to express by this last word I do not know. I looked up at the drape on the ceiling and said: "Look —you and I are here as in a crypt. And how quiet it is!"

" 'She merely smiled back sadly for answer.

" 'About ten o'clock she said she felt hungry. We passed into the front room. But she ate little, and so did I; for the most part we drank. Suddenly she looked at the cold things I had brought and exclaimed: "Silly-billy, what a lot of stuff you've bought again! Don't you dare do it the next time!" "But when is the next time going to be?" I asked. She looked at me oddly, then let her head drop and rolled up her eyes. "Jesus, Mary!" she uttered in a whisper. "What are we to do? Oh, I want you, madly! Let's go, quick!"

" 'After some time I glanced at my watch; it was already past one. "Oh, how late it is!" said she. "I simply *must* go home, this very minute!" However, she didn't even get up, and added: "D'you know, I feel that I must get away as quickly as possible, yet I can't stir from the spot. I feel that I shan't leave this place. You're my doom, my fate—the will of God! . . ." All this was something I could not understand. Probably she wanted to say something in keeping with what she wrote later: "I am dying not of my own will." You think that by this phrase she expressed her defenselessness before me. But, in my opinion, she wanted to say something else: that our ill-starred encounter was her doom, the will of God; that she was dying, not of her own will, but by God's. However, I did not attribute any particular significance to her words at the time—I had long since grown used to her eccentricities. Then she said, suddenly: "Have you a pencil?" I wondered once more. Why should she want a pencil? But I hastened to give it to her—I had one in my memobook. She also asked me for one of my cards. When she began writing something on it, I said: "I say, it's rather awkward to be writing notes on a fellow's visiting-card!" "No, these are simply notes for no one but myself," she answered. "Leave me now—I want to think a little and take a nap." And, having placed the card on her breast, she closed her eyes. Every-

thing became so quiet that I fell into some sort of coma. . . .

" 'Not less than half an hour must have passed thus. Suddenly she opened her eyes and said, coldly: "I forgot: I came to give you back your ring. You yourself wanted to end everything yesterday." And, raising herself a little, she chucked the ring on the wall-ledge. "Why, do you really love me?" she all but shrieked. "I can't understand how you can calmly allow me to go on living! I'm a woman—I haven't any firmness. It isn't that I fear death—it's torment that I fear; but you could, with a single shot, put an end to me, and then, with another, kill yourself." And at that point I comprehended more fully, with fearful clarity, all the horror, all the despair of our situation, and that it was on the verge of some solution at last. But as to killing her—no, I felt that I could not do that. I felt something else: that the decisive moment for me had arrived. I took the revolver and cocked the trigger. "What, you're going to kill only yourself?" she cried out, jumping up. "No, I swear before Jesus—not for anything!"—and she snatched the revolver out of my hand. . . .

" 'And again that excruciating silence fell. I remained sitting; she was lying down. And suddenly, indistinctly, she said something to herself in Polish, and then spoke to me: "Let me have my ring!" I handed it to her. "And your own!" said she. I hastened to comply with this request as well. She put on her own, and, having commanded me to put mine on, too, she began to speak: "I've always loved you, and I love you now. I've driven you mad and have tortured you to the very end—but such is my nature, and such is our destiny. Hand me my skirt, and bring me some porter." I handed her the skirt and went after the porter.

" 'And when I returned, I noticed that there was a small vial with opium near her. "Listen," said she firmly, "now is the end of all play-acting. Could you live without me?" I answered that I could not. "That is true," said she, "I've taken all your soul, all your thoughts. You wouldn't waver about killing yourself? And, if that's the case, take me with you as well. I couldn't live without you any more than you could without me. And after you kill me, you can die with the realization that, at last, I am all yours— and that for all time. And now listen to what my life has been. . . ." And, lying down once more, after a moment's silence and calming down somewhat, she began telling me her whole life, from her very childhood. . . . I remember almost nothing of her story. . . .

XIV

" '. . . Neither do I remember which one of us was the first to start writing (I broke my small pencil in halves). We began to write in silence, and remained silent all the time we were writing. I wrote first of all to my father, I think. . . . You ask me why I reproached him with "not desiring my happiness," when I had not so much as attempted, even once, to ask his consent to my marrying her? I don't know—Why, he wouldn't have given me his consent anyway. . . . Then I wrote to my fellow-officers, bidding them farewell. . . . Then whom else did I write to? Yes—to the commander of my regiment, requesting that I be given a decent funeral. You say that means I must have felt certain I would do away with myself? Of course! But still, how is it I didn't do so? I don't know.

" 'As for her, she wrote slowly, I remember, often stopping and deliberating over something; she'd write a word and then stare at the wall from under her eyebrows. . . . She herself tore up the notes, and not I. She'd write, tear up what she'd written, and then throw the pieces anywhere at all. . . . It seems to me that even in the grave it will not be so frightful as when, at that late hour, in that silence, under that lantern, we were writing all those unnecessary notes. . . . It was her will that we should write them. . . . In general, I submitted without a word to everything she commanded me to do on that night, up to the very last moment. . . .

" 'Suddenly she said: "Enough! 'If it were done . . . then 'twere well it were done quickly!' " Was she consciously quoting? I cannot tell. "Let me have a little porter, then," she said. "Mother o' God, bless me!" I poured out a glass of porter for her, and she, raising herself a little, resolutely threw a pinch of powder into the glass. Having drunk off more than half, she ordered me to finish the rest. I drank it. But she began to beat about and, snatching at my hands, fell to imploring: "And now kill me, kill me! Kill me for the sake of our love!"

" 'Just how did I do it? I put my left arm around her, I think—yes, of course, it was my left arm—and clung with my lips to hers. She was saying: "Farewell, farewell—or no, let it be an *Ave,* and that for all time now! . . . If we have not succeeded here, then we may meet with better fortune up there, above. . . ." I pressed her to me and held my finger on the trigger of the revolver—I remember my whole body jerking. . . . And then the finger jerked, by itself, somehow. . . . But she had time to say, in Polish: "Alexander, my beloved!"

" 'What hour was this at? About three, I think. What else did I do for two hours after that? Why, you forget that it took me about an hour to walk to Likharev's. As for the rest of that time, I spent it in sitting near her; and then I began putting everything in order, although I myself couldn't tell you for what reason. . . .

" 'Why didn't I shoot myself? Why, I forgot to, somehow. When I saw her dead, I forgot everything in this world. I just sat there and could do nothing but look at her. Then, in the same wild unconsciousness, I began putting her to rights and tidying up the room. I would be incapable of not keeping my word, which I had given her, that I would kill myself after her; but a complete apathy seized hold of me. . . . Just as apathetically do I regard the fact of my being alive now. But I cannot become reconciled to being thought an executioner, apparently. No—no! Perhaps I am guilty before the law of man, guilty before God—but never before her!' "

XV

By ten years of penal servitude must Elaghin expiate his guilt before the law of man.

But before God—and before her?

God's judgment is not known. But what would she have said, were it in our power to make her arise from her grave? And who would then dare to come between them?

THE LIFE AND WORKS OF
IVAN BUNIN

By *GEORGES ADAMOVITCH*

THE IMPORTANCE in Russian literature of the work of Ivan Alekseevich Bunin is indisputable. Yet the start of Bunin's literary career was far from brilliant. At the age of forty he had attracted little critical attention. The critics preferred not only Maxim Gorki and Leonide Andreev but also a number of mediocre writers who are quite forgotten today. Bunin was ambitious and not disposed to take an inferior place, he must have suffered greatly from this indifference. In his old age, he sometimes spoke of revenge finally achieved, recalling with visible satisfaction that only Chekov had discerned his gifts and had, shortly before dying, predicted a glorious literary future for Bunin.

It is impossible to explain Bunin's early obscurity without sketching a picture of Russian literary life in the years preceding World War I. Toward the end of the last century, Russian literary circles were shocked by the appearance of a group of young writers, mostly poets, with a fighting spirit and strange aspirations. One of them, Dmitri Merejkovsky, a man of great culture and restless intelligence, published a still-famous pamphlet deploring the ever-increasing decadence of Russian literature, which he attributed to its incapacity to understand that art must stand on its own merits and not on the veracity of its political or social comments. To support his thesis he spoke of the literary renaissance in the West, enthusiastically invoking the names of Nietzsche, Ibsen, Verlaine, and Mallarmé, who were little known in Russia except as objects of mockery in the popular press. Merejkovsky's movement increased in importance with the publication of the review *Mir Iscousstva,* which was edited by Serge de Diaghileff, who later created the famous Russian ballet. The movement soon allied itself more or less successfully with the theories of the Symbolists, a school to which nearly all the Russian poets before 1914 belonged.

The counterattack was not long in coming. The upholders of tradition, "the old graybeards," remained imperturbably faithful to positivism, which they considered a form of definitive wisdom, and to the idea of *engagé* literature. In the midst of the controversy, a vigorous young writer appeared; self-taught, half-Marxist, half-Nietzschean, he seized the "torch" that was about to fall from the shaking hands of his elders. Without denying the importance of purely esthetic values, he became the leader of those who saw the chief reason for their existence and their writing in the struggle against the established social order. The pseudonym he chose was eloquent in itself: Gorki, which means "bitter." The troubled political climate helped him, for the various schools of thought were hopelessly muddled. Literary jousting for years absorbed all the energy of the critics, who were divided into two camps.

From all this Bunin kept his distance. Though he admitted the need for progressive reform in Russia, he was far from being a revolutionary. As for the theory of "art for art's sake," he agreed that the idea was reasonable; it was not by chance that he was an admirer of Flaubert. Nevertheless, he kept his head and would play no part in Symbolist literary circles, which he considered guilty of bombast and exaggeration. The bad taste of the period exasperated him.

In his youthful writings, Bunin used no flashy effects, no vague metaphysical pretensions with grandiose words to support them. His style was meditative, endeavoring to penetrate the mystery of everyday life, working incessantly to achieve a perfection such as few other Russian writers had done. From his early days he was obsessed with the notion that he must avoid anything showy, that he must write "true" in the manner of Tolstoy, the supreme model whom he "never ceased to adore." He said the same of Chekov.

The critics gave Bunin a word of praise from time to time but in a condescending manner, as if they found him somewhat tedious. They evidently found nothing exceptional in his short stories, not even anything to be indignant about. He presented no insoluble problems or peculiar characters, only calm, love, nature, melancholy, and reverie. How, they seemed to ask, can anyone enthuse over a literary work which, even if faultlessly written, lacks all driving force?

It was only in the years immediately before World War I that attention finally was paid to this quite individual and sometimes profoundly moving voice. From then on Bunin's reputation increased. But it was only in his advancing years that he conceived and polished his real masterpieces—*Zhizn Arsénieva* (Life of Arseniev, 1930, 1939), his only great novel, and his last collection of very short stories, *The Dark Alleys*.

Ivan Alekseevich Bunin was born on October 23, 1870, at Voroneje, the capital of a province in the center of Russia. He was barely four years old when his family left the city and settled on a country property miles away: "A sea of snow in winter, a sea of corn, grass and flowers in summer; the eternal, mysterious silence of the fields."

His family belonged to the old rural nobility and had once been well off; but Ivan never knew those prosperous days. His father, a retired officer addicted to the bottle and the card table, sold his estates one after the other and finally reduced his family to near destitution. But Bunin never bore him any ill will, always speaking of him as a good and loyal man. It was his mother, however, whom he remembered with emotion. Strong-willed and deeply religious, always prepared for self-sacrifice, she meant so much to her son that later he could rarely mention her name in front of a third person.

The family's poverty prevented Ivan from receiving a proper education. He studied for a few years in a small provincial school but did not finish the course; thereafter, his elder brother undertook to complete his education. But he never received any form of higher education and soon had to earn his own living.

His first literary ventures were in verse. He sent a few poems to the editor of an obscure literary review, *The Fatherland,* without much hope of seeing them published. Three months passed without an answer. Then the review arrived containing, in a prominent position, a longish poem, "The Village Beggar," signed by Ivan Bunin. "An unforgettable morning," he later described it. His father announced that he had never doubted his son's literary vocation; his mother, in her usual calm way, said that the boy evidently had something quite exceptional about him. The poet himself, then sixteen, believed he had suddenly become famous.

One of his first stories also appeared later in the same review, and several small provincial dailies accepted a few chronicles. In one of his later autobiographical essays, he writes, "Few authors can have had such a bad start as I had." Nevertheless, his literary achievements gained him a place on the staff of the *Orel Courier*, a local newspaper, as assistant to the editor. After working there for two years, Bunin visited Moscow and the offices of *Russian Thought*, then the most influential and highly regarded review in the city. The secretary gave him a cold reception. Seeing the young man with a manuscript under his arm, he said, "If that's poetry you have there, we've enough in reserve to last us ten years."

Though Moscow proved hostile, his newspaper, which seemed to have faith in the young contributor's future, engaged him to edit a collection of verse. This volume was greeted with only two reviews, one quite indifferent, the other, by the famous Bourenine, then the terror of young authors, short and acidly sarcastic.

But Bunin would not be discouraged. A great admiration for Tolstoy inspired him with the desire to become his disciple, not only in literary but also in ethical matters (which would, we may add, have been foreign to his nature). Full of ambition, he wrote to Tolstoy, then at the height of his fame, and asked for an interview. *The Kreutzer Sonata* had just been published and was being discussed widely. In his letter Bunin said that he could not understand *The Kreutzer,* and did not feel competent to profit from its terrible lesson. I have not been able to discover whether Tolstoy replied to this letter, but in any case Bunin was not received for three years; then the meeting made such an impression on him that, even after thirteen years had passed, when he spoke of it he was, according to his widow, as moved and shaken as if it had taken place the day before. At the meeting Tolstoy must immediately have divined Bunin's mistaken hero worship and seen that it would bear no fruit.

About the same time Bunin began a correspondence with Chekov, whom he did not meet until 1895, when he became one of his closest friends. Bunin first wrote to ask permission to send some short stories for advice. Chekov replied that he was a very poor judge but would read them carefully. Bunin, again according to his widow, reproached himself to his dying day for having written this letter, realizing the uselessness and vanity of such approaches.

However, thanks to his doggedness and belief in himself, Bunin's affairs gradually began to take a more favorable turn. A well-known critic sometimes would give him a word or two of praise, or a poet of the earlier generation would mark him out from his contemporaries. Nevertheless, the champions of Symbolism, still intransigent and full of fight, adopted the same attitude toward him that Lecomte de Lisle, leader of the Parnassians, had adopted toward Sully-Prudhomme: "He is of course a poet, but not one of us."

His contacts with prose writers were friendlier. He was often in the company of Chekov, who showed his feelings by treating him as an equal. Stanislavsky, in his memoirs, noted that "Nobody could amuse Chekov and put him in a better humor than Bunin." A letter from Chekov to his wife contains the following sentence which, from such an unsociable man, is highly significant: "What makes me happy is that Bunin visits me daily."

In 1898 Bunin met a beautiful Greek girl, and it was love at first sight; he immediately asked for her hand. She accepted, and they were married a few days later. But the marriage was a disaster; once first love was over their quarrels increased, developing into an open break and finally separation. Later, Bunin married Vera Mouromtsev, who remained his devoted companion until his death.

Bunin's literary output continued. *Listopad* (The Fall of the Leaf), a volume of verse, came out in the "Scorpion" series, which included the work of fashionable poets. The best literary reviews wanted his work and gave his short stories a prominent place.

He had by now settled in Moscow and had become one of the most prominent figures in society; he was at all the first nights and the gatherings of the intellectual and artistic élite. Among his many friends were Gorki, Andreev, Konprine, Rachmaninov, Chaliapin. However, as we have already said, he lacked the element that would have placed him definitely in the literary front ranks. In the years to come, not even academic honors could replace this respectful coolness shown to him by the critics and the public. He was now making money and traveling extensively, and he appeared to have nothing to complain of; but he was still far from satisfied.

The publication of *Derévnya* (*The Village,* 1910), a long short story in a style to which his readers were unaccustomed, was the turning point. The critics seized upon it, expressing violent and controversial opinions, concerning themselves not with its literary merit but with its portrait of the Russian peasantry. In the tradition of Turgenev's *Annals of a Sportsman,* it was usual, in Russian literature, to attribute to the peasant, the humble *moujik,* the virtue of good-heartedness and to regard him as basically superior to those who had reduced him to a state of semi-slavery. *The Village,* with its portrait of the peasant as surly, bestial, selfish, avaricious, and insanely jealous, caused a furor. But Bunin's sincerity was clear and although he was accused of exacerbating class hatred, all kinds of people read *The Village.* For the first time in his life, Bunin found himself in the front rank of Russian writers.

Other short stories and tales followed, all well written and closely followed by the critics. Then in 1916 came the success of *Gospodín iz San Francisco* (*The Gentleman from San Francisco*), the story of a rich, anonymous American who dies just as he is about to set foot on Capri to spend a few weeks of well-earned rest. Inspired by Tolstoy's *Death of Ivan Ilyitch,* Bunin here displayed his mastery of narrative.

The Russian Revolution of 1917 filled Bunin with fear and distrust. The author of *The Village* would hardly be expected to applaud the abdication of the Czar and the new era of equality and fraternity. He expected the worst, especially when Lenin came to power. On the outbreak of the Civil War he and his wife left for the south, where the antirevolutionary forces were gathering. They spent some time in Odessa, where he kept a full diary, later to be the basis of *Okajannye Dni* (The Cursed Days), a mixture of bitterness, despair, and anger. When the Red Army approached, they fled to Constantinople and then to Sofia, where they were robbed of all their cash and jewelry. They managed to obtain railway tickets to Belgrade, where a French visa and a sum of money awaited them, sent from Paris by an old friend who had left Russia some time before. From then until his death in 1955 at the age of 85,

Bunin lived in France—mainly at Grasse —and shared the uncertain life of the Russian émigré.

Bunin's works are rich and varied, yet they form a whole, for they are dominated by those eternal questions which people are always asking themselves, without ever receiving an answer: "Who am I? Where do I come from? What is life?" Love and death haunted him. His books have a vague feeling of Ecclesiastes, a constant sense of the futility of life, of everything that most people consider important, indeed of the unimportance of those problems that appear so pressing. All passes, he seems to say, all will disappear; only those "two divine infants, Desire and Death," are more than man's fantasies. It would be no exaggeration to say that the disappearance of the social order which he had known in his youth inspired much of his work.

Bunin's stories tell of an ever-changing world. They seem photographically alive. Bunin was not content with simple, moral pictures but could introduce that shudder into them which seems for a moment to make the tale hover between reality and unreality. Being never sure of anything himself, he never made assertions; yet when you read him, your fundamental beliefs are shaken and you are left wondering. If he is sometimes vague, he is never banal.

Bunin's best work was done in exile. He wrote little about the Revolution. But one of his best short stories, "Nesrotchnaia Vesna" (Spring Without an End), which appeared in 1924, refers with a kind of sad resignation to this period. He leads us through an old castle, its deserted rooms stripped of their furnishings, and reflects sadly: Where are we bound for? Why must beauty vanish? What will replace it? This tale illustrates better than any other Bunin's attitude to the Revolution. People may say that this is a purely esthetic approach, but I disagree. The fact that the splendors of the past were possible only thanks to a cultivated and indolent minority living on the produce of those less favored did not trouble Bunin; he might well have quoted Goethe's famous saying that injustice is preferable to disorder.

Mítina lyubóv (*Mitya's Love*), written a few months later, is one of Bunin's better-known works, translated into many languages. In no other book did he succeed so well in bringing human beings into contact with the vast silences of nature. The pages in which a poor boy wanders about despairingly in the rain before committing suicide are rightly regarded as his finest piece of prose.

The novel *Zhizn Arsénieva* took Bunin several years of hard work, and did not appear until 1930. It is not only autobiographical, full of the author's own fantasy, but it is also a vast landscape of prewar Russian life. He deals with the period before the Revolution in a most lyrical manner, telling of his childhood, his early literary efforts, and first love. With great richness of detail, he makes that life seem almost comic. Never before had the joy of living, all the more important because it is limited by time, and the feeling of gratitude toward the fundamental forces which give life, been expressed by Bunin with such vigor. Yet in his youth he was regarded as a convinced pessimist.

Zhizn Arsénieva is difficult to analyze because, in spite of its length, it seems to have been composed in one burst of creation, the chapters moving effortlessly one into the other. It is a book to read and reread, to ponder, not to read quickly to get to the ending; for the action is entirely without what is commonly called "suspense." Indeed, Bunin always considered dramatic subterfuges of this kind, for which he condemned Dostoevsky, as "childish." All is calm and serene, events moving slowly and inexorably, but the reader is nevertheless always looking ahead to some sort of conclusion. Bunin was often asked to write a sequel to this autobiography, but he refused, saying that he could not continue the tale. He gave no reason for his refusal.

His last collection of short stories, *Dark Alleys,* was his own favorite. He contended that he had never written anything better; certainly nothing gave him more pleasure. Love is the theme of *Dark Alleys.* By this time, Bunin had turned squarely against anything he considered of secondary importance, social, political, and cultural questions. For the first time, he attempted to portray purely carnal attraction.

But these stories were received with astonishment and hostility. Russian literature has always had something puritanical in it—*Anna Karenina* created quite a

scandal in its day—and in the U.S.S.R. this puritanical attitude became even more marked. Readers were amazed that this eminent Russian writer should choose such subjects, when he should have been dealing with serious, everyday problems. Bunin never got over this. "What!" he cried, "I, an old man, who intends to deal with the most enigmatic and mysterious subject in the world, who delves to the very depths, to touch the bottom of human existence, I am accused of frivolity! It's ludicrous!" Nevertheless, his detractors would not withdraw; they refused to see that, according to present-day standards of Western literature, his supposedly licentious stories could have been read in any girls' school. They are perfectly rounded examples of his literary art, and all are sad, for death is never far away. It is possible that one day Bunin's own judgment of them will be amply confirmed.

Georges Adamovitch is professor of literature at the University of Manchester. Translated by Anthony Rhodes.

THE 1933 PRIZE

By KJELL STRÖMBERG

IN 1933, Ivan Bunin (Bounine is the spelling which he himself used after settling down in France) won the Prize away from thirty candidates. He had been proposed for the Prize once before, in 1923, by Romain Rolland, who had won the award in 1916. Rolland also proposed Maxim Gorki, and from then on the names of both writers were proposed regularly every year, together or separately, for the consideration of the Swedish Academy.

After Tolstoy's death, Gorki was unquestionably the most widely known of recognized Russian writers. He had been the subject of a report to the Nobel Committee as early as 1918, but the report was decidedly unfavorable. "If Gorki had been proposed ten or fifteen years ago," the commentator, who was not a member of the Swedish Academy, wrote in summary, "he might well have been considered; today it is impossible." His political activity and the particular form it assumed, especially in the cultural life of his country, inspired no greater confidence in the commentator than did his "ambiguous personality." The vein of his literary talent, moreover, seemed to have run out long before. In short, he should be turned down, the critic thought—and he was.

A decade later, in 1928, another expert was called in for consultation. The new critic was not prepared to accept the severe judgments of his predecessor without reservations. Anton Karlgren, professor of Russian language and literature at the University of Copenhagen, did not fail to acquaint himself with the material, especially the autobiographical books, which Gorki had published after the Russian Revolution of 1917. In them he found evidence of a remarkable rebirth of Gorki's powers as a writer. True, Gorki had made common cause with the new regime from the beginning; he became a zealous collaborator in a cultural policy which was, to say the least, debatable, while dividing his time between Capri, his favorite home for over a quarter of a century, and Leningrad or Moscow. But he never quite succeeded in following Stalin's precepts to the letter, that is, to become an "engineer of the human soul," as the new master of all the Russias required from his official poets.

For a long time he was considered too much of an individualist, too inclined to sacrifice to the cult of the uprooted *moujik*, too much the eternal vagabond sprung from the backwoods and mixing in with the proletariat of the big cities, whose philosophical or sentimental lucubrations, distilled against a somber background, had brought Gorki his first world successes. It was only toward 1930, on his sixtieth birthday, that the Soviet authorities recognized that Gorki was a literary genius of the first rank and consequently well suited to exploitation for propaganda purposes. From then on, no effort was spared to keep him in Moscow, in a kind of golden captivity, until his death.

Perhaps it was the official honors heaped upon Gorki in his old age which made the members of the Nobel Committee think twice. He had been installed in a state-owned palace as a kind of Pope of Soviet literature, and his job as supreme counselor for cultural matters gave him dictatorial powers. The Nobel Committee had always sought to avoid an award which might seem like taking sides politically or even interfering in the domestic affairs of another country. This principle must have counted for something in the case of Gorki, in spite of the rather favorable opinion of the most recent expert and despite the cordiality shown by several members of the Swedish Academy toward his candidacy when it was first proposed in 1918 by one of their fellow Academicians. Finally Gorki was eliminated, although his partisans returned each year until his death in 1936 to reassert his standing as the most gifted and the most original of the successors of Tolstoy and Dostoevsky.

The members of the Swedish Academy were not very familiar with the Russian writers who had developed in Stalin's empire. Even so, they were eager to do homage to a great literature which until then had never been distinguished by a Nobel Prize, and they decided to turn to a Russian writer who was then living and working in exile. There were two possible candidates—Ivan Bunin, considered by western critics as the worthy successor of Turgenev, and Dmitri Merezhkovski, who was proposed at the same time as Bunin and generally supported by the same persons. Merezhkovski, a novelist and essayist, had an advantage because

translations of his books had been well known in the West, including Sweden, long before anyone outside a small group of Slavic specialists had ever heard of Bunin.

On the other hand, Bunin was supported not only by Slavic specialists from various countries but also by Emanuel Nobel, nephew of the donor of the Prize, administrator of Nobel interests in Russia until the downfall of the Czar, and the loyal executor of his uncle's last wishes as expressed in the testament which was long contested by other heirs in the family. This great lord of international finance lived in Paris, where he kept up close relations with the Russian émigré groups. Each year he was guest of honor at all ceremonies organized in Stockholm on the occasion of the distribution of the Nobel Prizes. Bunin was certainly one of his favorite authors, but since he had no voice in the selection of laureates, he could advance his candidate only through various Russian and French literary friends.

The most favored competitor of Bunin seems to have been the new Greek Homer, Costes Palamas, although among the candidates vying for the Prize in 1923 there was, once again, Paul Valéry. The author of *Charmes* had been proposed by eighteen members of the Académie Française and as many professors of literature from all the universities of France. One would have thought that the Swedish Academy would be impressed by such a show of support, comparable to the force which had conquered five years before when Henri Bergson won the Prize. It did not work in Valéry's case, however. The conclusions of the experts summoned to decipher his distinguished but obscure poetry continued to be negative.

There were two other French writers among the candidates—the aged J. H. Rosny, Sr., supported by President Raymond Poincaré of France and Maeterlinck, and, for the first time, the great scholar Joseph Bédier, who had shown himself to be a fine poet as well in his masterful version of the medieval *The Romance of Tristan and Iseult*. His name had been proposed by Professor Schück, a sturdy pioneer who had opened new pathways in the study of medieval literature. And also for the first time we find a Hebrew poet representing the new state of Israel—Chaim Nachman Bialik, together with a Czech, Karel Čapek. The Scandinavian countries were represented by the Norwegian Olav Duun, the Dane Johannes V. Jensen, and the Finn F. E. Sillanpää; the last two were later to win Nobel Prizes.

In Stockholm, the appearance of Bunin made a fine impression. On his arrival, Bunin was received by a delegation from the Stockholm Russian colony, who offered him bread and salt on a silver platter—the traditional welcome in the Russian countryside. The gesture moved him deeply. From his windows at the Grand Hotel, the exiled writer had the impression of looking out upon a familiar scene, so keenly did the snowy riverbanks, flanked by ancient palaces, recall the St. Petersburg of happier times. In his meetings with the press he spoke frankly of his horror of the new masters of his native land. He made no effort to conceal his contempt for Soviet literature, subjected as it was to an abject regime. He confessed, however, that he did not know much about it, and that only by hearsay. No wonder that Alexandra Kollontay, the charming and cultured old lady who was the Soviet minister to Sweden, immediately came down with an acute diplomatic illness which made it impossible for her to attend the various Nobel functions for the year, even if one of her compatriots was being honored. As for the flower-decked stage of the Concert Palace, where the distribution of Prizes took place, the centenary of the birth of the donor of the Prizes served as sufficient pretext to use only Swedish flags, thus absolving the Chief of Protocol from the thorny task of choosing between the Czarist tricolor and the red flag with its hammer and sickle to honor the literary laureate, the rule being that the national flags of all the countries represented by Prizewinners must figure in the panoply.

Translated by Dale McAdoo.